A Passage

Through Fire

Translated from the French by Irene Uribe

New York   Chicago   San Francisco

Jean Montaurier

A Passage

Through Fire

Holt, Rinehart and Winston

Translation copyright © 1965 by Holt, Rinehart and Winston, Inc.
Originally published in France under the title *Comme à travers le feu*;
© 1962 by Editions Gallimard

Published simultaneously in Canada by
Holt, Rinehart and Winston of Canada, Limited.

Library of Congress Catalog Card Number: 65-10135

First Edition

Designer: Ernst Reichl
85785-0115
Printed in the United States of America

"According to the grace of God
which has been given to me, as a wise builder,
I laid the foundation, and another builds thereon.
But let everyone take care how he builds thereon.
For other foundation no one can lay, but that
which has been laid, which is Christ Jesus. But if anyone
builds upon this foundation, gold, silver, precious stones,
wood, hay, straw—the work of each will be made manifest,
for the day of the Lord will declare it, since the day is
to be revealed in fire. The fire will assay the quality
of everyone's work: if his work abides which he has built
thereon, he will receive reward; if his work burns he
will lose his reward, but himself will
be saved, yet so as through fire."
I Corinthians, 3: 10-15

I   Solitude, 11
II   The Encounter, 69
III   The Questions, 135
IV   The Struggle, 179
V   The Journey, 261
VI   The Rendezvous, 305

I KNEW that his will named me his executor. He had said to me one day, "I think I have taken care of everything. After my death, read my last wishes carefully. You will be in charge. I want everything done with propriety. I warn you, you have nothing to gain, but for our friendship's sake, promise me that you will act in good faith."

I gave my promise, and he seemed very much comforted. Then we spoke of other things. We never mentioned this will again.

He died quietly, holding the crucifix from his first Communion (I found this out later) in his good hand. I was at his side. For several days he hadn't been able to speak, but he was still conscious. He would look at me; I think he was listening. I will never know what he heard. Perhaps footsteps outside his window, perhaps the calls of men plowing the fields in his faraway home, which he never forgot; perhaps his church bells, a bird's song, the rustle of leaves, or the sound of the sea, which in this season of spring tides came almost up to the walls of his presbytery.

He wanted the window left open. The wind came into his room, stirring things a bit. He smiled at the wind, and at night at the stars. One day (I remember that it was around noon),

9

a butterfly flew in and circled about his bed. He signaled to me not to disturb it, and his eyes followed its dance.

Another time, by pointing to the wistaria on his garden wall, he indicated that he wanted some flowers. I went and picked some blue hyacinths and a bunch of violets. He opened his mouth and tried to speak; then he wept, but I think it was for joy. With his good hand he tried to gather the flowers together and awkwardly covered the body of Christ crucified. When they laid him out, I slipped this poor faded bouquet between his fingers among the beads of his old rosary. Against the violet of his chasuble, it was barely noticeable.

Everything was done according to his wishes. His funeral was simple and dignified. Afterward, I proceeded to sort out his belongings. It was an easy job. His will was clearly drawn up; everything was in order.

In the course of my task, in that house where I still felt the warmth of his presence and his friendship, I discovered this manuscript. I had known of its existence. It was folded up, rather carelessly, in one of the desk drawers. He had instructed me to destroy all his personal papers. When it came to this Journal, I hesitated for a long time, and then, questioning his invisible presence, I thought I understood him to leave the decision as to what to do with it to me.

I have read these pages over and over. As I read, I entered by degrees into the mystery and secret of his soul, and with him, into the mystery and secret of my own. Did he tell everything? Enough so that others could understand in turn, as I had, a little, that this man, who voluntarily became a priest and never regretted it, spent his whole life in darkness, searching for the Light.

I sent this Journal to be printed without changing a single word, without hoping to impose a logical order on these thoughts, so alive with his life, his anguish, and his faith.

Part I

Solitude

THE WIND is blowing up a storm tonight. It shakes this poor
shack of a house so much, I am afraid the roof will blow off.

It is late, and I am afraid to go to bed. For some time now
sleep has eluded me—and I used to be a very sound sleeper. It
has reached the point where I am afraid of the dark. And this
house creaks all over. And yet, God knows I never believed in
ghosts . . . !

I decided to write. Writing has always been a satisfaction
and a joy for me. When I write, I read my own thoughts from
within; I confront myself, see through myself.

This is not something I decided on yesterday. Even as a
child, I dreamed of the day when I would tell my own story.
I remember one afternoon when, I'm not sure by what miracle, my mother had allowed me to go to a movie. A poor little
show in a country inn, with the screen hung up on the wall
and bare benches to sit on. What was the name of the film? . . .
I can only recall certain images: a beautiful castle, surrounded
by a garden with carefully tended borders full of flowers. Even
now I can see the steps where a young girl appeared several
times in the moonlight.

The children of the poor really should not be allowed to see
movies. When they get back home, they are sad. I called my

dog, and we sat on the steps leading to the barn. A lamp shed a feeble light. I was cold; I wanted to be alone. My dog leaned against me, and I petted him. My throat was tight as I talked softly to him, confiding my inner turmoil. "My poor Fidèle, if you only knew! There is another world—I saw it—where people are happy, where wonderful flowers grow in gardens without any cabbages or potatoes! If only you had seen that beautiful castle!"

Those things shouldn't be shown to poor children. They should never hear such music. "If you only knew! There was a piano just beneath the screen, and a blind pianist who lifted up his head in a strange way, as though he could read in some stars of his own the songs he was inventing. Now it is all gone. Here there is no more castle, no more garden, no more music. Look! Everything is dark."

My dog licked my cheek. He was braver than I. And it was at this moment of desolation, and many others like it, that I thought (I remember it clearly) that someday, some very far-off day, when I had learned to write without making too many mistakes, and when I had become whatever or whoever I was to be, I would write down these childhood impressions.

At last I am going to do it. But what can I say about my boyhood, my past? How can I tell enough of it? How can I tell it right? Have I changed in the process of growing up? I can feel the boy living in me. The man I have become must have learned to put up with him and work out a neighborly relationship. There are two of us, and he is the stronger— more alive, more real, more present. He imposes his memories on me; I could not banish him without destroying myself. He is there inside me, laughing, crying, singing. The man watches him. The man acts and thinks and talks like a man; but the boy constantly beckons, and the man seems willing to follow.

"Come," says the child, "leave all that and come. You are

14

me. You are the one who is playing games and I am the serious one. I am the wood and the sap, the flower and the fruit. I am everything. Yes, I know, you have to play. Play, then. But when your act is over, take off your mask, leave your circus costumes behind and come back to me. Become a little boy again. Listen! Hear that wind tonight. The wind isn't speaking to the man; it is calling to me, for me. You don't even remember my wind! I loved it long before you appeared on the scene. You are thinking of your roof. But I see my trees shivering, my wheat kneeling down, my vine quaking like a beggar. I see my goats gamely facing up to it. When it blows hard, as it does tonight, I say, 'Blow, blow, beloved wind. I don't want to tame you. Blow between my fingers, blow through my hair. Here I come—blow me away. I am laughing!' I don't hear the wind with your old ears or call it with your dry lips. You aren't the one who is laughing. You are thinking of your roof. I'm not afraid it will tear off the tiles. And even if, just by wanting to so badly, it finally blew your house away—would that be so dreadful? On the banks of my stream, my reeds are still growing. I will cut a bundle of them and make a roof between two branches, tied with a few willow twigs...."

THE WIND died down, I don't know when or how. This morning the garden path in front of my doorstep was wet; a hand had flattened my petunias; my roses hung their heads and looked at me upside down. It rained while I was asleep. There is nothing left in the sky. I love this night rain which works alone and leaves a faint fragrance of cut grass at dawn. My

15

branches, dripping, mocked me: "While you were asleep, an angel came to visit us. You didn't even see him, but we did; we felt his caress. Look, you can't deny it." I looked at my trees, touched my roses timidly; I scraped the earth to gauge the weight of its new wealth. Everything seemed to be smiling. My parishioners had new faces, faces of hope.

In the freshness of this new hope, the child I was yesterday spoke in me all day long. I yield; I yield to him.

It must be true that things have souls, for they speak to me and I hear them.

I hear the wheat growing, the vine twisting around the vinepole, the reeds preening their plumes in the pond, the morning glories opening and folding their petals, looking like blue butterflies. . . . things have so many ways of speaking —I find their language much more rich and varied than man's. They surrender themselves as no human being ever has or could.

Their presence is everywhere, in the air, in colors, in fragrances, in a ray of sunlight or moonlight. They come in my window, mixed, entangled, blended, and yet so distinct that I can easily sort out what they bring me, just as you pick out the best fruits from a basket. It depends on the season, the month, the hour, the color of the sky, the strength of the wind, the density of the clouds, and other influences too many to name. Under a thousand different masks, things always have their song, their smile, or their sadness. They greet me, and I stretch out my arms.

The scent of alfalfa being cut, and of alfalfa harvested and stored; the scent of wheat ripening and of wheat fully ripened; the scent of grapevines in flower, of grapes being crushed, and of new wine gushing from the vat . . . The stables, warm milk, animals' wet coats . . . And all the sounds, the murmurings of things, laments or cries of joy: day sounds and night sounds, morning sounds, sounds of midday and sounds of evening. Bread being cut, the door closing, the bucket handle falling; the scuffling wooden shoes, the groaning floorboards, the old chair, the ax, the cupboard. Everything that in my childhood filled my eyes and heart without my realizing it; all those things which it would mean betrayal to forget; that poetry of things, which emphatically do have souls—so much so that they get mixed up with my own, and I no longer know which is stronger, or whether I am drawing my life from the contact with something I believed to be only a poor, pale dream. When these voices of things are stilled, or when the noises invented by man drown out their song, I sleep and nothing exists. But it takes very little to wake me: a passing cloud, the cry of an unseen bird, a few raindrops, the mild fragrance of dewy grass, a falling leaf . . . even less, much less; as slight a thing as a breeze caressing my cheek.

All that is so deep-rooted in me, so alive, strong, and real that I have come to be afraid of it. I love it and fear it.

For after all, whatever may be the power of these enchantments or this murmur of voices, have I become a man, or am I still a child? What good have all my studies been; what use are the joys, the loneliness, the sufferings of maturity if, with the speed of lightning, a dog's bark, a cracking branch, a whiff of acrid smoke from smoldering grass can rob me of these riches and take me back more than forty years, inspiring me with a wild desire to reject and scorn all knowledge, and to find, in my restored silence and poverty, the enchantment and health of my boyhood years?

But this springtime of the spirit returns just at the approach of life's winter. Is it a beginning or an end? I have no way of knowing. I had forgotten what it was like. I am afraid of this new and irresistible embrace of life. I don't dare to sing, and I have forgotten how to weep. I would have thought I was too old for hope. Is it a revenge, the revenge of living things, their irony? Could it still be a mirage? But suppose it were not a mirage; suppose reality were to be found here, precisely at the moment when I began to live in this poetry of nature and this harmony of dawns and nights?

I am waiting . . . waiting . . . but I know that my door will never again open onto that wonderful forest where my life had its source. I know that I will never again tread the crushed grapes, never again step out of the vats all smeared with their fragrant blood. I know that the sea beating against my walls with its invitation to faraway places and dreams is calling in vain. I know that never again can I say, "my field, my wheat, my house, my animals," and that I shall have to find my joy in looking at other men's fields and wheat and, with a hand trembling like a beggar's, caress other men's animals. I know that this immense voice of things will never again be the voice of my own things, and that it will come into my house only to cradle the dream of a child long dead.

I wait. . . .

I succumb to the weakness of opening my window to hear those voices. Is it weakness?

I have enough light left to write by. Perhaps I have enough time left to solve the riddle.

I HAVE reread with a certain curiosity what I wrote yesterday. What is happening to me, and how is it coming to pass?

I never consented to any mutilation of soul, mind, or heart. I accepted the priesthood in the conviction that within it I would still be free to love the things that Christ loved, and no one told me anything to the contrary. I submitted to strict disciplines in the well-founded hope that they would be liberating. So this unconscious transition from serenity to restlessness seems abnormal. But I have succumbed to it. I am on a dangerous slope where it is impossible to keep one's balance. My chosen vocation is a joyful one. I know that some writers maintain that Christ is a source of division. This is nothing new to anyone who reads the Scriptures. But such writers present the idea in a false light. They compare that separation —or if you like, that choice—to a sinister dismemberment, or to some kind of tightrope trick. But Christ never condemned his disciples to public execution, nor did he ask them to walk a tightrope. That separation, that choice, once it is accepted in practice, ought to bring peace. What disturbs me, therefore, is the latent, imperceptible, unpredictable, and obvious work of my subconscious mind.

Last night, in this same lamplight, I let myself go too far, inventing romantic and subtle analyses of a priest sick in mind and heart. I refuse to recognize it as a portrait of myself. Christianity is not a neurosis; the priesthood is not a clinical state; the priest is not a man whose inner life falls within the jurisdiction of psychiatry. There are sick people and madmen everywhere. Novelists find them necessary, and would invent them if they didn't already exist. Stories of priests are no exception, for even among Christians, readers find the idea of a balanced, normal priest hard to accept. A priest has to have a few faults which make him likable, and he has to be diminished in stature either by God's grace or by some obscure demon. If a priest eats and drinks like everybody else, if he seems sound in body and mind, the notion that Christians will form of him is, pretty generally, that he is not quite a good priest. Novelists, of course, take this into account.

Well, I refuse to be sick, either in head or heart! I won't consent to being handicapped just to please my parishioners. I won't become consumptive to cater to their complexes. I will fight with all my strength against anything that might diminish me.

I won't put on an act either. I wouldn't be very good at play-acting: "Our curé's health is bad, poor man!" Then the solicitous approach, the tender glances, the so-called prayers for his recovery, people coming into his house as though it were a hospital. That spells: "At last he is ours! We have taken possession! It is safe to be fond of him." Wouldn't one be tempted to take advantage of such a situation and make one's ailment last like a wick that never burns out?

I have never wanted that kind of possessiveness, that kind of affection. I won't have any part of them, because they are lies; because you aren't showing respect for the minister of God, but for the man who doesn't belong to you, one way or the other. Your attitudes are full of contradictions. I can prove it: Just let the same priest, in top physical and intellectual form, decide to shout one of those old Gospel truths at you a bit louder than usual, and you think, "When will the bishop relieve us of this lunatic?"

I know—I've been through it. . . .

The Christian life, truly lived, is much too demanding and sometimes too cruel for Christ and a bishop to give it into the keeping of the unfit.

For a priest, the sin of sins is to love nature. The idea which pious souls have forged of their priest absolutely excludes his having the slightest weakness for the charm of beautiful things, God's creations. They might forgive Christ for bending over the lilies of the field, for looking tenderly at the ripening grain, for speaking lovingly of a sunset or the wind which goes before rain, but they forgive because after nearly twenty centuries these images have faded. The intense poetry emanating from the Gospel no longer affects anyone.

People's minds are so twisted that it takes courage for me

to pick a bunch of violets in my grassy lanes on a spring day.

And that is why I am wondering tonight whether I didn't fall under their demon's spell. There is a madness here which I must exorcise.

One day (before I came here) my doctor gave me massive doses of a strong antibiotic for some boils that were growing insolently in my nose. He was young. . . . The boils surrendered, but this "shock treatment" upset my nervous system and affected my vision. The pendulum of my clock seemed to be leaping like a carp. To recover my equilibrium I had to close my eyes and listen. My hearing was sound. The seconds ticked by normally. It was in my vision, because of the drug, that things had gone wild.

I felt extremely uneasy and I swore to treat my boils thereafter with old wives' remedies. Drugs are much too risky.

Stability is so important.

No one can ever convince me that spiritual remedies ought to sacrifice man in order to guarantee the triumph of grace. If man staggers, grace staggers, too. Reducing the man in me means, according to the Gospel, pruning the vine . . . and if I prune my vine, it is because I want it to flourish.

THIS MORNING I was waiting for the sun, but a wet fog came in from the sea during the night. It was an unpleasant surprise. I could hardly see the tops of my pines. My petunias were sad, and my rosebushes were crying real tears. The sea—I could see no more than the shore—was smoking as though it were on fire. It was cold. So, autumn has given us sudden notice of its presence.

I put on my black coat, which is too long; it makes me look like Torquemada—or at least what I imagine Torquemada looked like. I took the path along the shore to go and visit a poor old woman who is wearing out the rest of her days in a very humble little house. In her real poverty, this woman has preserved a nobility of soul, of demeanor, and of speech which heartens me. I often go to see her, especially when the weather is bad. She is grateful for my company, but if we could weigh the benefits of these meetings, I think I would come out ahead. I have the impression that she has seen through me and that she sympathizes with my loneliness, which makes us two of a kind.

On my way back, along the same path, I met two fishermen. Here, among my parishioners, I always feel a certain embarrassment; I am not one of them, and they know it. I know it myself only too well. Conversation becomes very awkward. To speak to them man to man, I would have to have a more exact and vital knowledge of their daily life. I am slow to adapt to it. I will never be completely successful. It is really true that you have to be born in a region, in a *pays*, as we say at home, to know its soul.

If I remember tonight the impression which that ordinary conversation made on me, it is because I still feel the pain of it. There are words, even innocent words, which can open a wound. And when that wound is not fully healed, you don't have to press very hard.

I said to them, "Bad weather!"

"Bad weather! Storm yesterday, fog today. The market won't be flooded with fish."

I continued, "But then . . . what are you doing here?"

They pointed to the sea. "We are watching her, and she is watching us. And it looks as though it will go on like that."

After two or three equally insignificant exchanges, we parted. But bad luck would have it that when they left me, they added in their dialect—which I already understand, although they don't suspect it—"What is he doing out in this weather? Wouldn't he be just as well off at home?"

At home...

Oh, be still, if that is all you have to say!

At home. I can't bear to hear those words any more. I forget; I get used to my exile. And then ... It is as foolish as that! Two words spoken without malice, and I long to rest my eyes on the lovely festoon of mountains at home, just when they catch the failing evening light. A willow, a twisted vine, a garden enclosed within its hawthorn hedge. I catch myself listening. Even my skin quivers. At home the air didn't have this stupid taste of salt, the sun seemed closer, the thorns weren't as sharp, and when I walked under the trees, in this season, my foot brushed against real leaves—nothing like these dead needles shed by the pines. Home, my real home when I was a boy, was a house, a field that had a pretty name, a stack of wheat that I guarded at night, a bridge, our salt-pork soup, our poverty, and all our hopes. . . .

When you become a priest, rather late, as I did, after being a peasant for so many years, a rented house can never be your "home." That I can't change. But when, at the gracious invitation of God in person, you leave your plow and your village, and to appease your brothers' greediness, willingly consent to be dispossessed of all your worldly goods, and when in addition you have to leave even your native countryside, its sky, its wind, its scents, its accent and even its customs, without any special vocation, but as a result of men's incomprehension and malicious stupidity—what can you call your place of refuge but an exile?

That is what I have come to, without rebellion, without hatred; but I am utterly disheartened. I have nothing left but God, and He doesn't seem to be excessively concerned. I find it hard to resign myself. My parishioners can't go into these

23

trifles. I realize that what attracts me in that old woman's house is the fact that I am her curé without being an exile ...

(For example, I cannot stand the idea of being buried one day, far from the horizons of my youth, in this sand! After all this time, how fast that earth of my own country still clings to the soles of my shoes!)

I RECEIVE the most unexpected visits. I don't think I am mistaken in supposing that it won't last. I am "new" here, and what is more, I am an outsider who doesn't know the people. I don't mean my parishioners, who don't raise many metaphysical questions. I mean the few restless men and women from the neighboring town, the ones who have wearied all my colleagues, who have obviously been disappointed in all of them, whom I myself am sure to disappoint before many moons.

Thinking of this, I smile tonight as I have often done before, at the naïveté of so many priests and brothers, from every conceivable order, who are absolutely convinced that their brief presence (a triduum, a mission, sometimes no more than a single feast day) is supremely necessary to bring peace to the five or six tormented souls who are to be found in every parish of a thousand or so. These few confide in them their doubts, their spiritual afflictions, the fundamental incompetence of their parish priest to find any solution or remedy. Not all clerics are that naïve, but, thank God, one can always find a few who are. From then on, there is no end to exchanging letters and visiting, which is a boon to the parish priest, because he is left in peace.

When I was a vicar, I was well acquainted with one of those Reverend Fathers, a Jesuit, who came to preach a retreat to the "ladies" of the parish. In this instance it was a group of those idle ladies who pride themselves on their abstract theological knowledge and their "culture." They spend their time on charitable organizations, and do their bit, which would be fine if they stopped at that. Unfortunately, most of the time their committee work in these charities, which is unnecessarily complicated, is only a pretext. Woe to the priests who are taken in by it!

At any rate, my Jesuit managed to get entangled. I gloss over the details. Then he began his last little "talk": "Ladies, since, by the blind force of events, I am now obliged to leave you in the hands of your wretched parish clergy, let me, in the sadness of my priestly heart, give you my final advice ..." Not one of those ladies protested; not one stood up; not one slammed the door. I regretted it for the sake of that Jesuit, because it might very likely have done him some good. Still, there was one who made a report a few days later to her "wretched parish clergy." Even belatedly, this small show of courage had its worth.

What could I say to that intellectual who confided this morning, "I am losing my faith ..." I heard him perfectly well, and I transcribe his words faithfully. He no doubt expected one of those apologetic reactions which I suppose one should show in such a grave moment of a man's life. Losing his faith! To me, that is meaningless, and when I can't see any meaning in something, it leaves me cold. Can one lose one's faith? What reason would ever be strong enough, in any circumstances, to darken one's memory, understanding, heart, and soul to the point where one could coldly decide not to believe any more? Lose one's faith! it means abandoning absolutely everything that makes life real, everything that gives it a direction, a purpose, a reason for existing. For me it is unthinkable. I suppose that my intellectual must be joking and making fun of me a bit. One can be without faith. But lose it...?

I asked him, "What do you do in life?"

"I am bored."

"That is not a very lucrative profession."

"I am a professor of mathematics."

"Mathematics and I . . . Do you try to be kind to your students?"

"All of them failures!"

"All the more reason . . . And your family?"

"The family! You believe, don't you, that God is the one who is responsible for that?"

"If I denied it, I would be saying that the Scriptures lie."

"Your Scriptures!"

"What does the Church mean to you? Do you——"

I didn't have time to finish my sentence. The blood rushed to his head. He leaned forward in his chair and cried, "The Church! The Church! a vile heap of bigots, of pretentious fools, givers of advice, Boeotians. The Church and the social problem! The Church and her clergy, both high and low! The Church and the money question! The Church! Leo XIII and the so-called Christians of the end of the nineteenth century. The family instituted by God, and the Church founded, so they say, by Jesus Christ. If in all that you can find an intelligent man who hangs on to his faith, well, it is because that so-called intelligent man is really an imbecile!"

What to answer?

I said, "Listen here. One day a man came to me to announce that he would soon kill himself. For the same reasons as yours, if I remember correctly. I answered him, 'If you absolutely insist! Hanging or poison? I have seen some suicides. It is an ugly business. Be clean about it. I can't stop you. Is your will drawn up?... Yes. Then I ask only one thing: when you have really made up your mind, telephone me.' That man is still alive. And don't think I had anything to do with it, with such arguments as that! He didn't actually want to commit suicide. He was playing a part. So, you too, you want to kill yourself? Good. But before putting the rope around your neck (after all, that is what losing your faith means), think of me; I am perhaps an imbecile, and I accept it, but never, never could you suffer as much from your family and from the Church as I have suffered and still suffer from my family and from the Church. So in dying, you will have found a twin soul...."

"And you have kept your faith?"

"Come now, why would you want me to lose it?"

"You don't call those decisive reasons, to see a Church, founded by Christ..."

"The family and the Church are the supreme ordeal. But as for losing one's faith because in this family and in this Church there are men who have never had faith, or who are not strong enough in it, or who only think they have it—that, Monsieur le Professeur, is an entirely different matter! I have solved the problem for myself. You have to do the same. I am certainly not a great mystic, but I would at least like not to be too great a fool...."

When he had gone, although it was not particularly stuffy, I felt the need to breathe some air. I plunged out into the fog, which hasn't let up for three days, and found it soothing. Yes, I must be a poor apologist, but what can I say about something of which I have no knowledge? Lose one's faith! I was always taught that minutes are precious, and for me such considerations are a waste of time.

RECEIVED this morning, a letter from my professor. I will copy it down:

Let me inform you, Monsieur, that I consider you in effect an absolute imbecile, the epitome of nullity made man. I wonder by what unfathomable mystery the hierarchy could not only ordain you a priest, but to make matters worse, entrust you with a parish. You have shown me (something I already knew) why the Church is like a dead stump in the very midst of our world bursting with life and in constant evolution. The world doesn't ask the Church which path to take, and it is easy to see why. The Church is being built without you, that is, without priests. Luckily for Her, there are teams of laymen here and there who are thinking through the world's agonizing problems for you, and who are humbly working out solutions. I want you to know that I head one such team. A renewed Church will be born, you may take my word for it (you and all your colleagues) and in it you will look like a ghost.
I came, I heard, I understood.   Q.E.D.

I crumpled up this letter and went out.

Today, toward noon, light won its battle against the dark. It must be a decisive victory because, contrary to their custom, the men all went out in the afternoon. The port was absolutely empty. The women were pleased. "It's no life, Monsieur le Curé, when they don't do anything. Everyone has a job to do. Tomorrow they'll come back in better humor."
After an outsider's glance around the port, I followed the

path up the little hill, where I am sure to be alone. There the only local crop is planted: grapevines. The leaves are slow in falling because as yet there has been no frost. They shrivel and pile up in the holes in the path, in the bushes, behind the hedges. I walked through them on purpose. Their little shell-like sounds, their last cry—perhaps of joy—their last offering of their beauty, reminded me of autumn's lament in my far-away land. I was myself again, on home ground. My lungs filled with air; I smiled to myself. It was a real vine, and those were real leaves. I was walking in my own paths, inspecting my vines. They aren't pruned the same way here as at home, but they are just as fine. And one by one their leaves fall off, slide down, seek their place, nestle into it and die, mingled with the rest, just as they do at home.

At home...

Was it really worth while to leave everything behind just to reach—after so many years of that impossible work of a priest—the point where I inspire letters like the one I received this morning? I don't hold it against the man. I just couldn't play his game. . . . I would have had to appear on the stage of his theater, assume an inspired air, and pronounce words which I know well enough, but which diminish the man in me, and make me sick when I say them. I would have had to take an interest in his system, admit more or less that the Church is wrong, hold out the bait in front of him (that is what he was waiting for!), let him get caught by it and then gently reel in, still playing, guiding him or letting him go where the water near the bank is less clear. Then he would have wriggled with pleasure; I would have been acknowledged and declared very intelligent, and I would have received an enthusiastic letter announcing that he would soon visit me and also that I had been elected chaplain of his team.

That is what certain laymen (not all) today call their apostolate. They don't just say "yes," "no." They sit down, they exchange smiles, they plan their stage effects, they prepare their transitions, they drape words around a few vague ideas, and part delighted, convinced that they have built the Church. I am not sorry that I vexed that man. If he does some good, so much the better. I cannot hitch myself to his wagon. I don't reproach him for his rather heavy ruse or for his letter. I only note that as far as "they" are concerned, things are going to be the same for me here as they were back home. . . .

It has to be written in the form of a parable.
Once upon a time there was a vineyard. . . .
Once upon a time there was a field. . . .
There was once a man, vinegrower and plowman, who, for love's sake, left the vineyard and the field.
Once upon a time there was a parish, and that man took it into his head to prune it like a vine and plow it like a field. But the parish was surprised at being considered a vine and annoyed at being treated as a field.
The man waited. The parish watched. The man was stubborn, in love with his work, proud, patient, and clumsy.
The parish said to the man, "I want you to be like me. My branches grow without pruning and I bear fruit without your seeds."
The man understood then what it was to suffer from love. He persisted in his stubbornness . . . until the day when the postman handed him a letter in a familiar handwriting: that of his hierarchical superior. He had been expecting that letter for years. He had known it would come, that it had to come, that it could not fail to come. He knew what was in the letter. He didn't have to open it. . . .
One evening the man set off down the road of exile, wrapped in his long coat that made him look like Torquemada. . . .
What then? What then?

30

And then . . . I'd like to shout to my visitor of yesterday: "Oh, yes! I am an imbecile. You are right there. Even more so than you imagine. But I still won't be imbecile enough to gamble my faith on the toss of a coin. If you please, fewer words, fewer bows, fewer smiles, less indignation, less glibness, less trickery, less agility—just the truth."

Truth? That signifies flesh and blood. *Without bloodshed, there is no ransom,* to quote St. Paul.

"So I am an imbecile! But this evening, pushing my stick through those dead leaves—perfect images of my life—looking at the clouds just starting to turn red, going over in my mind your letter (for which I thank you), in my loneliness and exile, which (in all innocence and thinking you are doing right) you only make more bitter, I felt my flesh, my blood, my heart, being transformed into a cathedral, and I wished that one day, crushed by beauty like this, cowering as I do in the light, completely immersed in an ocean of joy, you might hear the symphony that floats beneath these arches and look out through the stained-glass windows, and see, outside, in 'our world bursting with life' the writing of the luminous Gospel Story."

I came back to my presbytery. It was night.

How foolish I am, indeed. . . . I was as happy as a child!

I LIKE our little trolley.

Some say that soon they'll do away with it, which would really be too bad. Before I came here, I sold my old car. I don't need to be "motorized" any more. When I go to town, which isn't very often, I take the trolley. Usually it is crowded. I catch hold of one of its copper hand-rails, and look around me, talk, listen.

Today was market day in the district. It was also a feast day and the Dean had invited me to preach. My parishioners were wearing their Sunday best, but they weren't on their way to church. They didn't have the time or the inclination. Most of them didn't even know it was a feast day.

"Are you going to do your marketing, Monsieur le Curé?"

"Yes and no.... I am going to preach."

"Oh? And what is the occasion?"

I didn't make an issue of it, but I realized then what my congregation would be like. By now, as they say, I have a nose for such things. No peasants or their wives, but the widow of the former public prosecutor, the bailiff's wife, the notary's sister, the veterinarian's daughters, the tax collector's mother-in-law, and so on; a cluster of pious little ladies; two or three men, a few women from the choir—bustling; the Ladies' Aid Society—chattering; the girls from the Catholic school, their thoughts elsewhere; the Sisters, apparently serene. The shop owners would stay behind their counters waiting for customers and keeping an eye on their competitors across the street. The Dean, somewhat reassured, would press my hand neither too much nor too little (which is natural, since he knows all about my situation) and would remain on his guard. He would be, so to speak, on pins and needles during the first ten lines of my sermon (which is still perfectly natural).

In the trolley there was at first a strong smell of low tide. As we traveled inland past the fields, that odor of seaweed, fish, and sand evaporated, giving way to smells of planting, of freshly plowed earth, of rotting husks, stables, the brook, the farmyards. I felt more at ease. Each stop carried us a little farther from the sea. There was a switch in the conversations.

32

My fishermen's wives began talking about the price of wheat, and I fell to daydreaming.

I wasn't thinking about having to preach soon. I felt good. I was happy. These people were my people. They didn't know it, which was too bad. I knew it though. The women drew back from me a little on the pretext, half true, that their baskets would get me dirty. They excused themselves. I was less happy. I said to them silently, "I am of the same breed as you! I am a peasant! I used to carry baskets like yours, long ago. I can still feel the pressure of the handle in the crook of my arm...."

But I mustn't disillusion them. I must accept, without lying, something of this middle-class lie. This priest, a peasant? Then he isn't quite a priest. It has come to that. Did St. Peter have to make excuses for being a fisherman? Times have changed. New times have come, haloing me with the light of a star long dead. Suddenly I remembered the irrepressible laughter of an old shepherd to whom I said one day, "You put me in mind of my old job."

"Come on now," he replied, choking with mirth, "folks like you, they never dirtied their hands!"

What can I do? Accept the situation so that truth can seep through in spite of it.... Suddenly I felt like preaching right there in the trolley. That is where Christ would have preached.

"The kingdom of God is like unto a handful of yeast, unto a grain of mustard seed, unto a field of wheat, with its cockles and good grain, like all the things you are carrying there, like everything you see about you, like the seeds you sow, the rain, the sun, the wind, like all that! You are the kingdom of God...."

I preached my sermon for myself alone, in my empty heart which is groaning in its chains. The people aren't aware any longer. I felt sad. I didn't dare to look at them any more. I felt like a doctor who has stopped taking care of his patients. Somewhere something is blocked. Between the people and God, a wall has been built. Joy can't flow through any longer. We are afraid. We have worn shoes with buckles. In certain cases, especially when it seconds inaction, the habit makes the monk. I felt like a stranger in their midst. Still. . . . There is no end to it, then! Everything will be a failure. I thought . . . I used to think . . . Youthful illusions! It isn't true. It isn't true any longer. I am not the breach in the wall; I am the wall. And yet I am the one who was ordained a priest to serve others. A little child clung to my cassock. It felt like a breath of fresh air. I thought I might talk to him. We would understand each other. He would be my Host for the trip, my tangible presence of Christ, my nourishment, my banquet. Wasn't I in need of it? His mother, scandalized, pulled him roughly away. "Come now, look out! Don't squeeze against Monsieur le Curé like that!" So now even the mothers deny me the very ones whose angels contemplate God's face. Times have changed indeed.

I tried to calm myself. I was almost at my destination. My sermon in the trolley was a failure. I still had another one to preach.

The canton is just like all the other cantons in France, like my own, in times past. I decided not to look about; in fact, it wasn't necessary. Here, of course, the doctor. There, the notary's rusty yellow plaque and his office window full of house plants. This passageway must surely lead to the town clerk's office. The shoemaker. The pharmacist. The grain merchant. I didn't see them; I sensed them. Behind those blinds, "they" were watching me: "Who is that? . . . Yes, but who is that new one? . . . Oh, of course, that's who it is. You know, the strange one from the parish down by the shore."

A car passed . . . the bailiff, I know the species. The police sergeant came up, greeted me obsequiously, and asked me

34

some questions which on the surface were quite harmless. "So! You're getting used to it here? It's not much like where you come from." Where I come from! So he knew. He looked at me very closely. The rectory housekeeper did quite the opposite, viewing me from on high, knowing, circumspect, and cautious. I felt as though I bore the weight of the world; I was marked on the forehead. Then I took hold of myself. Once again I was back in the milling crowd. "The good news shall go forth to all people." The noises of the covered market hadn't changed, except that the wave of sounds coming out had a different lilt. That accent of theirs! . . . There was the church. I went in.

Heads turned. Necks stretched from behind pillars. What did they want of me? In what way was I different from others? What penny thriller were they writing inside their heads? They made me think of a hair-raising spectacle I once witnessed, long ago, in a farmyard: a poor unfortunate fowl was trailing a piece of intestine from her rear orifice. And all the other hens swooped down, tugged, snatched, swallowed, until everything was gone, even her lungs, even her heart. What had that poor hen done? Nothing. It was so horrifying that I wouldn't believe it if I hadn't seen it happen.

I knelt before the high altar. "This time," I said to Him, "I am no better treated than You. They are pulling at my intestines, at my heart. You spoke of turning the other cheek, and I have done it. But when I have no more stomach, no breast, no heart, then what more will I have to give them?" He didn't answer me. He understood. But I knew I must remain poor. There must be a vocation to poverty, to true poverty, that is. I felt like prostrating myself, there, before His tabernacle. But it wouldn't do. What conclusions would they draw from that?

Once, a very long time ago, I knew a woman who was very distinguished and extremely intelligent; she ran a business and was very level-headed, but humble, ascetic, and doubtless

35

poor in spirit. One day, on coming out of my confessional, she felt the desire to pray like Mary Magdalene, on the bare stones. That was all right in itself. She knelt there like a statue. (I would have stopped her if I could.) Unfortunately, she wasn't acting like everyone else—and if she wasn't acting like everyone else—since she wasn't crazy—it must be that she had terrible sins. And if she had such terrible sins (and it was more than sure that she had!), it must be that she wasn't as honest as she was reputed to be or as she pretended to be, the vixen! They talked about it for a year in that parish. They are probably talking about it still. She lost her customers into the bargain. Finally, when she had very little heart left, just enough to keep her alive, I said to her, "You have to make up your mind: either you hold on with this tag-end of life, and God will be the air you breathe, or else you must let go!" She held on and she has not let go since then. She hasn't even aged since that time. But when she smiles, the birds in Paradise want to perch on her lips.

And I, too, shall have to go that far....

On my knees before the altar, I was fine, but that wasn't my place. I knew that my colleagues had seen me through the open door of the sacristy. I told myself, "I ought to love them, I am going to love them; I know that it is going to be possible for me to love them." But their conversation had sunk to whispers. And I knew that "he" was there! "He?" Not the Dean, a good man whose eyes are too clear to harbor any hidden shadows. But "he"—the one who knows everything, passes judgment on everything; the virtuous, pure, holy, untouchable, unattackable, untouched; the one before whom in every diocese the bishop fumbles; the one who, in a few "well chosen" words, tells a man off; the learned one, with his degrees, rich and powerful; one of the four or five "powers"

36

who, like the Gray Eminence, govern, impose their laws, arrange promotions, play their cards shrewdly; that high clergy type who knows by heart the contents of the social encyclicals; my censor, my judge, my attorney general.

Yes, "he" was there. I recognized him by his soft hand, his patronizing manner, his fatherly way of putting his arm around my shoulders and, speaking for them all without any authorization, saying to me, "We are delighted to meet you at last..." That "at last" was going too far. I wished the others would say something. Anything, about anything—the good weather, my health. Silence. I outfaced it. I asked for a surplice. The Dean helped me put it on. I fastened the straps about my neck. I had trouble with them, and I noticed that my hands were shaking. I saw "him" looking at them. The bit of intestine. He was about to lunge for it. He attacked: "But, my dear colleague, where is your mozzetta? Surely you were a dean? When you left your beloved parish, before you came to us here, weren't you named honorary dean, which authorizes you, in canon law, to wear the mozzetta?"

My eyes blurred. My heart rocked like a swing. I was swimming in an unreal world. There was no more past, no future, no sacristy, no church. I heard a voice: "We are going to begin with the singing of the *Magnificat*, and while we are singing, will you please go up into the pulpit?"

Go up into the pulpit. That's right! I was supposed to go up into the pulpit. To preach—what? This was my entrance examination. But where were my ideas? Last night everything was clear; I remembered that it was all clear, but just what was it that was clear? That confused mass of ideas that the wind was scattering? Nothing left. Emptiness. Dizziness. My God...

"*Magnificat! Ma-a-gnificat!*" "He" was intoning it. The Dean must have given his own stole to "him." His voice rose like a *Te Deum* of triumph! It descended and fell on me, as it was meant to fall on me, just as he wanted it to fall, like lead. "Sing, sing louder! The higher these verses ascend, the harder they crush me down. Mercy! Have mercy!" I closed my eyes. I was not praying. How could I pray? To whom could I pray? Is there a saint to call on in times like this, the way you call on St. Barbara when it thunders? I was living outside of time. The Dean must have come over to me. I was vaguely aware of a hand pressing my arm. The time had come. I had to preach. I had to open my eyes at least to see the steps leading up to the pulpit. I opened them and saw right in front of me, relaxed, laughing his *Magnificat*, my mathematics professor.

The congregation was sitting down. Looking at me. Waiting.

I want to write down that sermon so that I can remember it. It is the only one of my whole life, up to the present, which rose to my lips without passing through my brain.

The first thought that came to me, like a bolt of lightning, was that I didn't have their accent . . . the lilting way they end their words, their "r's" that grind out through gear cogs, their "au's" caressed with a feather, which I pronounce "o." That calmed me. I noticed that the edge of the pulpit was not worn or dirty, and I concluded that the Dean must preach from the communion rail. I wasn't thinking of God or the Blessed Virgin or the devil. My lips were going to open and I would listen, like the others, to my entrance examination. The situation struck me as comical. Those were the only impressions I had.

"In the name of the Father . . ." (slowly, that much time gained, two breaths.)

"My brothers in Christ . . ." (yes, there it is. I am on my way. My lips will just have to shift for themselves. I want to repeat "My brothers in Christ," but if I give in to the slightest

38

stage fright now, if I stumble over a single word, I am lost . . .
the bit of intestine . . .).

"We are all poor, and sons of the poor. . . .

" 'Poor!' you say. 'What about our social position? and our
property?' Others say, 'And our academic degrees? And
our training? I am a doctor, a lawyer, a professor.'

"Excellent!

"Let's go back a few years; the doctor's father herded goats
(a very honorable calling!) and was a tenant farmer. The
notary's father wore wooden shoes lined with straw (a splendid kind of footgear). The professor's father spoke the local
dialect (the most beautiful language in the world all the
same). That farm had no electricity. Those wooden shoes
went to the well to draw water. That dialect prayed to the
Blessed Virgin.

" 'What kind of a speech is this?' you ask. 'And what is its
connection with the feast we are celebrating?'

"And if I go back even further, they were poorer still. And
it isn't a bad thing that their children have television sets,
automobiles, and running water on every floor. I say to you
that it is a good thing, a very good thing, on condition . . .

" 'Ah,' you say, 'there we are. So then, these conditions?'

"My brothers in Christ, it is hard to be a notary; it is hard
to be a doctor; it is hard to be a professor; it is even harder
to be a priest. And not because of the law, or diagnostics, or
algebra, or the cassock. Why is it so hard? Because it is hard
to lend your hot-water bottle when your own feet are warm,
particularly when your own feet are warm! And when your
soul is warm, it is even harder to give a part of your cloak to
souls who are shaking with cold! It is hard, because first you
must love; because charity is worthless unless it goes hand in
hand with—unless it runs ahead of—our gift. The man who
gives without loving is a merchant in the Temple. . . .

" 'On condition,' you say?

"On condition that you don't have scales over your eyes and a hard shell around your hearts. The birds fly, the fish swim, the stars shine, the dew refreshes the plants. Do you ask what your heart is made for? The wealth you may have, your learning—God rejoices in these things, but if you do not love, if you love only yourself, and that badly, what good does it do you to have television? What good are your studies if you don't share your knowledge? What good is your wealth, if all you do is hoard it? What good is it to be a Christian, if you worship only your idol?"

A few chairs creaked.

"He" inched forward a bit in his seat in the choir stall and crossed his fat legs. His right hand supported his head, the index finger indenting his flabby cheek.

My professor wiped his glasses....

" 'On condition...?'

"These are not my conditions." For the first time, I risked a gesture. I pointed to the tabernacle. "They are His ... these are His conditions.

"There are certain fires which never go out. There are odors which cling. There are trees that don't die if you cut down only the trunk; you have to kill the roots. There are poisonous mushrooms which always come back up.

" 'Give us an example!' you demand.

"My brothers, what does God want?

"Here is your example: once there was a man (and this was not so very long ago) who considered his race the superrace, the race of rulers and of gods. As long as that race, his race, triumphed, the other races were branded like animals at a fair. Only the elect, who were chosen, screened, numbered, selected, and labeled, had any right to breath, words, life. The air belonged to them. The earth, too, with its yield, and its treasures both visible and hidden. The roads were theirs. Men. All other men. The Temples. God!

"That was called racism. I can tell you something about it, because for five years, I was that monster's property....

" 'And so?' you say.

"So? So? So? If this morning, into this church, were to come peasant women laden with their baskets, fishermen smelling of the sea, the schoolmistress smelling of secularism, those mothers with their messy kids, the Protestant with his Bible, the Jew with his beard, the blacksmith on the corner with his suppressed desire for God, the worker with his demands, the Freemason with his certificate of civil burial, the abandoned wife whose heart is fugitive, that streetwalker with her curiosity, her halfhearted repentance and her search for the one lover who will at last be faithful, all those who are out there, on the other side of these walls, on that market square, all of them, the way it used to be in the catacombs or in our first Christian basilicas or in our famous pilgrims' shrines, Jerusalem, St. James of Compostella—how would you love them? Would they be your own race, the race of sinners, of suppliants, of God's poor, the race of joined hands and open hearts? Of hearts offered up?

"Or would you simply chat with them about the latest styles?

"That is His first condition.

"And those among you who at this moment secretly rejoice at the idea of this sudden and, unfortunately, as yet impossible onrush of all your brothers into this House of the People which is called your church; who welcome them, and embrace them, and offer them your rented pews, and stand up so that they can be seated, and intone for them a *Magnificat* as light and airy as the one the Blessed Virgin spoke to St. Elizabeth; who are saddened at the thought that this beautiful dream is only a dream, and that we must be only at the beginning of the Christian era; who lift their arms toward heaven to plead for the hour to strike when the flock will be gathered together, and for the victory of Love—all those are of the race of Christ, and in spite of their sins, their hearts are warm enough to love."

After that I hesitated a moment. I knew I should speak of the others. I was afraid I would express myself badly, and sound vindictive. I have never been able to speak of those "others." They have always imagined that I didn't care for them. It is my fault. But I don't know how to learn. It is the one single reason for all my disappointments. I speak in churches and I never speak to the ones who are in those churches. How can I expect people to understand me?

I therefore waited, searching for words, more words, and finding none, I said, "Amen."

At the meal afterward, the Dean seated "him" opposite himself and placed me on his right.

I wasn't hungry or thirsty, except (it is an affliction) for my craving for the crowd which was beginning to ebb away, and for solitude.

"He" talked a great deal about "his" reminiscences of Rome. "When I was in the French Seminary in Rome . . . When I received my doctorate in canon law, . . ." and so on.

One thing that struck me as odd and irreverent was that he called all the bishops (with whom he seemed to be very well acquainted) by their family names, not mentioning their titles. Everyone was laughing, but without conviction, a sickly kind of laughter.

He added, "They all think they are Napoleon; a bit of red braid and they think they own us. Don't look for any other explanation for my being named Canon."

Why did I have to answer, "Do you think that with that bit of red braid our bishop could lead his Canons to Austerlitz"?

I heard, "After Austerlitz, my dear fellow, there was Waterloo."

42

That didn't mean very much. I replied, "They were there too, his men, with their bit of red braid." Then I was very spiteful. "But the sun of Austerlitz and the rains of Waterloo no doubt would not agree with certain capes. They would turn pale!"

Then I heard a roar. "I should like to inform you, Honorary, Would-be Reverend Father Dean, that the chief concern of bishops is to keep their clergy in a state of mediocrity. No glory, no shame. No nonsense. And you must admit that with certain individuals, they succeed only too well."

When I stood up to leave by the last trolley, the Dean said to me in front of them all, "Would you be so good as to hear my confession?"

It was a long time since I had heard confession. My parishioners hardly ever confess.

My little trolley, the last one of the day, was almost empty. I took the opportunity to recite my breviary.

When I arrived here, I don't know why, I switched on my radio. An unknown orchestra launched into the fourth movement of the Ninth Symphony, the only music in the world which I listen to on my knees, weeping. The Hymn to Joy.

I feel God's nearness in these coincidences.

THIS AFTERNOON a priest came to visit me. One of those who were with me the other day in the canton. (Not "him" of course.) He was probably just taking advantage of the good weather, or rather of what they call good weather in these parts.

What can I say about his visit? There are certainly some things which don't change: these meetings of two priests for instance. Here or back home, the images are the same.

Two men (who are priests) sit looking into each other's eyes. That is the way they usually talk when there are only two. It is hard to say whether they mean to be more open about themselves, or whether each is trying to fathom the other, or whether they aren't both playing a kind of hide-and-seek which allows them to dissemble behind an outward show of frankness.

The conversation drags, but only on the surface, only by a lay observer's standards. A tape recording of it would be pitiful. They don't choose their words with care. Their exercise is different, more on the order of grammar: the agreement of words with a thought, an orthodoxy (even a restrictive one) which they learned long ago; with what was said by a certain teacher, or with what they read in a book, in Latin, or with an experience which fell behind or beyond the Letter. For they both are familiar with the Scriptures: Does Christ approve of what I am saying? Would He, will He ratify it? In this particular instance, what is His will? And men being what they are, changing very little, where is that cleft in the rock of their souls where this Will of Christ can penetrate?

They speak or keep silent like tourists at the edge of great cliffs or immense valleys, where they have been told that their voices will echo. And when they interrupt each other, they are not listening for a human answer, formulated by the lips of men, but for that yes or no which comes out of God's silence. Their waiting is full of calls launched into the Infinite, toward some unknown shore or mountain or fathomless vale. It is this reply, always slow to come, which is the point of departure for the next sentence. It is not very complicated. One has only to join in the game, or, in a word, enter into the mystery.

This kind of thing can't go very fast; it never does. But they aren't anxious for it to go any faster. They are only bystanders, children throwing a ball against a wall, beggars holding out their hands. It looks rather worthless on the face of it.

When two priests talk to each other about something other than the administration of the diocese—a hopeless topic—or the latest incomprehensible promotions, or the gossip from the capital, it is always like that. For conversation to be lively, there have to be at least three priests. Then it means nothing at all. It is just small talk.

We talked for a long time, about nothing apparently; about everything. Our last remarks were on the subject of saintliness.

"I love the saints," he said to me, "but where are they? How does God manufacture them? I have been trying to make saints for a quarter of a century. I am a total failure. I have been varnishing cracked plaster."

"The saints are first of all men. Have we molded men? What do you expect grace to fasten onto? In this, am I not most traditionally orthodox?"

"Yes," he replied. "Men. Real men, fully human. . . . Wouldn't that be a marvel . . . a canticle to the glory of God?"

"Can it be that the Church is afraid?" I asked him then.

"It seems to me that it isn't the Church itself that is afraid. But within the Church, too many liars would be afraid of sincerity, too many cowards would be afraid of courage, too many of the diseased would fear health."

"Isn't there any solution?"

"There is no theoretical solution. Every saint, I mean every sound man who wants to become a saint, has to blaze his own trail through the wilderness." He added, "I think you made an enemy the other day, at the deanery."

"Tell me what I should have done to become his friend."

"Nothing different. But—you did say something spiteful."

"I know I did. But suppose I hadn't said it, would I have acquired any claim to his friendship?"

"No," he answered, pressing my hand in farewell. "It wouldn't have changed anything, not anything at all—on his side—but you? You?"

"I?"

He added very gently, "You would have been purer."

TODAY it is raining.

It is raining in a way that makes me feel it will never stop. It almost seems as though it is raining even on the sun. The sun comes out, then it hides. It is raining on the sunlight which is tarnished by contact with this horrid drizzle.

After my Mass, I tried to light my fire and filled the whole house with smoke. I opened my window wide and, as long as it remained open, my stove "drew." When I closed it, the smoke came back.

Finally I gave up. I had to put my coat on to keep warm. Was this the way it would be all winter?

I asked a man, "Does it snow here?"

"For half a day, every four or five years."

"Oh, and what kind of weather do you have when it doesn't snow?"

"Like today—rain."

In anger, I retorted, "That's unnatural; that's no kind of a country!"

Those were my words; they just burst out. Try and call them back....

The man looked at me closely. I guessed that he had his answer ready. Something like, "If you don't like it, try and

46

change it . . ." or "You didn't have to come here!" But the answer remained unspoken. He only shrugged his shoulders and turned his back.

Exile! The feeling is coming back. . . .

Be a man first. And be "pure."

While I am going about here and there, greeting my parishioners with a fairly cheerful face, my mind is working. This thought has been bothering me for a long time: it is not my fault if everything goes wrong. Maybe it is normal for everything to be mixed up. But why—why—were we taught that everything ought to go right?

Once again I mentally criticized our so-called classical teaching methods.

Consider this: from the sixth grade on, in all the secondary schools, Catholic and non-Catholic, what do they teach? Excellent subjects. I don't condemn the content, only the form. They tell us: "A French composition begins with an introduction, continues with the development of the subject, and ends with a conclusion which should briefly sum it all up and leave the reader with a feeling of intellectual satisfaction. Read the great writers and imitate them! Read Racine, Corneille, La Fontaine, inimitable in their perfect balance. Read Giraudoux, Mauriac. Don't read Léon Bloy yet, or Claudel; they mix everything up. Later on."

From this French composition, a simple formula for organizing our thoughts, we deduce, whether we want to or not, a practical formula for organizing our lives. A life well led, well ordered, ought to resemble this French composition. You let yourself get caught in a cogwheel. People congratulate you for being caught in it. You live in it; you live from it. There it is: the mold. Into this mold and not outside it, never outside it, we have to pour our days, our years, our lives. Anything that doesn't fit into the exact shape of this mold is called excessive, false, abnormal, out of bounds, blameworthy, and condemned.

Next, or simultaneously, come religious ideas. Who can deny that they ought to conform to this program, take their place, too, within the mold? We press down. We force them. We break them if necessary. In you go—in, or else!

Isn't this a mistake? How can it be corrected? What other method can we invent?

For, in life, two and two never make four as they do in that French composition. Who pays any more attention to it once he is out of school? But even those who ignore it have a bad conscience. Should one be a St. Francis of Assisi or only a cut-rate Christian? How many cowardly compromises, how many discouragements have their origin in the impossibility of being St. Francis? And when discouragement enters into a soul, when it is accepted (which sooner or later happens), the devil is not far from taking over.

I know, I know that one becomes subdued, one mellows, one soon learns to be satisfied with half measures, but always as a second-best, which makes the cowards gloat. But there are others besides cowards in the world. There are also all those who think they became what they are, because on a day which strangely resembles yesterday or the day before, two and two for them added up to three or to zero.

All my disappointments, most of my human and spiritual anxieties have come from my inability to arrive at this figure four. When it was too hard for me to reach it by inner resolve and will power, I tried action; I made gestures which committed my will from the outside. The desired result then seemed assured, theoretically, according to the laws of French composition.

But, in these matters, "theoretically" is an empty word.

And so, I had a few material possessions, slowly, painfully acquired by hard work.

On the day I was ordained a priest, I played at being St. Francis of Assisi. I gave everything to my brothers. "They will understand," I told myself. "They will become better because of it." They understood nothing, and I think they became worse. It was all a failure, outside the mold, all within a false front. Two and two didn't make four.

Those possessions didn't mean so very much to me. It wasn't these and tried to dispossess me of them. From then on, I am learned was playing in my head, the prescribed formula, the well-assimilated French composition. I knew that there existed, by the will of God, that other fortune which neither moths nor rust can destroy.

I was pure, classically pure, evangelically pure.

And what was the result?

It was precisely from that day on that they began to consider me a madman, for different reasons of course, each one for his own reasons, each one according to his own beliefs, but the conclusion was identical: "He has lost his mind."

I ought not to have played at being St. Francis.

For, once I was poor, once I was just a poor man, once they saw me wearing only my poor man's rags, my pride, my honor, my freedom, my joy in being a free man, they aimed at too painful to give them up. And the music of the words I had sure that they held me in contempt.

They hadn't changed: they couldn't. It is not their fault. They aren't evil. They were incapable of changing. God himself could have come to them and said, "Try to understand!" and they wouldn't have done anything about it. In their eyes, the poor man is a failure. I had put myself in that class in their eyes. There I am still.

For years I have lived with this useless humiliation.

As far as I can understand these complex things, I think I was wrong, but my mistake was not in offering, in giving, in dispossessing myself, in saying to them, "Take what is mine, and let it be yours from now on." In itself, in the absolute, that was right. I was right according to the formulas I had learned, according to the lesson, the Masters, the mold. I was wrong in thinking that, once this act was performed, a certain conclusion must necessarily follow, as it does in classic drama. The conclusion didn't follow.

Where, then, in God's plan, is this "two and two make four" to be found? Where is the truth? How can we reach it? How can we distinguish it from opportunism? Mightn't there also be an "opportunism of the Gospel?" Perhaps. . . . Did God want me to make these humanly foolish gestures in the world of reality? Why? For whom? Who was to benefit? Do I have to re-examine my whole spiritual life? Even if I was wrong, I don't regret it. But who profited by my mistake? "When the facts contradict the principles," St. Thomas wrote somewhere, "it is the principles that are wrong."

Unless my error consisted solely in the false conviction I had of my own inner purity . . . All those things are indecipherable. . . .

But I wouldn't advise anyone to play at being St. Francis of Assisi!

Now it is over. . . .

I mean that no one can convince me that I am wrong. I have struggled for forty years. Every morning I have found myself back at the same point, and no sense of guilt has ever so much as grazed my soul.

My mother was a Jansenist, and I must have been one, too. I must still be one in some ways. It is no help; it upsets everything. Luckily for me, I was one of their poorest disciples. I took a great deal from them. I left much alone. The result was a struggle, but I have stopped struggling, because it is futile, vain, and false.

I accepted everything that I was taught, and I don't deny any part of it. However, in my eyes, in my ears, in my heart, there are springs which were not evil, but which have never been sanctified.

My temptation? I love the earth. I love it passionately. The earth and all that it bears, all that it nurtures, all that flowers upon it. I love sunlight. I love the stars. I love everything.

Where is the harm in that? I'm sure I don't know.

The earth . . . I feel happy to think that death will give my body back to it. I would like to be buried like the Carthusian monks, without a casket. It would be easier and quicker for the earth to make me part of its liturgy.

What spirituality for a priest!

Of course, if I stopped at that . . . But in a way I do stop at that. The earth exists, too. Jesus the Christ loved it before me. Was it in such a very different way?

"Detach yourself from it all." From all what? Let's be a bit more precise!

One day a priest, one of those whose cassock seems to be turning violet, as you might expect (today it is violet) made this remark in my presence: "There is a whole class of our colleagues who can't be expected to climb very high . . ." His sentence was never finished because just when he was going to continue, our eyes met. . . .

So I am one of the species who creep. I don't feel it.

It could be dangerous (the tune is familiar!) to love God in His book of nature. Everything is all mixed together there. Agreed. Is it then sounder (it is certainly easier) to set the Throne of God so high in the clouds that the creeping kind

like me never reach it? Yes, it is less difficult to speak of Him
... in the clouds! But, as He is far away...

When God called me, when He called me—I am sure of it
—by my name, I was sixteen years old and I was mowing in a
field of alfalfa. I can still see the spot. I could find it within a
half-inch. I was mowing. It was on one of those mornings that
are so clear, so pure, so light, that I could think of nothing
except mowing light. I cut it into slices, and it came back; it
ran away laughing in front of me; it dared me to run after,
crying, "Cut, cut! Come! But see, you will never have done;
the farther you go, the brighter I am!" I offered my bare
arms, my chest, my head. We were talking together, and it
was then that God spoke to me. I can't say exactly how. In
that light, I didn't see Him. He was one with the colors, with
all those flowers which so graciously bowed before my scythe,
shaking off their dew in a thousand sparkling stars. I felt as
though I were in a church, the most beautiful in the world,
as big as the world. I didn't smile at this vision. At that time
our family poverty was not conducive to extraordinary oc-
currences. But this was not at all extraordinary. It is not
extraordinary to encounter God in the light. At least, as I
understand it. I saw myself a priest. I had to be a priest.
I would be a priest.

I became a priest, but I still remained a mower of alfalfa, a
shepherd, a peasant from back home who will never "climb
very high." In calling me at that precise moment, in molding
me from that very instant, God did not say to me, "I detach
you." He said, "Come! Come just as you are, with your scythe
and your ignorance. We'll manage. You will see."

Since then, my life has been spent looking for the harmony
between Him and His earth, in His light.

My PRESBYTERY is something of a shack, old and in disrepair. There hasn't been a priest here for twenty years. This post was re-created for me, which would hardly make sense just now when there is a shortage of priests, except precisely for the fact that it was I. I am not a renegade, or afflicted in spirit. I am just the one who never made a success of anything. So it's quite natural. For, of course, one must succeed. Whatever may have been said on the subject, in a certain way one must succeed in the worldly sense. Bishoprics, diocesan administrations make a great point of the holiness of priests, but all the same it seems that they prefer the skill a priest displays in not causing too much trouble by his inability to adapt to a given parish situation. (If he is also holy, so much the better.)

Now, I realize that everywhere I go my very presence irritates those in power. The powerless—that is, the poor—have never stood up for me because the poor are the poor in all the parishes in the world, and even if they want to they can't help those against whom the powerful are fighting. They are too dependent on them. The poor, the humble folk, have always honored me; they have loved me, I am sure; but they have kept silent. I am not even disillusioned. I don't hold it against them. That's the way things are. Can you imagine a poor man, poor in everything—especially lacking fine language— knocking on the bishop's door? Coming into the bishop's presence, timid and stuttering, on the heels of the doctor, the pharmacist, the factory manager! It just isn't conceivable. In fact, it would be contrary to nature.

My case is not unique. But I certainly was particularly well "taken care of"! I write it and think it tonight without bitterness. If only I had known better how to defend myself! Take the offensive! Explain my problem with more persuasive force! I could have done it for someone else, I am sure. But for myself? Defend myself against what? No one reproached me with not being a saint, but, because of my clumsiness, they said I was "useless." I answered, "At my age, do you think I can change?" which only reinforced the case of my "powerful" accusers. What a miserable reply! I don't deny it. I provided everyone with weapons to use against me.

The individual doesn't count for much in the system. The important thing is for the wheel to turn, the way those in power want it to turn. Sometimes I let it depress me. I know perfectly well that I will be depressed again, that here, all alone, I will cry out. Those cries won't disturb anyone. No one will hear them. Even if they heard, it wouldn't matter to them. I'm not the one to change anything.

The Church is both divine and human. Her garment of flesh is cumbersome. Those who are scandalized by it always exaggerate one way or another. But those who suffer from it perhaps too often keep their peace.

I don't want to be a coward. And I haven't been one. I am here because I couldn't defend myself, it is true, but the reason I couldn't is that I didn't want to be a coward. What would it have meant to undertake my own defense? The apparent truth is that I was wrong. I didn't know how to talk more effectively. They didn't understand me, which means that they understand everything except silence. And here I am. I didn't even think for a moment of unfrocking. How could a man think of unfrocking when God has called him by his name, in a field of alfalfa, while he was mowing light? I think my former bishop guessed at least that much: that I would never unfrock. Otherwise, in my opinion, he would have been less brutal than he was. Every administration han-

54

dles with care those who might create a scandal. As for me . . .

I was always "catalogued." I would be curious to read the record under my name in the ultra-secret files in the bishop's office. I imagine it would read something like this: "Average intelligence. Goodhearted. Spontaneous. But so impulsive and lacking in tact that it is impossible to entrust him with a post of the slightest importance." And later on would be added: ". . . after making blunders which this time are irreparable, he was sent to another diocese."

I fervently hope that back there the wheel turns better without me.

This presbytery suits me because I am not at all fussy. I look out on the sea. It fills my eyes and ears. It fills my shoes, too; for on certain days it comes up almost to my walls. I have a very broad view. It couldn't be more so. A little path leads to my door. I think that in summer I will go barefoot; it will be easier. I have sand everywhere, especially in my bed. Behind the house there is a little hill with vineyards. Pine trees just about everywhere. That is all, or that would be all if that old woman hadn't kept up the little garden in the dooryard. Petunias, roses! What an excellent idea!

Four rooms under the shakiest of roofs. I made one of them into a classroom, one into a kitchen, or reasonable facsimile. The others serve as study and bedroom. Not everyone has as much.

Little by little I am visiting my new parishioners and getting to know them. Here as everywhere, there are those I call the poor. I don't know how much money they have. To me, the word "poor" means manual workers; they may be rich, but their minds aren't complicated. And here, as everywhere, there are the others. I have no second thoughts when I use this word. The others, as far as I can judge, are a few pensioners of the army or the government—here they call them "people

55

of means"—rather ill-natured. Their wives seem shrewish, malicious, gossipy, quick to lie, and full of self-satisfaction. I hear, too, that the only time they ever agree is when they are skinning their neighbors. I will try to take all this into account, without much hope of getting results. Up to now, with my fishermen's families, everything is all right. With the others, I can't tell. The canton is too near. The good ladies have high society friends there.

One thing I can be sure of is that I have been fighting the dust and the spiders for a good month, and not one of these ladies has felt the slightest urge to help me. They don't seem to be disposed in my favor. In church, from their reserved pews, they look at me rather strangely. How exactly? It's just a feeling I have.

It seems that my sermon of the other day wasn't very well received. One of my fishermen told me so in his own way this morning, in the port. He started to laugh when he saw me. "What in the world did you say to them the other day in the canton? You're off to a fine start! If you keep on like that, you'll get the same treatment as another one I knew when I was young . . ."

"What happened to him?"

"They cut off his ear!"

I didn't dare tell him that I had only one left. . . .

A VISIT . . .

A lady of high society. Handsome coat. Authoritarian manner, rather haughty and a bit too familiar. That manner of theirs . . .

56

She didn't even introduce herself. She began her first sentence with these words, "The Colonel, my husband, sends you his respects." And without waiting for my answer, she pivoted around, inspecting the room. (I omit the gestures.) "What a charming presbytery! Oh, how nicely you have decorated the walls! And this window on the sea . . . They tell me this house was vacant for twenty years. What a waste! The Colonel and I live in an ugly building—so ugly!—in keeping with our income! If we had only known! What an ideal weekend cottage! The sea, a fine sandy beach two steps away! The sun! No neighbors! Paradise! . . ." And with a note of regret: "Yes, and a very suitable house for a priest. You will find God here —how shall I express it?—right under your hand! Do you think the municipality would have authorized us to use it? I tell the Colonel over and over, 'My dear, you are too timid, too soft, too simple-minded—in a word, a fool.' Thank God a priest has this delightful chalet! Do you like it here? How could you possibly do otherwise?"

I would have been happy to show her the door. Instead I begged her to have a seat, which she did without a break in her monologue. She had an affected way of speaking that was like an electric current passing over my skin. In moments like this, I call on St. Rita, patroness of lost causes.

"Oh, just imagine that I couldn't hear your sermon the other day! What a pity! It was our little maid's day off. How sorry I am! They tell me you were very personal! I like that! Personality! Always personality! And more personality! Those are the words of my conceited husband. It seems to me that you aren't lacking in personality. In my opinion, the Colonel is—yes, I repeat—too soft! My motto is: daring! Always daring! And more daring! The only ones who succeed are those who are daring. Everything at sword's point! Oh, if only I had been in the Colonel's place—you understand me— I wouldn't have retired with those five miserable stripes! Five stripes! Just imagine! When I know hordes of men who have their stars and who aren't good enough to be adjutants. . . . Do you like it here?"

"Enormously, Madame. I——"

"Oh, I've heard all kinds of things about you! I'm going to give you a piece of advice, like a true friend. Follow it, and you will be better off for it! Do as I do: listen! Say nothing! It is the only intelligent way to live in peace! Have as little as possible to do with society. Don't imitate your colleague in the canton, the Dean. A good man, but so naïve! Rather, follow the example of—oh, it's simply a question of outlook—of the Canon, such a distinguished person, and on his way to win those stars! You surely must have noticed him the other day! A bridge addict! He is a familiar visitor in our home! Bridge opens every door, even the bishop's. . . . Of course this is a nice little house, oh, very nice! but really just a cottage, barely adequate for a vacation, a little hole in the wall, a "shack" as the Colonel says. And your apostolate, your apostolate! Do these coarse folk tempt you? You will be wasting your time on them! Have we got such a surplus of priests that we can bury them alive? I'll speak to the Canon. . . ."

"I beg you not to, Madame——"

"What, an orator like you? A sensitive person, I can tell. Don't deny it! You can't fool me! It's perfectly clear. . . . By the way, I came here to ask you some advice, as a priest, as a friend——"

I burst out, "I have so little time!"

"To waste, you mean! . . . I understand you so well! In this odious canton we naturally have to keep up some social relations, entertain! Can you think of anything more detestable? No! How fortunate you are to be living here among fishermen with no malice, no spiritual problems! Simple folk! That is the only thing I understand—simplicity! But a Colonel's wife . . . When we were living in Paris . . . Oh, yes, I forgot to tell you: the Colonel was on the Army General Staff for

58

eighteen years. Evening parties, cocktail parties. A bore. But it was Paris! We entertained a lot. . . . Can you play bridge? The Colonel is a terrible partner. He prefers chess. That's not for me. I have no time to waste. Do you like chess?"

I cut in as tactfully as I could, "Since you desire the advice of a priest, Madame, the Dean——"

"The Dean! What an idea! A priest without culture! A priest of peasant origin, with no experience of the world, with-out——"

"He is a priest, Madame."

"So are you! Here's the problem: the Colonel doesn't love me! Can you imagine? No! A lifetime of silence and devotion at the side of a man to whom you have sacrificed everything, given everything——"

"Your case is not unique. I am quite ready to advise you, but on one condition——"

"Not unique! I suppose I must accept that, although it isn't very original. . . . On what condition? There are always con-ditions it seems, the same as the other day in the canton. Well —on any condition you wish! Any condition! I have had enough! I will be docility itself. It would be hard for me to leave him, although I often think of it! It would be easier to be unfaithful, but as a solution it has too many drawbacks when you try to carry it out. And there are our Christian principles! And my conscience! Just think, I teach the cate-chism to the girls in the neighborhood! Hopelessly stupid creatures. What a bore! . . . There, you see before you an hon-est woman who has nothing with which to reproach herself, whereas he——"

"This then is my condition, Madame: I promise to take up your problem only if you speak to me about it in front of the Colonel."

She stood up, knocking her chair over, and, at long last, was speechless.

I added, "That is the condition set by a priest who was once a peasant, and who has retained from his former state the habit of calling a spade a spade, and your plea for advice a breach of confidence and an indelicacy toward your husband and toward me! Can you expect me to be a party to it? You are not two; you are one. You were told that on the day of your marriage. But allow me to repeat it in front of him. I will be free tomorrow afternoon between three and four. I will be very pleased to meet the Colonel. Come back with him."

I won't see her again.

And if I keep on like this . . .

I AM TIRED. I feel that I reach the limit of my strength more quickly than I used to and I have trouble recovering. I am aging. I can feel it, but somehow it doesn't make me sad.

Once, in a theater, I saw a play—I can't recall just what it was. But it made use of a complicated, invisible mechanism called a "revolving stage." As soon as the curtain fell on a scene, a new set neatly replaced it, and the play went on almost without interruption. Sometimes the lights were simply put out for a few seconds. When they were turned on again, there was a new set, and the play continued.

I am aging, but in a way the play continues. Soon it will pursue its course without me. I am making way for younger men.

It is more than fatigue. I am worn out. This has no effect on my will. The things I did in my youth out of enthusiasm, I do now as a matter of principle, out of conviction, as a consequence of faith reduced to its starkest, most pitiable state. Once one has reached this point, one can live a hundred years.

I can still hear my mother saying, "If you lose heart, you will have two burdens—the one of giving up, and then the one of getting back your strength. So stop being childish!" As a line of argument, this is irrefutable.

But what is more fundamental, what really touches perhaps the deepest part of my being, is of a different nature: I am sick of spending my life, of offering up my life, my various ordeals and my few rare joys, in vain. Apparently in vain.

There was a time, not so long ago, when "holding out" this way in the face of almost continual failure, or else obtaining such mixed results that even one's accomplishments couldn't be called successes, when facing this depressing emptiness was viewed by our superiors with evangelical understanding of the pastoral ministry. They gave us encouragement, not often, but enough to help us persevere. "The sterility of your life is only on the surface," or "Have you forgotten the Gospel? Unless the seed die, will it bear fruit?" That was not very "original," to use my lady caller's expression, but it was, every time, a dip into the Fountain of Youth. I came out cheered up for six months!

Today, I hear again and again, I read: the "outlook" has changed; the "approach" to the apostolate is no longer the same. A kind of pragmatism has insinuated itself into our thinking. What has become of true and false, of virtue and cowardice, of holiness and its opposite? It is the man who acts according to the formulas who is held in high esteem. These formulas are all catalogued. Prudence and competence require us to conform to them. The apostolate is no longer the loving, anxious, silent search for the lost sheep, but a scientific experiment; the apostle is no longer a shepherd, but a research worker.

I am too old to change. I know some colleagues who have used these techniques to great advantage, and I applaud. But I am just not made of the same stuff.

A colleague who understands the problem from bitter experience once wrote me: "My dear friend, have courage. Don't be in too much of a hurry. The Hebrews wandered for forty years in the desert before they crossed the Jordan! Perhaps, like Moses, you will see only from afar that 'land flowing with milk and honey.' But what would have happened if Moses had lost heart?"

His words are a comfort to me.

I'LL NEVER get used to this coastal winter.

Back home it is foggy, too, and damp, but the air is healthier. You take deep drafts of it. There are very cold days, filled with sunshine which, completely under winter's spell, doesn't give much warmth, but is exceptionally bright. And often, in the early morning, the dawn tints the branches that are heavy with hoarfrost. That is how our trees take their revenge for being deprived of leaves. The sun delights in making their diamond ornaments sparkle. As it rises, its plunging rays invade the woods; the branches lighten and straighten up, as the frost crashes to the ground with a dry, shell-like sound; a faint mist appears, and in exaltation my sun, back there, takes possession of the world.

Just the memory of it gave me the courage to go out into this pea soup, happy in spite of everything. I was thinking— not for the first time—that the lives of saints have never been —will never be—fully known. I myself live at an immeasurable distance from sanctity, and yet in the lives of saints presented for public consumption I can easily discern what has been left in the inkwell.

The method is well known. Could it be any different? It ought to be. First one goes through the archives. One selects certain actions and manufactures a saint, transparently designed for propaganda purposes. This saint is then used to justify traditional propositions. One wants him to be ascetic, pious, and obedient, so that is what he will be. He will be because, in fact, he was. It is not a lie. Everything falls neatly into place. One declares, "We were right! He was, indeed, a saint." And when the reader closes the book, he should declare, "Everything turned out right."

It all turned out so well that if this saint were to come back, he would laugh as, in saints' memory, a saint has never laughed. Am I leaning toward heresy? It is so easy! Once I preached on this theme, but I was most circumspect. One of the misfortunes of our orthodoxy is precisely this perpetual necessity of being circumspect. I can just hear our resuscitated saint! He wouldn't go all around Robin Hood's barn. He would say: "How naïve you are, and how little you ask! Of course, I slept on a board. I fasted a little more than most. I even obeyed my bishop, all the while retaining my right to speak frankly to him. I prayed a lot, too. My sanctity? ... You have bound it to these actions with strong ropes.

"Only I assure you that when I came before God, I saw the picture in a different light, and before I was judged, I had a chance to look at my true portrait as long as I wanted to. Your book wasn't of much use.

"Finally I was admitted, it is true, into the company of saints. I will spend eternity trying to find out just why. I am slowly beginning to understand that it was because at a given moment of my life on earth—in that immense silence which filled me when I sought out my soul and took hold of it, heavy as it was and too tightly attached to my body—I had the courage not to lie. Who knew of it? Who could possibly know? These things passed between me and myself, by day and by night, in that abyss of light and shadow called my soul, at the precise moments (very numerous) when I took that soul by the shoulders and pushed it forward, saying, 'Look here! This is the way to go!'

"A body is heavy, opaque, refractory. They say it is the one that makes things go wrong. And the soul? . . . Do you think it is so light and docile? I launched my soul (and my heart with it) a thousand times toward the stars. They never found their orbit. They fell back down. I picked them up; I launched them again.

"It is easy and painful to lacerate one's skin; it is spectacular; it leaves scars; it causes comment. Fasting also disciplines the body, whether imposed by will power or by force. The Germans knew the trick: stale bread (a hundred and fifty grams a day) and tap water. After a week, there was no need for guards. No one had the slightest desire to escape. But to become a saint, that isn't enough.

"The hardest thing about becoming a saint is getting one's soul accustomed to dizziness, one's heart to disgust; and everything in us that is unseen, to that NOTHING—understand me, that NOTHING—called believing. Christian civilization, which is so highly prized, the conversion of unbelievers, the acquisition of personal merits (which are too highly acclaimed)— they all exist, of course, but they hardly count at the moment of choice; and in order to plunge oneself alive into that nothing of 'I believe,' one has to have, I swear to you, less flashy reasons. The rest is given in addition. We don't count for much in the process. It happens all by itself, whenever a Christian decides to be a little less of a coward."

Oh, yes, I hear very well. That is how my saint talks. So it is easier for me to recite my breviary, thinking of the hoarfrost back at home, of my woods amazed to be so beautiful, of my sun and my winter sky, than to get up and start for the seashore in this thick air that looks like soot. And why? What

64

for? To say what, while shoving my soul forward by the shoulders the way you push a child along, forcing a smile to my lips?

But I did go out: "Good morning . . . and your boy? Is he better? . . . Come now, tomorrow, believe me, you'll be able to go out fishing again. . . . You come to choir practice this evening, little one. . . . No, it wasn't nice of you to misbehave, but it would be even worse if you didn't try again to be good. You wouldn't want that?"

I'm not very good at that sort of thing.

TODAY I took my walking stick.

I brought it with me from home. I had cut it in a beech copse. Now it is dry and light, just right for my hand. It doesn't have a handle like a cane. I don't like canes. A childhood complex. A cane looks bourgeois; it suggests an old gentleman, a stroller, a time-waster, a good-for-nothing. My stick—much longer than a cane—I carry like a shepherd's crook. I reinforced the end of it with three big nails so it wouldn't wear down. It helps me to walk and makes me feel young again.

As soon as I take it in my hand, my flock is there in front of me, my dog Fidèle at my side. I feel like whistling, so I whistle. I look for nettles, to knock off their tips, but here there are only a few stunted brambles. I'm on my way . . . I'm setting out for my meadow. Soon I will find my ditch, the arbor of branches where I built my cabin, my "house-in-the-meadow," my enchanted domain. I can see it still. At the back, the great root of an ash, which I used for a bench. There I would be at home, with my dog, my birds, my spiders, my ants eternally passing, my flock before my eyes. My dog would look at them and at me. If men knew how to look at each other the way a dog looks at one, there wouldn't be any wars.

When it rained, my dog would huddle under my coat. Only his head poked out, and we would tell each other our secrets. I have never confided as much to any man as I did to that dog. Youngsters have a lot of troubles. How do they bear them if they have no dog?

I must get a dog here. But would he be as intelligent and good as Fidèle? Poor Fidèle! He developed rabies and my father had to shoot him. I wanted to bury him myself. I can still see the spot.

And they expect me to forget! To be fair, no one told me that I ought to forget. But they implied that I ought not to let my memory be encumbered with dead images.

Dead?

Let me live, then! Don't cut me off from my roots. Isn't it enough to have transplanted me? I can't help it. I have nothing left, after God, except my meadow . . .

Look, there, the stream. Beside it, my willows with their silver-lined leaves that turn their backs to the wind. My old elms full of knots, with ugly, pointed toadstools growing at their feet. You mustn't pick them. They rot there or dry out.

To reach my meadow, there are three bridges. They aren't all alike. The last one has no railing. I used to be afraid of it. Farther on, a great ditch where my grandfather used to steep his flax. The water from the stream flowed into it through a sluice-gate.

I don't know the scientific names of the flowers. No one ever taught me. There were flowers everywhere, in all seasons. All colors, all shapes. In the spring, the snowdrops with their peaked hats, tender as dew. You don't dare touch them. Then the violets, the little daisies, the buttercups. When June comes,

66

with the haymaking, there are the tall daisies, which always grow higher than the hay. Like snow flakes swinging to and fro. The dark bushes had already bloomed in April, rather comical with their flowers coming out before the leaves. Frost is dangerous as long as their fragile petals haven't fallen. And then come the hawthornes. That is in May, the month of the Virgin. In the evening I used to go to May Devotions. The path through my meadow smelled good, so good that it almost made one want to be an angel. The hay was already high. The wheat was growing. "It prickles," they used to say, for "the month of May never leaves without putting ears on the wheat." The breeze would caress them, and they would bow down, then straighten up again. They were happy. It is nothing, but it grips your heart and you feel a strange happiness that is like anguish. Strange, perhaps because it is real, not adulterated, not fabricated, real! The alfalfa was almost ready for the first holocaust. The grapevines began to bud. They would flower, at exactly the same time as the morning glory. Of all fragrances the grapevine in flower is the most delicate, the most subtle. Anyone who hasn't smelt that perfume doesn't know what perfume is. I will smell it here next June, or probably sooner, for the vines here should be a bit "ahead" of those at home.

And then, in the evening, when I came back from the meadow, the festoon of my mountains! The sun would go down, and I would follow its descent, accompany it to its setting. It took its time. I loved to watch it disappear. When there was nothing left but a tiny slice, brilliant, gleaming, the color of orange peel, another kind of anguish gripped me (I don't know which one in the scientists' list!) and I would have liked to run, follow it, never leave it, not lose it. I wished it would stand still! It had no right to disappear, since I didn't want it to. But it would disappear nevertheless. I would look for its last rays in the clouds, in the sky. I envied those clouds for possessing it still, without me. Night fell. The hay stood straight. It was the hour when the sparrows gathered in the Virginia creeper. There was no end to their chirping, and you could hear the rustling of their wings among the leaves. Then the dogs would begin howling from farm to farm. What makes dogs howl at night? Owls passed over my head so impudently near that, trembling with fear, I bent my neck to avoid being touched by them. . . .

And then? And then? Always the same question. . . .

Part II

The Encounter

.

I WILL get to bed late if I want to write it all. . . .

I am anxious to have a written record of what happened today. Something serious has entered my life, which may very well upset its tranquillity. Time will tell whether I am exaggerating the importance of these events.

The walk I took day before yesterday gave me the desire to take another. My intention was twofold: (1) to seek God more intently, and to try to glorify Him by a more explicit acceptance of my exile; (2) to take visual possession of my domain. I don't like to live without an exact idea of the topography of my surroundings. From the hillside, I can see my whole parish with its rows of houses set along the shore, and, turning my back to the sea, I can make out the canton at the far end of the little trolley line. I gauge the distances. I feel less isolated. Taking possession visually like this, elementary as it is, satisfies me, reassures me, cheers me.

The wind was blowing from the sea, not steadily, but in gusts, wild, incomprehensible. Because of its violence and even more because of its caprices, I wasn't quite at ease, not quite in communion with the elements. Soon my presbytery looked minute, and on the side toward the sea, everything blended into that mysterious and moving immensity.

When I reached the top of the hill, where the municipality has installed a few benches (for the summer tourists, I suppose), I looked toward the plain and saw the Dean about a hundred yards away, signaling to me. I hurried to meet him.

In full daylight, in the full wind, almost under the full sky on this plateau, it was easier for me to look at him than it was the other day in the sacristy and in his house, where I was hindered by my heart beating a call to arms.

He is of medium height, thick-set, broad-shouldered, with a rather short neck; darting eyes whose flame is slightly dimmed, a shrewd mouth which could easily become bitter, prominent forehead widespread as a fan.

He gives the impression of being an intelligent, realistic and practical man, without complexes; a good sort, prone to irony and to gaiety; but also of being a man who has suffered, and whose spontaneity has been dulled by it. I noticed his heavy, thick hands, made to hold tools; his knotty fingers, his clean nails. He was neatly dressed, but his shoes were very worn. His step is firm, his gait is sure. He walks straight ahead, right through the puddles. His handshake is firm. His voice is tenor verging on baritone, musical, rich in overtones, very pleasant. He speaks easily, rather too fast, using precise words, but with humility. He seems to be straightforward, careful both to avoid weakness and not to wound others. I was instantly drawn to him.

"I was coming to visit you," he said without affectation, "and here you have come half the way. What shall we do? Shall we stay here, on this bench?"

"Monsieur le Doyen, we won't be half warm enough here."

"Well then, let's go to your house."

We began talking without difficulty or embarrassment: of my health, of my getting settled, of the climate. We walked

72

along slowly. He is more sure-footed than I, and less cautious. I avoided the rocks. I prefer climbing. We went toward the sea, where the waves were invading the beach and making the boats dance. The wind blew full in our faces. It carried our words away. We had to walk closer together. Before our eyes, my parish spread out, growing from one minute to the next. I think it was the sight of its low red roofs which made him say, without warning, "Naturally you are feeling a bit melancholy. Even the strongest go through it . . ." Then, stopping a moment and pointing to the houses: "Are they starting to grow fond of you?"

What could I answer? He guessed my perplexity and was about to relieve it when I said, "One thing I'm sure of: I am already very fond of them."

He stopped again, a fraction of a second, and turned to look at me.

I went on, "Surely you know that as we grow older our hearts don't feel quite so much the need to receive . . ."

"We all say that. But it would be too bad if those words, which have been repeated for centuries, expressed the truth. Words are like newsprint; they convey a great many misapprehensions." And, after a moment: "So they sent you to us! Bah! Here or there . . ."

He wasn't looking at me then. There are some things you don't say to a man's face. He was trying to capture my sympathy.

"Ah, yes . . ." Then he came out with: "Our bishop spoke to me about you . . ."

He didn't finish his sentence. My answer was supposed to follow, and he was waiting for its impact.

"If you want to do me a service, Monsieur le Doyen, keep me in ignorance of it."

His hands, which had been clasped behind his back up until now, fell to his sides. There was a silence, neither light nor

73

heavy—just a silence. He shoved a stone aside with his foot. The wind, separating us, entered into our exchange.

Without raising his voice, seemingly indifferent to whether or not he was heard, he said, as though to himself, "Another one beaten and bruised . . ."

Stopping abruptly and touching his arm, I replied firmly, "Those who have been beaten and bruised don't like to have their wounds probed, Monsieur le Doyen. The only important thing is to carry on without flinching and without complaining, and get one's work done."

His eyes were looking into mine. We made contact for the first time on the level of mystery. If there had been a wayside calvary at that moment, we would have looked at it together.

He said, "Yes."

We had reached the village. Some children greeted us. I resumed the conversation: "What kind of man is the bishop? I have dealt only with one of his vicars general. I haven't met the bishop himself."

"Upright. Ascetic. Inclined to traditionalism and therefore without major preoccupations." He laughed. "Traditionalism is an automatic distributor. You pull down the handle and the answer falls out, wrapped and ready for immediate consumption. He is fair, I think, but too easily influenced to be completely so——"

"But I thought that the traditionalists——"

"No, you didn't think that at all. You know, as well as I do, that traditionalism is for external use only." He went back to his description: ". . . somewhat more papist than the Pope, and more sensitive than he seems. Kind. Aloof from life. Stubborn, which does him harm. All in all, a good man."

"A good speaker?"

"Always the same sermon, but at least he does preach. What a strange job a bishop has! . . . He has nothing against you. He is waiting——"

74

"What is he waiting for? Miracles?"

"No. He is waiting just for the sake of waiting, because it is an attitude to adopt—you know it very well. . . . Come on, let's go into the house."

He stopped me on the threshold. His hand dropped rather lightly on my shoulder and he said, almost roguishly, "God sent his Son into this world on a 'perhaps.' Our bishops give us their trust only on a 'for sure.' The history of the Church"— he lowered his voice—"is written between those two phrases. That is why there will always be an ambiguity."

"And what can be done about it?"

"We must always go back to the beginning: 'Peter, do you love me?' "

These words, plunging us straight back into the strictest orthodoxy, relieved the tension. I motioned to him to come in.

"You've fixed the place up very nicely," he said. "Good, good!" Then, sitting down, "You are really in luck."

He was throwing me a rope. He was going to speak his piece. For a few moments, I would have to listen to him. I tried to distract him from this position, and divert the discussion into lighter channels.

"In luck, Monsieur le Doyen? A man who has been beaten and bruised . . . ?"

His eyes fixed on the ceiling, he said wearily, "I am curé of a canton——"

"And so? 'Peter, do you love me?' "

"It is ungovernable! I am not the only one of my kind, but I am what I am."

"In a canton, Monsieur le Doyen, there are too many people—and not enough."

"Ah, yes. And that is why the architect's wife thinks she is the Queen of Sheba, the tax collector thinks he is Minister of Finance, the doctor fancies himself a famous specialist, and the leader of the bugle corps imagines he is Bruno Walter in person! And so on all down the line! Don't laugh! What do you expect a poor curé to do in the midst of so many prodigies unless he is the Pope himself? And I am only a peasant." He caught himself. "When you come down to it, all those demigods, every one without exception, are just like me. You did well to tell them so the other day. But that doesn't change anything; it just annoys them."

"I beat my head against the same wall for ten years."

"I have been at it for fifteen. But that would be nothing if 'they' understood us; if there was a little opening, a little blue sky, from the direction of our superiors."

"Can I offer you some refreshment, Monsieur le Doyen?"

He wasn't listening. He had begun to pace the room.

I said, to get a discussion going, "Were you ever a soldier?"

"I was even a sergeant in the French army."

"Under fire?"

"Under fire."

"That's no picnic! And did you always bless our High Command?"

He stopped pacing and had the grace to smile. "I like that, coming from you."

I caught the ball. "Would you believe that I have already received calls from two of your parishioners? A mathematics professor——"

He burst into laughter, clear, ringing, contagious. I laughed with him.

"That one is dangerously close to being a Jehovah's Witness. In a couple of weeks he'll get himself rebaptized by immersion. He has another mania, letter-writing."

"I am already aware of that. And . . . a Colonel's wife . . ."

"The President of the Catholic Women's Club—and indomitable. We'd better drop the subject, if you don't mind."

"Just a word about the Colonel?"

"No! Or else I'll talk for an hour and go home disgusted with myself—and you!"

His eyes turned light. His lips were pursed in a peculiar way. He was laughing inside. Perhaps because some image had connected in his mind with the preceding one.

"You read, I see?" he said to me. "Perhaps you also write. You have the time. Not I. Lucky fellow, I tell you!"

And after a silence. "There is a book here for you to write. A sort of comic novel, a play of marionettes who look as though they stand up by themselves, but whose strings are manipulated by their own selfishness, ostentation, gossip, opinions, ambition, stupidity, a lot of knowing lies, even more spitefulness, egoism, and a so-called solid piety. I needn't go into detail. You can guess the rest . . ."

"I have only to consult my memory. The flood-gates would never be closed."

"I haven't been down to the beach for a long time," he said. "Come on. I love the wind."

"Is it the wind that attracts you?"

"No."

"Well, then, let's go and see *them*," I said. "You need it. So do I."

I took my long coat, my walking stick, my beret. We were just going to cross the threshold when a sudden force—strong as a lightning flash—paralyzed me. It didn't surprise me. That hand which rivets me to the ground; that sudden blindness; that inner voice with its imperative command to speak, to speak at once and say everything that comes, not from my head, but from that well of words in my breast; my inability to react; all those fruits of emotions too long repressed, or sparked unpredictably by some uncontrollable contact of ideas or contradictory feelings—all that is part of my hidden inner being, below the level of my will. So I knew that I was going

77

to pronounce—that I had to pronounce that very minute—
the words which always prove to be my doom. My enemies
have only to gather them one by one, as though in a basket,
and present them with cunning, to make me look like a madman. I am no longer master even of my tongue, which articu-
lates with frightening slowness, adopts an Italian pronuncia-
tion, and acts like a cowering slave of this hidden force. But
my ideas are brutally logical, images come to me, the intona-
tion and the transitions are true.

I gripped the Dean's arm very hard. He looked at me, surprised. Had my features altered? He leaned slightly forward,
opened his mouth to ask me something, but the flood had
already begun:

"Monsieur le Doyen," I said. "I haven't introduced myself.
I was introduced to you by someone else. But I owe you the
truth, even if it doesn't conform to the truth of my superiors.
I don't bear any grudge against them. Their decisions have a
place in the plan of Providence, entering by a secret door, the
one which opens onto the Mystery of God. They never cross
its threshold. They push others through, never knowing the
joys and tears which God has in store for those who have
passed over. They direct—the word is accurate—they direct
without knowing it, without understanding it, blindly, with
the help of reports and records, with the intelligence of wise
but fallible men; they direct in that desert where God holds
his counsels and arranges his rendezvous. They direct in that
silence where, as the prophet has said, God speaks to the heart,
where the eyes of the blind and the ears of the deaf are opened,
where the parched soil is changed into springs of running
water. They direct, with a precision which cannot have any
other but God for its author, where the passing wind carries
the songs of angels, where the Devil stumbles, where the
Church is being built. So who could imagine that I feel bitter?
Even the simple-minded couldn't get lost on the path I am

following. Yes, I agreed to leave—and I left. They are glad to have me where I am. I don't delay them any more. I have entered alive into a vast night. To go forward, I now look for my way in Heaven. They can breathe without feeling my breath. My mistakes no longer slow down their machine.

"That is one aspect of the case, my case. It should be enough to put your mind at rest. I am not a renegade. I am not a rebel. I am a free man. A peasant doesn't unfrock, or if he does, he is a false peasant. He may be given another earth to plow, another field to sow; it doesn't matter much, if at all. Wherever a peasant may be, he lives and dies with a spade in his hand. If he doesn't, he is a traitor. Traitor to God, to his land, to his planting, his wheatfield, his vineyard, his dog, everything. And a coward. A real peasant never breaks his word. He isn't even the lord and master of his oath. The words he pronounces, the promises he makes, are those of a hundred—a thousand—generations who have gone before him; and the echo of a loyalty which stretches from century to century back to his origins. I am not a hireling; I am a shepherd."

He stood with his hands at his sides, as he had done on the path. His eyes widened, his breath came faster. With an extremely gentle gesture, almost the gesture of a woman, he drew my coat back onto my shoulders from which it had slipped.

"It was time," he said.

"It was the time, Monsieur le Doyen, when one doesn't refuse to give oneself to God. The time when the fires are lighted at the stake. There is no lack of wood. All those one has loved bring their fagots. Nor are arms lacking to lift you onto them; nor ropes, nor shouts, nor laughter, nor songs. You just have to leave it to them. They manage everything. You have no one but your dog left to look at you with loving eyes. If they notice it, they kill him."

"And your family?"

"Nothing left . . ."

"Then we are twice brothers."

"There is another aspect of the question: I have never been so naïve as to think that a pastor could firmly establish the practice of charity in his parish. That would be too good to be true. Heaven doesn't come down to earth like that. But when a pastor—contradicted by the Queen of Sheba, by the Minister of Finance and all their associates (which wouldn't be much and would even be quite natural), contradicted furthermore by his superiors, who give audiences to the Queen of Sheba, the Minister of Finance and all their associates—can no longer even see justice done; when in his parish the poor man is crushed and the proud man triumphs; that pastor ought to shake the dust from his feet, and go away, anywhere, any way he can; just leave, escape. Otherwise, what is he accomplishing?"

The Dean said softly, painfully, "You really want to hurt me?"

"Are we still at that point? Hurt you? Because your heart is beating as fast as mine? Because your head is feeling light? And because your hands, like mine, are seeking support? If justice itself is absent, where can you introduce your doctrine? When a priest's word runs up against a stone wall, it falls back onto his heart heavy with the wrath of God. We must accept this void, enter into this desert. But we mustn't cheat. Do you know why the world is in such sad condition, and the Church is still so small? It is because priests have been afraid of death. I couldn't live that way any more in good conscience. I was suffocating. I was only a clown doing my act. They had won. They had succeeded in wrapping the Gospel as I preached it in the wrinkled rind of my daily blunders. I wasn't unhappy. They still consented to have me say Masses for them. It isn't the least bit dangerous to have Masses celebrated, and it made it look as though, in addition to offering prayers for their dead, they were paying for their curé's sermons. They were sorry for me when I was sick. They greeted me politely; most of them went to church and to confession; they received communion on feast days. They all had acceptable alibis, and supported by them, their luke-warm souls were untroubled. But in the deepest part of their being, in that place where resolutions are made, where transformations take place, where we hesitate to say 'no' when the truth rends us, I could not touch them. In fact no one had ever touched them there. They were fond of me in their odd way, which accepts falsehood if it is well decked out. And I was no saint. . . ."

"Where are the saints?"

"Everywhere. But if you look for them, the Devil makes them so ridiculous that they faint with shame in the midst of the laughter. What are saints good for? God knows. We don't."

"You needed to have more obvious faults . . ."

"I have been told as much. But take those obvious and vulgar faults, those faults which make a priest popular—let's not talk about cultivating them; I could never acquire them. I used to know a priest who got drunk almost every day, and when he was drunk, he used such foul language that children had to be kept away from him. I am not making this up. The whole canton went to his funeral, and he was genuinely mourned. From the pulpit, at his funeral Mass, a vicar general pronounced the eulogy. I celebrated the Mass in anguish, weighed down with gloom. It still distresses me. I can still hear that sermon. I kept saying to myself: What about me? Should I take to drink too? Should I get myself picked up out of ditches night after night? I just can't do it. I don't want to. They trample on my heart; that is to be expected. What good is a priest's heart? But I still have my head. Should I offer it to them, throw it to them? Go mad, not with that lucid madness which leads to the rendezvous with God, but mad with wine, mad with alcohol, mad with delusions; really mad, curled up on my belly with my cassock all muddy, drooling from the mouth, my eyes out of focus, having to be dragged up by my arms? At that price, I would have the right to their pity, their patience, their love; to such words as 'Poor thing! Well, he's a good fellow all the same'; to their tears, to their affectionate presence. I can't do it! I simply can't. To me, a ditch means a garden where violets grow, and night is the starry stage where Christmas first was sung! How could I possibly look upon them with a drunkard's eyes?"

"Shall we go out?" he said.

I had sat down. I remember that I was sitting. My stick had slipped between my legs. I was afraid. Afraid of dramatizing myself, of putting myself in the spotlight. A flame died.

"Yes," I said. "I need it."

"You said you needed to see—your own kind."

The spark suddenly flared up again. But this time I was able to restrain it. I answered in a tired voice, "My own kind. Yes. They have their faults, too. They are weak, too; not excessively straightforward, often sly, cunning, not always as poor as they pretend, avaricious, but ... they don't prevent me from breathing. I can wait for them. I can watch them, I tell you, and they don't frighten me. I listen to them. They listen to me. I am fond of them. It's unreasonable. Why is it so? Why? Race? Blood? The same origin? The same human condition? Am I prejudiced? Then is it—could it be—purely sentimental? Are they my last branch? ... For there still has to be one ..."

We went out.

But I am tired of writing tonight....

82

I WANT to be objective.

I am watching myself from day to day.

This will lead me where life usually leads us, which means we never know where. My art will consist in being faithful to this plan. A man as clumsy and unlettered as I cannot embellish things. Objectivity is the only honest path I can follow in keeping this Journal. A documentary film of the truth, the record of events as they happen, in their outward form, and in whatever I can grasp of their inner meaning. This presupposes a certain naïveté, but I don't see why that should disturb me.

So, before getting back to the Dean's visit, which at its very end took on a character of extraordinarily tragic intensity—to be objective and leave out nothing that I feel is important—I will relate another event which took place after this visit, and which therefore dates from this morning.

After a very bad night spent thinking over the meaning of the Dean's attitudes and his parting words, I went out quite early. I had two aims in mind: to see whether the *Marie-Jeanne* had sailed, and to visit a family who have a son and daughter in my catechism class. In the only street in the village, a car caught up to me, slowed down and stopped, its occupant obviously meaning to speak to me. It was the bailiff of the canton. He is the perfect physical type for the job. Thin, almost floating in his suit, which is very clean and well pressed, an angular face, ashen complexion, the outward appearance of a sick and nervous person. He has cultivated a habit of speaking softly, cautiously, as though while chatting with friends, his mind is on the summons in his pocket. He must be an excellent bailiff, silent, conciliatory, and wily. He was very polite, very pleasant, and apparently pleased to have met me.

I was scrupulously careful not to ask why he was visiting my parish. Out of discretion, for one thing, but also to avoid hearing news which was sure to be disagreeable: tenants thrown out, family quarrels, and so on. Why should I know about these things, since there is nothing I can do? But, since he seemed to be intelligent and sincere, I applied a rule which I have adopted as a law for conducting conversations: to avoid as far as possible the usual commonplaces and clichés which do not afford anyone any enrichment. So, as soon as the ice was broken, and we were able to exchange impressions freely, I allowed myself to ask him a question which I have been mulling over for years, and which, to tell the truth, I have never had the courage to ask a man of the law.

"My dear sir," I said, "you are in contact with a great many people in your office and elsewhere. Usually, these contacts come about because of people's difficulties, in which their honesty, their frankness, their Christian or pagan attitudes come into play. Now, here is my question, and I would like a candid answer: Do you find any noticeable difference between the behavior of a practicing Christian and any other baptized person who has forgotten the way to church, or to be more exact, between a Christian and a Jew, between a Christian and an acknowledged Freemason, between a so-called man of the Church and a fervent secularist, obsessed with secularism?"

His answer was not immediately forthcoming, though I sensed that he could have replied at once. His delay did not proceed from an intellectual doubt or the need to consider. He hesitated because he wondered for a few seconds whether

84

he could choose between a pleasant lie and the distressing truth. Then he answered firmly, "No difference."

I thanked him. The conversation became jovial, almost too much so, with each of us making an effort, out of evident good will, to help bury this answer. But we were both thinking about it to the end.

Dramatic aspect of a Redemption misunderstood.

How long, O Lord?

The *Marie-Jeanne* has sailed.

When we left my house, the Dean didn't want to go through the village. We took the path along the beach, the one that goes to my old woman's house. Gusts of wind blew the salt spray into our faces. I took care not to complain, although it was very disagreeable, and I ended up not even bothering to wipe my face.

Here, no one ever gets angry with the sea. The sea is never wrong. It is the wind, the storm. No fault of the sea's. They are rather sorry for it. They don't say so, but they really seem to pity the sea.

"The *Marie-Jeanne,* now," the Dean said to me suddenly. "I know the captain. His boat is named for a girl he didn't marry. She married someone else because his 'hair was blacker.' Try to figure it out! She left this part of the country long ago. I wonder if he even knows what became of her. He never married. He lives on the sea. Someday he'll die there."

A man was coming toward us. "That's the man," said the Dean in my ear.

Immediately I began to rack my brain for something to say to him. A complete blank. The Dean called out to him, "Oh, don't worry about the ropes. They'll hold."

"Yes," replied the man, "but I'm going to take a look all the same."

The Dean smiled. The man walked into the water heedlessly, jumped onto his boat, and inspected the mooring ropes. He didn't touch them. We heard the motor start, accelerate once or twice, then stop. The Dean shouted into the wind, "When do you sail?"

"Tomorrow."

"It won't be any calmer."

The man made a gesture expressing indifference, and looked at the waves with eyes which saw there something I will never see. He was wearing flat wooden shoes, roughly made, and much worn. Trousers rolled up, head uncovered, chest bare, he went about on the boat, busy with chores which were incomprehensible to me. The waves bounced him, mocked him. Surefooted, he paid no attention to them. He made me think of those clowns children play with, which have some hidden mechanism to keep them on balance.

I said, just for the sake of saying something, "If the sea is this rough on the beach, what must it be like two or three kilometers from here?"

The Dean smiled again.

The man came back. He didn't even look at me, and I felt hurt. He was dripping wet, but he wasn't shivering, in spite of the cold wind. His eyes were dark and resolute as he said to the Dean, "She has weathered others much worse. Today I was wrong to hesitate. Now it's too late, but tomorrow . . ."

The Dean answered, seemingly with the intention of being persuasive, "Will you be going alone?"

"Who knows?" And, leaving us: "With her, I am never alone."

The Dean gave a deep sigh. From this short exchange, I knew that he felt proud, that he might well have said, "You see what they are made of here!" He was silent, because, I sensed, he was absorbed in other feelings. I couldn't pin it down. I think he was happy and apprehensive. Apprehensive

86

chiefly because of that sense of destiny which clings to these men of headstrong, passionate character who risk everything for their love.

Night fell. The water turned black. Soon I would hear only that tireless, everlasting sound like that of a pendulum—the waves breaking on the sand. No one can say it offers much variety. In the daytime, I can stand it, but at night it frightens me.

"Let's go through the village," said the Dean.

We passed a few men in doorways. He greeted them by their first names. He laughed, but now in another key, more gently, much more gently, somewhat absently. Within him, anxiety was breaking through. Some drinkers lingering in an inn saw him and invited him to join them.

I looked at him. "Come to my house," I said. "We'll have time before you have to catch the last trolley." And I added, with somewhat feigned gaiety, "I can offer you supper at least."

He didn't answer. I no longer existed for him. He straightened his shoulders, which had been slumped over for the past few minutes, and went toward the inn with a firm step. I was alarmed. "Who and what is this man?" I wondered. "What demon possesses him? Why does he want to drink? What secret is he harboring? What suffering does he want to drown in wine?"

I followed humbly, my heart heavy. Beneath the sad electric bulbs, the faces of the men around the table reassured me. These men weren't making fun; they didn't want to play a joke on us. They were real, sincere, happy, not drunk in the least. The Dean sat down among them and was immediately at ease. He accepted a little hard cider. He held his glass in his large hands and rolled it back and forth as the others did. I saw his demon depart. For how long? I was prepared to spend the night in that inn at his side, out of dread of what would happen when we left. He was calm, very dignified. He was completely absorbed in the conversation: the children, the sick, the old folks, the sale of fish. . . .

As we were leaving, he turned to me, put a kindly hand on my shoulder, and said to them, "This one won't ever go fishing for lobster, but he's a good sort. Pay attention to what he says."

I was grateful to him. When we were alone again outside, I wanted to thank him, but he wouldn't have it. He replied dryly and ungraciously, "Soon they will be as fond of you as you are of them. Why should you doubt it?"

He looked at his watch. I heard him say, to himself, "I have just time, but then, what difference does it make? I can just as well walk back." Again his shoulders hunched over, his head bowed into the wind. His fingers worked in his closed fists as though kneading something in his palms. He was facing something heroically, but he was nothing more than a hunted animal. At times he lifted his head and his eyes stared into the night.

We were slowly nearing the trolley shed when suddenly in my head a veil was torn away. I began to blame myself: "That man didn't come here to see you or to hear you, to take a walk along the shore path or even to drink that bit of cider with a few fishermen. He came because he couldn't stand being alone any longer, because he wanted you to be in communion with his suffering, because he was expecting you to take him down from his cross! What secret, what suffering, what dark night is crushing him? Into what depths has he fallen? That was why he came. 'It was time,' his 'time,' the time of extinguished dawns, dead hopes; the time for the death knell. That was the point he had reached; that crossroads, that hesitation, that despair, that last cry, which bursts forth just before the heart stops loving! And I saw nothing, felt nothing, guessed nothing! I talked about myself, my

88

problem. He was patient enough to listen, accept, hold on. During those moments, he had been searching for my soul, timidly, like a child who knocks on a door and listens for signs of life inside, a footstep, a lock squeaking, and who wonders, faint with fright, who will open to him, and whether he will be welcomed or rejected. When he suggested that we go out, he hadn't heard anything but my complaint. He went out when he was sure that he would hear nothing more. And then he went in quest of the water, the wind, the sand, a boat, a bit of human warmth from that fisherman who is closer to him than I am, an inn, and a drink of cider. But there was no contact. No cleft opened in the rock. The angel of Annunciations was silent. I hadn't understood that this man was bleeding to death; that he was suffocating in the dark. I hadn't seen that he was agonizing, screaming, dying there before me. At least I would treasure that gesture of his when he drew my coat back over my shoulder! At least I would have that gesture, and it would stay in my eyes now wet with tears and in my heart which had softened too late. He was going ahead; I followed. Where was he heading? I no longer existed for him. I had proved to be just like the rest, just as self-centered, just as distracted. I wanted to stop him, throw myself in his path, say to him, 'Speak, for heaven's sake, speak! Don't go off without telling me your trouble. Stay with me tonight. Together, by lamplight, we will search in your mystery, in God's mystery, for our harmony, our music, our song, our cry, our tears—and your peace! Your relief, do you understand? Your smile. We will find your smile again. . . . I will keep silent . . . I will only look at your wound and pull your coat back up around your neck. You won't be cold, and perhaps I will become the one you are waiting for.' "

But it was too late. He was too tall by that time; his head was lost in the gliding clouds. His lips moved, but I couldn't hear any sound. His immense hands continued to crumple his anger. His joints cracked. I was no more than a ridiculous dwarf stumbling along beside him. The storm was so violent that the waves seemed to pursue us. Would it never end? Is this, then, what agony is?

I felt a guilty relief when I saw the light of the shed swaying behind the pines. Crooked branches projected their ghostly shadows across the path. I prayed: "My God, let there be enough of that feeble light left! Let the trolley be still there!" I was ashamed. His hour had struck. He had become too tall, and by now I was crawling. I was crawling; I knew that I was crawling, that I hadn't risen with him, that I was not rising, or even trying to rise; that I was afraid to rise.

The streetcar conductor saw us. He would wait. . . .

The Dean stopped short. He stood there, speechless, and then turned around, looking for me. His hand reached out to press mine. He seemed strangely strong and calm. In a new and very gentle voice, he said, "What time is your parish Mass on Christmas Day?"

"Nine o'clock, Monsieur le Doyen."

"Fine. My Mass is at eleven. You will have time to come up. I want you to be there that day, near me."

"I will be there, Monsieur le Doyen . . ."

I wanted to embrace him, but he didn't seem to notice as he took his place beside the conductor—and then he disappeared from view.

"He disappeared . . .," I wrote last night.

It is true. I have lost sight of the immense body, the head that touched the stars. What caused that vision of great height and of enormous disproportion between us? Perhaps it was because, walking beside him, I suddenly had a revelation of our true dimensions. I felt that I was very small, a pigmy walking beside a giant. At these moments, the eyes see something other than the physical. They take the measure not of the body, but of strength, courage, loneliness. It must be quite rare, but it does happen sometimes, so it would seem. . . .

He could have taken a seat by himself, but he sat down near the conductor, because he is the master of his soul, and can command his suffering and his secret. During that short ride, he must have made small talk, laughed, been just "the Dean," familiar in these parts for the last fifteen years. That is really not so bad!

That scene of yesterday is hard to forget. But I have to pay attention to business, and there are only three more days before Christmas. I have a brand-new crèche to finish. My youngsters made cardboard houses, a church, some really fine boats. Everyone is going to be pleased with it. And I have to rehearse the littlest ones for the Midnight-Mass procession, another of my innovations. A three-year-old will carry the Infant Jesus, and the others will follow behind him. All in white robes, the girls dressed as angels with wings. There is so much to be done. This paraliturgy is full of charm and freshness; my fishermen's wives were quite taken by it, and they are working, too. My choir is modest, but they will do their best, and I hope the people will join in and sing.

Although the memory of yesterday's scene may never altogether disappear, it will fade. But today those images, those few words have been haunting me. I am sure that the Dean would think me wrong. Writing to him would be meaningless. What could I write? How would I reach him, re-establish contact, touch his soul persuasively enough to gain admittance? I don't have time to go and see him, and if by some chance I could, he would be put out. A man of his mettle doesn't indulge in sentiment. The best I can offer him is silence. He would give me a cordial reception, keeping his own counsel. "What fair wind blows you our way? I have a hundred things to do. Don't you folks have to prepare for Christmas in your parish?"

He has closed the book. He will open it to the same page at his High Mass on Christmas.

His visit caused some comment in my parish. Favorable comment. Here, that priest is loved and respected. I knew that before I came he used to visit here often. He would go into my fishermen's homes and sit with them. He would stay until late, and some of the young people would walk him part of the way home.

The storm has let up after all. A fine mist lingers on, but it is slowly dissolving. The weather is almost warm. The sea is still rough, for no apparent reason. The winter, local people say. Mainly, it is dirty. I went out to gather shells for our crèche. At low tide you can find any number of them. I went by way of the path, and at the end of it I was pleased to find the old woman on her doorstep. To tell the truth, I would have been disappointed if she hadn't been at home. But when does she ever go out? Smoke was coming from the chimney. I went in and immediately felt at home. I feel at home wherever I don't have to talk. I set down my half-full basket and looked at the fire. The old lady burns pine cones mixed with a few branches. Her soup was boiling in a pot. I forgot everything, even her presence, and returned in memory to the fireplace of my earliest years, its great pot, and our bowls set in a semicircle in front of the hearth. Each of us had his own bowl. Mine was decorated with big red flowers, and as far back as I can remember, it was cracked.

"Clear soup? Thick?" My grandmother would cut bread for each of us the way we liked it. The vegetables would float on the surface of the soup. The bunch of leeks, tied with a string, was for my father. I liked the potatoes. They stayed firm during the cooking. I would eat them first, without mashing them. We would eat our soup standing up, talking. The flames from the hearth would light up the kitchen. The day was over, the cows milked. I would not have been able to express what I felt, but I knew obscurely that this was happiness. I have eaten a great many other soups, but never better, never even as good. We were poor, but we were never hungry.

Like my grandmother, this old woman knows the quality and worth of silence. She was listening to my inner thoughts. I picked up a branch and poked the fire. I love fire, just as I love wind and water—running water, not the rolling waves of the sea. Sitting in front of those crackling pine cones, I was filled with a vast sense of well-being, which I didn't analyze. You can't cut happiness up into little pieces. I was alone. I felt warm in body and heart. Long ago, at moments like this, my grandmother would say, "Stay there. Rest, my little one," and her words were like a caress on my forehead. Or, "Listen to the wind blow! We must say a prayer for the men at sea." She hadn't seen the sea; she never saw it. But some dread of it clung to her memory, perhaps from reading old sailors' tales. She was afraid; she trembled "for those who are on those boats, in the storm. The poor things," she would moan. "We are snug inside, but what of them?"

The old woman had put on her apron. We still hadn't said a word. She went out, probably to feed her animals. Where else would she be going and what would she be doing outside at this hour? I went on poking the embers. The end of my stick caught fire. I buried it in the ashes, then started all over. All I needed was my dog. Only one thing was different here— the smell of the fire. At home, it was less pungent, less resinous. I sat there in the half dark. My elongated shadow was dancing. I didn't see it, I sensed it. It took off from me, crossed the floor of beaten earth, outlined my shoulders and head on the wall. This projection of my self comforted me. No, nothing was changed. I had left it all behind, but nothing had changed. I had brought my home with me. My conversation with the Dean slipped away and sank into an unreal world. Everything he said, everything I felt when I was with him, that prelude to tragedy, that prologue before the curtain rises on the play, had been effaced. I will go to see him on Christmas. The half-opened book will be closed. We will laugh together. We won't even allude to what happened. Things can be so pleasant, so agreeable, so comforting. Like this fire which, without any searing flames, gives warmth and smells good.

She came back, took off her apron. She stepped lightly. I could not even feel the weight of her glance. She avoided looking at me, for fear that her eyes resting on me might shake me out of my well-being and break the spell. She came close to the hearth. Yes, the soup was ready.

"Dip me a bowl of it," I said.

She was happy. "How do you like it?"

"Thick, with a lot of vegetables."

She offered me a place at the table, but I refused.

The time had come to talk. You talk while you eat soup—what else can you do?

"We have made a fine crèche," I told her, "and the children will look beautiful. Are you coming to Midnight Mass?"

"I know that you have been making great preparations. I am happy about that Midnight Mass. I will surely be there. I have been wishing we had one for a long time."

"And will you sing?"

"As loud as I can. I know all the old Christmas songs by heart." And after a pause, "Keep on the same way. The people are fond of you. They like you because you work with your hands."

I smiled. "What else are they for?"

94

"When I see a priest," she said, "I try to picture him as a peasant, a workman, a fisherman. I say to myself, 'If all of a sudden he had to use his hands, his arms, to earn his living, and obey a boss, would he be able to do it? A boss is not easy to take!' If I can answer yes, his sermons do me good."

I didn't reply. I wanted to look at my hands, show them to her, open them wide in front of her, talk to her of my plow, my first pair of oxen, my field. But I kept quiet.

She continued, "I never go out any more, though once upon a time I was like everybody else. I have known priests of the sort who, in my opinion, talk too well to have much real spirit. Is it so easy to talk? But it isn't everything. It isn't even very much. It has to be a man who does the talking, a strong man, a leader."

Was she saying this for some purpose? The Dean's face passed before my eyes. I always hesitate to force the conversation in any one direction for my own ends, but wasn't this the moment to do it? I lowered my voice so as to leave her free to choose (whether to pursue her own idea, or take up mine) and I ventured to say, "I think our Dean is a man like that...."

She nodded and said softly, "Yes, he is such a man! To stay fifteen years in that place, he had to be."

I was afraid that she would sense my curiosity. Now was the moment when she would speak, or keep silent; it all depended on that intangible ingredient called trust. "What are they like in the canton?" I asked.

"Mostly decent people, and a dozen false witnesses. And for a man like that up against those false witnesses, it must be worse than a storm at sea. They have done everything they could do to him. And it was not the Freemasons they say such awful things about, not the Communists, some of whom go to Mass. We found out, a long time after it happened, that he had even been called before the bishop, who trusts those false witnesses. The Dean went on trial without even knowing why, and sentence had already been passed before the accused was heard. He went there in full confidence, thinking that the bishop had a few routine questions to ask about his deanery. I don't consider that very straightforward. That's all I heard, but one thing is certain—he never spoke of it to anyone. One of his accusers let it out one day when he was dead drunk—yes, there was a drunkard among his accusers. What else can you expect? That's how it is! Those people know how to talk. They have money, power. They think they are something special. Without them, there wouldn't be any more religion, you understand, because they *are* religion. It's just too bad for the priest who doesn't agree with them, doesn't join their party, and dares to say it out loud! It means that the priest is against religion, against the Catholic schools, against the Church!

"The simple people are helpless to defend him. They feel bad for him, but they aren't the ones who make the laws. If they took it into their heads to defend him, they would be in a fine fix. The doctor wouldn't come when they called him. The notary would draw up their wills wrong. The police-court magistrate would find against them. Their cows would die without the veterinarian. The pharmacist would ignore them. The assessors would increase their taxes. Put yourself in their place! They are bought, sold, bound, weighed like grains of sand. They have to think like the doctor, vote like the magistrate, read the same newspaper as the notary, bring chickens and chops to the schoolmaster. And when the notary isn't speaking to the doctor, when the mayor is running for re-election, when the assessors all belong to different political parties, the road-mender doesn't even know which way to hold his shovel, the rural policeman feels his cap swinging back and forth on his head, the sick don't dare call the doctor, the secretary at the town hall adds up names to find out who will win the election, the nuns pray for the 'best man' to

96

win. Look at them all. They lose their appetites over it. They wear out their brains. They don't know who to call friend or foe. They are given slogans and stories to repeat by rote. The streets are full of rumors. During the night, papers are slipped under doors. People won't face each other, but they are all out to kill. They write anonymous letters. They flatter, threaten, calumniate, assassinate. They buy one vote, five, ten votes with wine, or with pot roasts as the case may be. 'So much to the good,' say the poor. You see strange bedfellows. There are secret consultations, ears to keyholes. Friends quarrel, relatives insult each other, the women weep, the men come home drunk. You can't tell the right from the left after a while. They hark back to the Flood, looking for skeletons in closets. All you hear of is thefts and thieves, adulteries, children who look like this one or that one, those 'who would do better to clean their own houses,' and women 'who are virtuous now that they aren't good for anything else.'

"The morning of the elections, before sun-up, cars from the two rival parties meet by a strange coincidence in front of the houses of all the paralytics in the town and surrounding hamlets. They fight over them, push them around, snatch them away from each other. 'Come with me, I tell you . . .' 'If you don't get into my car, you can wait for your veteran's card, a good long time!' and 'I swear that the whole world will hear what your filthy father can stoop to!' No one even knows for whom such people would vote if they weren't given the ballot all filled out, in spite of our guaranteed secret ballot. When they have cast their vote, no one gives them another thought. They are forgotten on a bench like travelers in a waiting room; it is just as though they had dropped dead. They have to find their way home as well as they can.

"After four or five years, things calm down, and then they start all over again.

"And the men aren't the worst—it's the women! Not that

97

there are many; you could count them on the fingers of one hand. But they make enough noise for a hundred! We call them 'the Ladies' to distinguish them from the small fry who don't trot out their Sunday best every day of the week. If they had plain common decency, they wouldn't be any less sharp or any more stupid than ordinary people. But they have one serious and incurable disease: they lack simplicity. They put on airs; they talk with a phony accent. They hold their heads at such a strange angle that it must give them a stiff neck. They spend their time gossiping, making trouble, and exchanging hypocritical smiles. They all hate each other, and besides the confusion they create and foster so artistically, they have to concentrate on who can wear the finest hat, dress in the latest fashion, have the fanciest living room; who knows the best people and marries her daughter to the most desirable young man—and that doesn't mean the handsomest, it means the richest. For them, 'wealthy' always means 'honorable and distinguished.' They exert themselves so much with all their picking and choosing, their snubbing one another, turning in circles, handing out advice, that each one finally ends up alone. That is when they begin to accuse humanity of all kinds of crimes, to discover all kinds of vices in the parish, to find monstrous egoism and incurable stupidity both general and particular. All you hear is 'I told you so. . . . If they had listened to me . . . I saw it coming a long time ago. . . . But with people like that . . . and especially with the Dean we have . . .'

"For even though they have done everything they could to make his life unbearable, they pride themselves on being Christian and they can't get along without their Dean. So he is trapped in that basket of crabs, both his words and his silences are weighed, his visitors are counted and identified, the length of their visits carefully recorded, his absences are investigated, his friendships (if he has any) sifted and screened, his moods analyzed and his every step counted. If he talks to the schoolmaster, he is a Communist; if he drinks

98

an aperitif twice a month, he is a drunkard; if he stays at home, he is too strict; if he smiles at the women in the choir, he is too loose, and he is irreligious altogether if he doesn't preach their kind of gospel. He has been our Dean for fifteen years, and I often say my rosary for him. . . . That's how it is in a canton."

I sat listening. Then I set my bowl down on the table. Anyone else might have laughed, but I didn't feel in the least like laughing. I was reliving my own story. The woman didn't know who I was or where I came from. So all the cantons in this world are just alike! I was thinking of the Dean. He had stood firm. I had walked out. Maybe I hadn't had an old woman's rosaries to help me. Not even that! So I had left. But the Dean and I are brothers; that is the plain truth. Brothers twice over, since neither one of us has a family to turn to for refuge. That is one hardship Christ didn't experience, although they say He shared all our sufferings. The Dean is alone. He has to swallow his loneliness, and in moments like that it isn't often that one finds God. Perhaps we two were destined to be friends.

The fire had sunk beneath the ashes. The woman threw on a few branches. Night had fallen, just like last night, save for the wind's violence. I didn't want to leave. I sat down again in front of the fire. I wanted to pray. Not to question God, but to listen. All was silent once more. I didn't notice what the woman was doing. The door was open; I could see a few faint stars and hear the sea. My basket of shells still stood in the same spot. I watched the flames.

I will not tell my secret to anyone. It is good for me to be anonymous at last, a priest without a past, without a lineage, without roots. That woman must see into my innermost visions. In the half-light I could feel her reading my mind. She wanted to talk. In spite of my precautions, the conversation had changed direction.

"Yes, he is such a man. . . ." Then she immediately added,

without transition, "You preached there the other day. They already know you."

I swung around abruptly. I instantly regretted the movement, but it was too late. She was wiping the table and gathering the crumbs into her hand. Negligently she added, "That's for my chickens."

I looked at her. Who can this woman be?

I looked at her as I never had before. The flames lit up her face and outlined her profile clearly against the shadow.

You never really look at an old woman. You take it for granted that they all look alike. But this woman is different, I suddenly realized. I can't be mistaken.

What can her background be? What is her real name? What is she doing here? The Dean hadn't mentioned her, and I hadn't asked anyone for information about her. Until that moment, I had thought of her simply as "my old woman." Her ease in speaking had surprised me a moment ago, but my habitual intellectual laziness had prevented me from drawing any conclusions. I had just listened and poked at the fire. Now that medallion-like profile struck me and I noticed the slow and studied grace of her gestures. She possesses a distinction, a refinement, an indefinable perfection which are the sign of a mysterious past, where suffering has entered in to shape and finish the advantages of birth and breeding. No, I cannot be mistaken. That play of light and shadow, like a Flemish painting, gave her away even more than her voice. She has become, either voluntarily or by constraint, "an old woman." She has found her center in that acceptance, in prayer and forgetfulness. But her voice, her gestures; the way she smooths back her hair when a few rebellious locks fall onto her temples; her facility of speech; her psychological penetration —I cannot be mistaken. She is the very image of a breed whose lot is sorrow, sorrow delicately veiled by God's grace.

How long, O Lord? And why always these shocks?

She didn't turn toward me. She threw the crumbs out of doors. I went back to poking the fire. I asked rather too quickly, trying to sound indifferent, amused, curious, "And what do they say about me in the canton?"

"The same thing they say here: that you look like a fighter. That is the general opinion." She added in a confidential tone, "My own opinion is that you have suffered a great deal, and that as a result you aren't afraid any more." Then very firmly, "They say (I mean people in general) that you are like the Dean and that you will go the whole way, whatever it may cost. They express it differently—they say it won't be easy to shut you up—those are their words."

"Good for them."

"Yes . . . only one thing startled them: your accent. They say that you aren't from this part of the country. I suppose they are right."

To avoid discussing the point I asked, "And the others? The dozen 'false witnesses'?"

For the first time, I heard her laugh. She has a very young laugh, like a child's. "What difference does it make? I hardly think you are one to be bothered by them. They are watching you. What else can they do? You know how their minds work —they are like hunters watching for their prey. At the first opportunity, they will shoot. It will be hard for you not to give them that pleasure. If you are the Dean's friend, you are fair game for them. It is up to you." She added to herself, "It is not the choice that counts, or that hurts the most; it is the consequences of the choice."

I expected a complaint, but none came. I stood up. I purposely turned my back to the fire. She was in front of me, and I could see only her eyes. They made me think of those great lakes in my own country which they say lie in the craters of volcanoes; they are the stillest in the world. She couldn't see into mine.

"It is getting late. I have to go back. Let's pray together for a second. A decade of the rosary...."

Then I left.

Something crumpled inside me. My fears, lulled for a moment, flared up again.

My parish is taking a great interest in the construction of "their" crèche. I follow their lead, for I really think they are ahead of me.

That is the difference between parish priests and our higher echelons, who have lost contact with life. They are one step removed; they draw up plans and collect statistics. But they usually lack humility and practical sense, which explains why they hate to admit that they need us. They appear to be consulting us . . . are they only pretending? That seems absurd, and yet after surveys based on information furnished by us, their set ideas crop up again. Through a learned exegesis of the findings, they even manage to convince us that we were the ones who suggested them....

I have stopped trying to change anything in this pattern. I am not anxious to involve myself here in the same thing that brought me such misfortune before. I have an unpleasant memory of their offices and antechambers (not that I was in them very often). I am also of the opinion that parish priests often lack courage and do not have confidence in their fellow priests. It should be easy for them to impose their point of view, but they are afraid. Of what? It is still a mystery. They all act as though they felt guilty about something.

Those in command are perhaps not lacking in good will.

All they need is two weeks of effective work with their troops. In times gone by, when the means of communication were less efficient, bishops and their vicars general visited their dioceses on horseback, eating in one place, sleeping in another. They were shepherds. What would become of the sheep if the shepherd didn't share their life? To be a shepherd means at least living with one's sheep.

I am not one of those who say irreverently that "the Holy Spirit and the bishop don't work in the same office." I am not opposed to the high command. But I ask the impossible of them: that they see how we live and consent to admit that the Holy Spirit hasn't completely forgotten us.

Anyway, all that is past.

My old woman came this morning to help the others. I noticed that they called her "Madame." We scarcely said hello. I was surprised that she brought a dog with her. I had never seen that dog in her house. She must tie him outside during the day. He is a spaniel, very affectionate, but of doubtful pedigree, I suspect. I petted him with real pleasure. He returned my caresses lavishly. Those dogs have no enemies, except for gypsies. They bark, but they don't bite. They are sensitive and friendly creatures; a perfect dog for a priest. He made me want to own one.

When school let out at eleven o'clock, the crèche was nearly ready. The children all came to see it before their catechism class. It is very beautiful and expressive, accessible to their young souls.

This afternoon while I was alone in the church, seeing to the last touches and connecting the electricity, a young priest came by. He was riding a motorcycle, dressed in modern fashion, like a real garage mechanic. I vaguely recognized him. He was in the canton the other day. He is curé of two small parishes, nearer to the deanery than mine, and in the opposite direction, inland.

He is a nervous person, who soon becomes unbearable.

"What are you doing there?" he asked me.

"I'm trying my hand at electric wiring, as you can see."

"Our superior in the seminary always held that those jobs ought to be left to laymen."

One must control one's self; go to the very limit with concessions and compliments, whatever the cost.

I answered, "Very good advice! I'm glad to see you here. I guess you have finished making your crèche. You work faster than I."

"My crèche! Two silly old nuns have been doing it for the last twenty-five years, it seems. You can well imagine that I don't even go near it. They haven't changed one straw in twenty-five years. Everyone is happy that way . . . not to mention the curé!"

"Very good! That leaves you free."

"Yes, that way I can take a little air."

"Plenty of it here."

"In my opinion," he went on spiritedly, "one has to get out, see people, not stay shut up in one's presbytery and molder away. No one believes any more in that old law of staying at home as much as possible. I am not anxious to lose my mind."

I felt an impulse to ask him whether that was another of his superior's precepts. But one must control one's self.

"Well," I said, "I don't know much about electricity, but I guess it's going to work in spite of me."

He looked at my crèche and burst into laughter. "Whoever made that horror?"

(St. Rita, help me!)

"My . . . laymen. And I worked on it myself." One must be frank, face up to responsibilities, come what may. "It was my idea. I'm not going to set the world on fire. . . . Oh, there, it's going to work. It's a success!"

104

He tried another attack: "Do you like it here?"

"Frankly, yes."

I didn't ask him anything. He volunteered, "Those two dumps of mine make my life miserable. This is my first job as curé. I hope the bishop will be understanding . . ."

"The bishop is a fine man. He will surely be understanding."

"Luckily, I kept up my activities in the city. I am secretary of a social-action group and I direct an interparish choir. I have friends there, too. You see what I mean?"

A fuse blew, and I had to see what had gone wrong. I was acutely aware of St. Rita's protection.

"Very interesting, social action," I said insinuatingly.

"Fascinating! Contacts with the best people in the diocese! Meetings where you think the problems through! A good way to get the laymen out."

I burst out, "Out of what?" But I quickly got control of myself. "You don't happen to carry fuses, do you? A motorcyclist ——"

He fell into the trap. "I'm on my way to the canton. I'll send the electrician over."

"No, there it goes, it's working again. It wasn't the fuse; I pulled on a wire here. Must have been a bad connection. I'm not very good at this. . . . You're going to the canton at this hour?"

"I can see that you don't know your way about. It's just on my way. And I have a militant Catholic Action man there, a math professor."

"A—what?"

"A charming fellow; if you prefer, a layman, intensely committed. Just one like that in an inactive parish, and it is on the way toward resurrection. You never did any Catholic Action?"

"With workers and peasants . . . intense, too, in its way. That was a long time ago."

"Oh, yes, but with the workers it is mostly supporting their grievances, and that is a bore. And with the peasants, it is snail's pace Catholic Action."

"I am slow myself."

"Our world moves fast."

"Very fast."

"And the Gospel is behind the times."

"Very much behind. . . . Help me here one second. Hold this step ladder while I put in a bulb."

"You must excuse me, but I want to get back before dark, and I'm afraid you'll be at it for quite some time. My professor is waiting for me to plan our next meeting. A very independent fellow—sign of a strong personality."

"Can't I offer you some refreshment at least?"

"No, thank you."

He looked at my crèche and he looked at me. I went on working. It is extraordinary how soothing manual labor can be.

"Good-by," he said.

"Good-by, my dear colleague. Get home safe."

He went out in a hurry; the door slammed.

I thanked St. Rita and put in my bulb.

Ah, well, he is young and I am old.

Day after tomorrow at eleven o'clock, I'll be with the Dean.

Christmas Vigil.

It is 10:30. There were very few confessions: my youngsters, a few women, one or two old men.

106

After Midnight Mass, 2:00 A.M.

The weather is quite mild. (At home, Christmas Eve is almost never this pleasant.) It almost seems as though the wind died down on purpose. The stars are shining with a clear light and they seem neither too far away nor too close.

Those were marvelous hours. All my people were there in that old church, so poor, where Midnight Mass hadn't been celebrated for years. I won't be able to describe it. I would do better not to try. Some things I find impossible to write, things which have moved me violently, in a special way, which have made me want to weep. I feel able to describe almost all the rest. Not that.

It is two in the morning. I don't feel like sleeping. The church is closed now. My parishioners are going to bed. They are talking together about that Mass. I am sure of it. I closed my shutters tight so they don't let any light pass through, which is completely unimportant, except that it satisfies my secret instinct for privacy. To keep the tradition of midnight supper, I just ate some cheese and drank some water tinted with wine. What could be better, when one is alone?

But I wish I weren't completely alone. A physical presence has never been necessary for me as long as I can call to someone from my heart. I like to express my feelings openly. Right now I would like to be able to write a letter to a flesh-and-blood being who was my friend. But who?

I could write to my bishop. That would seem natural. I would say that I am pleased; that my parish kept Christmas well. I know that I would let myself be a bit carried away. But that would never do. The bishop is a leader, and he isn't interested in anything that resembles emotion.

I might write to friends, on this night of friendship, but how many do I have left?

My brothers? We spent so many wonderful Christmases together long ago. That is all water under the bridge to them now. They all think that I have "changed," that being a prisoner of war made me "another person." Among themselves they call me "that lunatic." The recent events which brought me here are apt to have confirmed their opinion.

A lunatic doesn't write letters from his asylum. Such letters are read with a faint taste of embarrassment, and no one takes them seriously. Anyway, the last letters I received from them were full of insults: they called me unjust, biased, mean, dry in heart, fanciful. The only reason I wasn't put away is that there are a great many madmen in the world who aren't in asylums. They wondered how my attitudes toward them could be reconciled with "the rest." "The rest," which they didn't dare to specify, probably means my vocation to the priesthood, my Mass, my state in life, my cassock. What attitudes? Their attitudes show a serious and total lack of comprehension of my solitary life. Family ties are necessary for a priest. Their Christianity hasn't made them understand that. They will never understand now. It is too late. But if despair could take hold somewhere in my soul, it would be there, at the point of that "too late."

I have to accept it, and no more feeling sorry! Whatever I do from now on, I am a lunatic. That's what I told my math professor: "The family and the Church are the supreme ordeal."

If my grandmother were still in this world, I could write to her tonight. I would write carefully, so that she could read without straining her eyes. She would receive my letter like a visit, a present, a blessing. She would sit down in the old worn armchair in her little bedroom, and there between her bed and her chest of drawers, she would repeat my words to herself. She would think, "That poor boy! My poor little boy! How far away you are! I can't understand why they punished you. I don't listen to them when they say bad things about you. I love you. . . ." And she would cry slowly, really cry; she would sob out loud; she would let her sorrow run its course; she would be transfigured with love. I would have said to her:

Dearest Grandma,

It is late, but it is Christmas Eve, and I can't go to bed without writing you how warm my heart is. Of course I missed you. I wish I could have seen you as I did one day back home, in front of the sanctuary rail of my church, with your fluted bonnet and that fine ribbon that you fixed onto your head with pins, and wore so proudly. With your shawl, your missal printed in large black type, your poor man's glasses, your twisted fingers, that smile sweeter than any other I ever saw. I missed you because tonight I didn't have that piping hot chocolate that you used to make for us every Christmas Eve. It wasn't instant chocolate like the kind they make now. You used to break up the bars, melt them, stirring them with a wooden spoon—I can still remember. You would pour it out into an earthenware pot, smiling, and you would wrap the pot in a blanket, like a child in his cradle. . . .

We would say, "Do you think it will keep hot, Grandma?"

And you would answer, "Don't worry, children."

That was our Christmas-eve treat, your Christmas-eve treat, your joy, your ocean of joy. We would come back from church running, do you remember? The house was warm; our bowls were already full; the chocolate, too rich (it was the only time!) foamed on the slices of white bread.

I missed you, but since I can write to you, you'll be happy to hear that the children in my parish behaved very well. They marched in procession from the sacristy, twice around the church, and then to the crèche. The littlest ones stumbled a bit. The one who carried the Holy Child was as serious as a pope. Of course, I had attached the Child firmly to the cushion. The parents weren't looking at me, but at them. . . . There were five little girls dressed as angels with golden wings. Others had big paper stars on their foreheads.

In the sacristy, where no one had been for so long, I had

discovered two rusty censers. We polished them, and two of the older boys marched ahead of the procession swinging them. The girls sang, "*Il est né le Divin Enfant . . .*" You used to sing it, too, in the old days in a sweet, soft voice. It was your voice that I heard. I wanted to cry, but I controlled myself.

When we reached the crèche, the children formed a semicircle. I took the Child Jesus in my hands, like the Blessed Sacrament, and I laid Him delicately on the straw. The church was full of a great, silent emotion. Kneeling, I incensed the Child, and said to Him, "Protect us, kind Jesus. Keep us simple. Grant that no one in my parish may ever be afraid of You. Bring to my Grandma, far away over the mountains and plains, a little joy! If she weeps tonight, let it be tears of happiness."

Angels dressed in blue and pink hung from the branches above the crèche and little houses constructed by my youngsters lighted up from the inside. You would have been happy to see all that. You would have said, "It turned out very well; you have done a good job!"

And then I sang the Mass, in my vestments which are old, but not worn out. I was almost as well dressed as I used to be when you would send me to school with my smock all ironed, my belt shined and my wooden shoes waxed with tallow. I preached my sermon (you know how I love to preach), and the congregation was very attentive. I can't see them so well now that I wear glasses—supposedly in order to see better—but I feel their presence, and that is enough. Not many received Communion, but I assure you that if they understood God better, they could all have received Him, their hearts were so warm.

Above all, don't think that I am unhappy, dear Grandma. Don't try to figure things out. Say your rosary for one of my intentions. I am afraid that something may happen to me today.

Now I am going to bed. I am still your little boy who loves you and sends you a kiss.

I am astonished, now, that I wrote that letter. My grand-mother has been dead for a very long time. What does it mean? Is it true that I am mad? *Could it be true that on this Christmas night there is so little love on this earth that a priest, dying of loneliness, doesn't even know anyone to whom he can cry out that he is happy?*

ALL THESE events are beyond me.

I have tried to play my part. I leave all the rest to God.

I will record here from day to day the essentials of what has happened and what I know, and also whatever will happen in the future, which I have no way of predicting. I won't dramatize anything. My mind is calm. I am living in a vast peace.

After my nine-o'clock Mass on Christmas Day, I took the little trolley, as I had promised. It was just about empty, and I knew there wouldn't be many getting on along the way. "A slow day today," said the conductor when he gave me my ticket. "I won't earn my keep today . . ." He added, looking at me, "Aren't you tired after all those celebrations?"

Yes, I was tired, but it was the kind of fatigue that leaves the mind free and makes it more receptive. The main thing is not to be drowsy. Sometimes I even enjoy that state of weariness which creates a certain nervous tension, sharpening my powers of reflection and intuition. My body doesn't interfere with the mechanics of my brain.

The weather was still very mild. I opened the window and

let the air blow in my face. A peasant got on; he was going after medicine for his grandson. He had been a prisoner of war in a camp not far from mine. We talked about those raw German winters, that painful lack of in-between seasons, the wind which is sovereign master of those lifeless plains. The man was a poet. The beauty of those German sunsets had remained in his mind's eye. I became absorbed in the conversation, and traveled along toward the canton without thinking of the Dean, except when his face rose up from time to time out of some uncontrolled region of my soul and superimposed itself on the image of those twilights. It soon faded, and nothing was left of the fugitive apparition but a trail of shadow which blended into the crimson clouds. Without knowing it, the man had touched a sensitive spot. I still dream of those sunsets of my captivity. Shall I ever see them again?

It was a quarter to eleven when I arrived. The church was still almost empty. The choirboys were lighting the candles. One by one the singers arrived, scarcely bowed, took their places behind the altar and started chatting. It was warm in the church. The smell of incense still lingered from the previous night. Some people class it in the category of romantic frills, but it brings me happy memories of my youth. You can't deny your own past. I didn't even remember that I had suffered on this very spot only a few days back. What good does it do to nurture the memory of pain? Of joy, yes, but not of suffering....

I stopped a few moments in front of the crèche in the north apse, in a corner of St. Catherine's chapel. It was in very good taste. The Dean hadn't mentioned it to me, but I had a feeling that he had worked on it himself. He certainly hadn't entrusted the job to a few "silly nuns." As I knelt before the altar, I heard the Dean giving orders and silencing his assistants.

He greeted me very warmly, but he didn't linger. He went on systematically preparing for the ceremony. "I have to plan for everything," he said to me in a mild tone. "I can't count on anyone else. But that's nothing new to you."

The ornaments. The missal. The burettes. The seats for the choirboys. He spoke to the singers. I watched him go through all the motions I know so well. The church began to fill up. I felt at home. I thought, without nostalgia, of my canton of years past. Decidedly everything was perfectly normal; everything was in place, in its proper place. This was exactly how a curé prepares for the celebration of the Sacrifice. I must have dreamed, that was all. I was right to think that nothing would happen. This brought me a feeling of inner contentment. It was just like me to imagine things, to indulge in fancies. I went so far as to accuse myself of magnifying things. I thought of the good talk we would have together after the Mass. After we had eaten, I would really be sleepy. I would invite the Dean to take a walk with me, and I could catch up on my rest the next night. I resolved not to go home too late. The Dean would appreciate that, since he would be at least as tired as I....

Everything seemed to be all right.

Then, at that very moment, a few minutes before the Mass, while the Dean was putting on the alb, the Canon rushed in like a whirlwind. I noticed that he had pouches under his eyes, his hair was badly combed, he hadn't shaved, and he walked as though he were too tired to stand. He didn't greet me, but rushed over to the Dean, who hadn't turned around, and exclaimed, "Oh, dear Monsieur le Doyen, what an abominable night! If I hadn't feared to scandalize your good folk, I should still be in my bed."

The Dean made no reply. His lips were moving. He was reciting the prescribed prayers.

"Imagine," the Canon continued, "just imagine that after

singing Midnight Mass, *"in splendoribus"* you have to admit, and celebrating two following ones—a bit hastily, I confess (what an idea to impose three Masses on us on Christmas Day!), she cornered me! . . . You know who! The Colonel also insisted, but she would have been enough by herself! How could I refuse? Not all charity is bread! She had it all planned—midnight supper at the Carlton. And the Tax Collector's widow opposite me.

"There were four of us—which, of course, suggested a game of bridge. I was the dummy most of the time, which gets on my nerves, because she insists on taking the bid even if she gets no answer to a low bid in clubs. She just never will learn to bid. It went on until dawn . . . until seven-thirty in the morning. She kept on losing. The widow, who is a thousand times more intelligent, won without any effort. I don't have to describe the scene! The Colonel's wife in a murderous temper, the widow cynical, the Colonel exhausted. And I had to bear the brunt of it all. A nightmare, I tell you.

"I had just time to throw myself down on my couch, without even changing, when your church bells woke me. The worst, the thing that frightens me, is that just as I was finally able to break away, she said, 'Don't think, Monsieur le Chanoine, that the wife of a Colonel ever accepts defeat. We must play again this evening, seven o'clock sharp. In the meanwhile, get some rest. That's the best thing you can do. And try to be a bit more lively.' You see what a position I am in! Frightful. I really doubt that I will go back. What would you do in my place?"

The Dean didn't look at him. He was ready to celebrate. His hands were folded on the credence. The organist struck up a joyous Christmas air. I had put on a surplice. Motioning to the choirboys to proceed, the Dean whispered to him, "I would have appreciated it if you had taken into consideration in reporting your activities the fact that these children were present." Then, after the clergy had started their procession, he said over his shoulder, "Yes, go back tonight, but I warn you that you won't touch a card."

I was just in front of the Canon, but I felt that he was turning around. Had he noticed a pallor, a visible sign of fatigue on the Dean's face, or did he want to attract attention, or make amends? "By the way," he said, "who is preaching at this Mass? I can very well do it."

In a cutting voice, perfectly audible from where I was, the Dean replied, "Anyone as conceited as you ought not to be concerned with preaching the poverty of Christ."

We were in the choir, and the bell rang. It was too late for the Canon to answer, but as he headed toward his seat, he remembered me and whispered in my ear, "What got into him? He's out of his mind! I'll make him pay for that one!" I had just time to say, "I think he has already made up his mind to pay the price."

My intuition hadn't been wrong. My desire for tranquillity hadn't changed the course of events. It was only a question of time. In a warm, rich, very true voice, halfway between earth and heaven, the Dean chanted the Epistle: *"Multifariam, multisque modis olim Deus loquens patribus in prophetis: novissime diebus istis locutus est nobis in Filio."* (God, who at sundry times and in divers manners spoke in times past to the fathers by the prophets, last of all in these days hath spoken to us by His Son.) Whatever may come to pass, nothing will ever be more sublime! He incensed the Book of the Gospel. I felt that he gave special emphasis to the words, *"In mundo erat, et mundis per Ipsum factus est, et mundus Eum non cognovit. In propria venit, et sui Eum non receperunt."* (He was in the world, and the world was made by Him, and the world knew him not. He came unto His own, and His own received Him not.)

He took off his chasuble and came forward toward the congregation, his eyes fixed on the pulpit. Then he decided to remain at the communion rail. He crossed himself. I expected a storm. I can best compare what happened to a powerful river rolling forward almost soundlessly. I know of no better way to express it. Nothing can stop the onrushing water; nothing can break its force.

"My brethren, I give you notice that tomorrow morning you won't hear the Angelus ring. The nuns and the few persons who assist at my daily Mass can stay at home, because this very evening I am leaving the parish.

"This comes as a surprise to you. Let me therefore state clearly the reasons for my departure.

"You perhaps think that I have been appointed pastor of another parish. That is not the case. Nor am I under any canonical sanction. I don't think I have lost my mind. So what is left by way of hypothesis? This: I am leaving you of my own accord, because I consider that the honor of the priesthood and my fidelity to my vocation are at stake.

"For fifteen years, as you know, I have been your pastor. Like all men, I have my faults. But God doesn't choose angels to be his priests. A priest, even though he isn't perfect, has a legitimate right to hope, especially after so many years of effort, that his presence and his work will have some visible effect. But it is plain to see that I have prayed, labored, preached, waited, and suffered here for nothing. Those we call the good haven't become any better. The others have been afraid to become good. Spite and malice, calumny and falsehood are rampant in this parish. The rich remain hard of heart. And what is worse, the attitudes of a few dangerous self-righteous individuals prevent all those who seek the truth from taking the first step toward it and from sharing in their turn in the blessings of the Redemption.

"When I was first appointed to this parish, His Excellency the Bishop did not conceal from me the difficulties that I would encounter. 'Go there,' he told me, 'like a missionary.' But what more does a missionary do than preach Jesus Christ, and Jesus Christ crucified? You have paid too little attention to this message. I led you to the foot of the Cross; your hearts were touched, and then you hastened to forget. I have sowed my field untiringly; the harvest is not worth reaping.

"What should I have done or invented that would have been more effective than preaching the Gospel? 'Go forth and teach,' Christ said, sending his apostles into the world—and Christianity was born. Here, paganism has prevailed.

"I have spoken several times to His Excellency about my difficulties and my projects. In spite of his prejudices against me (prejudices which some of you so skillfully insinuated into his mind), he has always refused to let me leave. But I have endured all this as long as I can. Now I have reached the point of complete exhaustion, the time when a priest would have to give up the struggle and, just to please his parishioners, consent to preach a disfigured Gospel.

"If this unmistakable resistance of my parish to God's grace is the result of my inability to adapt to your personal conception of Christianity, I hope that my successor will be exactly the man you need to lead your souls toward God. If you are the ones responsible for this failure, then of all my acts in this place, the act of leaving you will be the most intelligible and the most disinterested.

"I have lived in poverty. I leave here with no more than my breviary and my worn-out cassock. I don't know where I will go, but wherever I am, I will pray for you. Like Christ, I pitched my tent among you. Like the Jews, you refused to acknowledge me as the man of God. I leave you without anger or bitterness, in the hope that my successor, preaching the same Gospel, may know the apostolic joys that were denied me."

He crossed himself.
His forthrightness and courage had created an unusual

117

atmosphere. One could feel that at that very instant the miracle of a new Christian community might have taken place. But it couldn't last. I looked at the people. They didn't dare make a move. They were wondering if it was true, whether those words had been spoken, and if they had been spoken, whether they were addressed to them. No one budged. They had not yet taken any stand, but it would not be long before they would. How long would it take? They didn't dare look at that priest who went on with the celebration of Mass. They didn't know exactly why they were there, paralyzed, emptied of themselves. They were searching. Not all of them. Just those "dangerous self-righteous people" whom my old woman called "false witnesses." They were searching; you could feel it. They were wondering how to ward off the blow.

When the bell timidly announced the Elevation, they stood up, on their guard, jaws clenched, eyes hard, necks stiff. They hadn't yet found a solution, but they acted as though they had. They looked at the Canon. Very self-possessed and relaxed, he had opened his breviary. At the *Gloria Patri*'s, which he prolonged, he glanced covertly at the congregation. He was counting his troops. They weren't all there. The Colonel's wife was still asleep at that hour. I didn't see the professor. But a few, whose faces were unfamiliar to me, exchanged almost imperceptible signals with him. He seemed to be saying to them, "Don't worry, it is another of his outbursts, and this time it is full-scale. But . . . let's wait and see what happens. This is just the beginning. Now it is my turn to take over. You can trust me. . . ."

I also noticed the others, the crowd of humble folk. They had already withdrawn into sullen silence. After Mass was over, they wouldn't form any groups; they would want to escape. This evening, or tomorrow, they would have sensed which way the wind was blowing. "They aren't the rock, they are the sand." They will take whatever shape the wind and waves decree. They love their Dean; they suffer with him, pray for him. But, in God's name, why did he do such a thing? Everything was going along more or less smoothly. He was wrong, since "they" are going to win out, since his wave is going to crash into their wave. . . .

I waited for the end of the service without anxiety. I didn't ask myself any questions. I just waited. The Dean celebrated slowly. He seemed so calm to me that little by little (am I then so much inclined to tranquillity?) I let myself believe that everything was normal. He came down from the altar. I didn't hurry back to the sacristy. My curiosity won out; it is very bad, and I gave in to it. I saw "the sand" trickle out rapidly, in silence. The "rocks" remained. After all, isn't this their home, their Temple? Aren't they Religion?

As though inadvertently, the Canon stepped out of the stalls on the side nearest the communion rail. He looked at them, then stopped. He didn't go toward them; they were the ones who must come to him. They surrounded him. But although they were already talking busily, they spoke in low voices, because I was still there, the spy, the enemy, the Dean's friend. "That madman's friend. Madmen both. So let's speak softly." This time I looked at them for a moment, smiling, compromising myself. I know that kind of confabulation so well! It didn't matter what they were saying. I didn't need to hear it. I knew the conspiracy was starting. . . .

The singers hesitated. Passing in front of the doorway into the sacristy presented a great problem. Finally, one of them took courage, and hurried ahead, walking sideways, almost turning her back to the open door. The others, comically imitating her maneuver, followed in her wake, as though into a narrow, difficult, dangerous passage, full of land mines; as though they lacked air and had to hurry to get through, so that, a yard beyond, they could breathe once more.

I followed them down the steps, at a respectful distance from the conspirators, who were now laughing noisily. Some of the singers must have nodded to them because I heard the Canon's voice: "Good-by, my children." He was holding his breviary in one hand, raising it in the air like a sword, or using it to give people who spoke to him friendly taps on the shoulders. He towered above them, his tall body swaying to and fro. He seemed very pleased.

When I entered the sacristy, the Dean was saying to his clerics, "Hang your cassocks carefully in place, and then go." One by one they went, almost backing out. They watched the Dean, who was taking off his vestments and carefully putting them away. He put his chalice into its black case. He wiped a bit of dust from the top of the cupboard with the back of his hand. Nothing was in disorder. He could go. . . .

Just at that moment, a nun came in. The Dean started to make a gesture of annoyance, then, smiling mischievously, he asked, "What is it?"

"You are my protector . . ."

"This is the first I've heard of it."

"But, of course, Monsieur le Doyen, it was through your intercession that I remained in the parish. Now our Mother General will send me away. Where shall I go? I suppose I'm not doing any good here?" She was on the verge of tears.

The Dean answered, "No tears, Sister. And put your mind at rest. You won't be sent away. I have never been of any influence in your life, but I can assure you that you won't be sent away. You—you are irremovable." He laughed when he pronounced the word. "Irremovable, I tell you."

Her eyes questioned him.

"You really want to know why? Well—don't you understand that no other Sister is as good as you are at bringing grist to the mill? Now, go in peace."

When she had left, he said, "Tonight she will be howling with the wolves. So . . . all that remains is to make my farewells to—him."

120

He hadn't arrived yet, because he had stopped a half a yard from the door. He had been listening. The nun ran into him, and he murmured something to her in a low voice. She answered with a nod.

He came in. I saw enough irony in the Dean's expression to reassure me. The Canon made the first move, in a honeyed voice, very paternal: "My dear colleague, have you considered your canonical position?"

The Dean replied, "I know by heart the articles of the Code which apply to me. And you—have you considered your—*evangelical* position?"

The Canon stiffened. "What do you mean by that?"

"What do I mean? Like one I won't name, what you have to do, do quickly. Anyway, as St. Augustine affirms, even that one could have baptized, which means, according to unchanging theological teaching, that you can also administer the sacraments validly. Your duties as chaplain of the convent aren't so very demanding. So I am entrusting the parish to your care until His Excellency names a new Dean. For the marriages, you can ask for powers from the Ordinary."

Pale and this time quite himself, the Canon lashed out. "His Excellency will hear of this scandal from me, the first thing tomorrow morning."

"It is charitable of you to take the trouble. You will find that it is superfluous. His Excellency will have learned of this—scandal—through a personal letter which I sent last night. But do go all the same. You can give him the details. And—don't forget—you have a bridge game to win tonight at seven."

The Canon turned his back, saying only, "Then I'll leave you with your—new friend." Then he disappeared.

The Dean looked at me. "Now I can go."

"Where are you going?"

"Against the wind. That is what I have decided. But which way is the wind blowing this morning?"

"Then you're coming home with me," I answered. "It is from the sea."

His eyes filled with tears.

"No tears. Those are your words. Let's go."

The church was empty. We remained a long while on our knees before the altar. He looked at the tabernacle, and said, "Let's pray together."

"To whom?"

"To Her."

And we recited the Ave Maria aloud, like two seminarians.

WHEN WE reached that turn in the path where, looking toward the sea, you can see the front of my house, I noticed that my door was open. I wasn't too surprised, since I never lock doors, and there is always a little breeze from the sea. The Dean said, "Is there someone in your house?"

"No," I answered, "and usually that door is closed." I went in, feeling a bit uneasy. A cloth and two places had been laid. The ashes on the hearth were still glowing. A meal was waiting for us. My old woman was there to welcome us. "So you are the ghost," I said.

As though she were the lady of the house, she answered, "I'm afraid that everything is a bit dried up and unappetizing. The broth is none the worse for waiting, but—the rest . . . ! How do you like your soup, Monsieur le Doyen? Thick or clear?"

I saw him hesitate, very moved. "I like it very hot, full of vegetables and seasoned with the devotion of the cook, which means that the one you are going to serve me will be exactly right."

122

He stole a glance at me. No, I had nothing to do with it.

"You must be hungry," she went on, "and you are surely cold. Sit right down."

She closed the door, served us, and then put two great logs on the andirons.

This past night I had a dream which has remained in my mind. This rarely happens to me; usually by morning my dreams have vanished. But these images remained very sharp. They come from that arsenal of old emotions, of whose presence I am not conscious, but which are always ready to explode.

I was back in my prison camp. It was winter, just at nightfall, that hour which is a torment to the sick and the exiled. We had just eaten that vile turnip soup which we called "cheat-death." Snow had taken possession of everything. It had lain for weeks piled up to the windows of our barracks. Our combined heat, which did us no good, attacked it just under the roof and melted a thin layer which formed icicles in front of the windowpanes, ironic testimony to our animal reactions and our will not to die.

That evening, the conversations of those two hundred men, all crowded together, formed a confused, neutral hum, whose depths harbored the terrible presence of sadness and boredom in their raw state. A sort of house of despair for men. No one reacted against it. Not a single voice cried out. But an omnipresent guitarist played and sang the same desolate refrain for the fiftieth time:

Farewell, Venice of my Provence,
Land of my lost loves, farewell,
Farewell, cicadas in the pines,
In the tall pines singing still.

After a while it became hypnotic.

One of my bunkmates, sitting in front of me (I saw him very clearly) hung his head without even supporting it in his hands. The hanging head of a man crucified. His hair tumbled down over his forehead. He was weeping foolishly. His tears splashed on the boards. He didn't try to hide them or excuse himself. He had gone under. I thought: If ever we get out of here, we will never have enough joy, never enough peace, never enough sun to restore our balance. We will always lean toward the shadows.

And that guitarist who never stopped! "Farewell . . . farewell. . . ." He had played and sung that song before. It had never lasted so long, or perhaps we had been less in agony? How long can agony go on . . . ?

I stood up. I knew the singer, a young man from Provence, starving, like the rest of us; perhaps a bit more than the rest because he was only twenty-two. He had let his beard grow, a sparse fuzz which he didn't groom. Of his face no more was visible than his angular cheekbones and two lights, two flames, buried beneath the forehead bones, shining too brightly. One would hesitate to look into them for fear of getting a dizzy spell. He frightened us. A figure from the dance of death, the kind you see in faded medieval frescoes.

I went over to him. I could read in my comrades' attitudes their sympathy, and gratitude, and a feeling of helplessness. I wouldn't be any more successful than they had been. One of them said, "We've been telling him for an hour to keep quiet..."

The young man didn't even look at me. He was squatting in a corner, his ear and cheek pressed to the guitar box. He was not a man with a guitar, but the instrument itself. To reach him, one would have to paralyze the guitar first. I put my hand on the strings. He said without lifting his head, "Once more..." Then, since he couldn't continue, he turned his two savage flames on me. He looked like the sorcerers one sees in pictures, but he was too young to play the part.

"Oh, it's you."

"Yes, me. Can't you play something a little gayer?"

He laughed nervously. He laughed the way a man condemned to die might laugh before the guillotine. Without anger, in a voice rooted in his soul's wounds, he answered, "For a priest, that's pretty feeble."

"I'm not asking you to discuss theology, just to change the record."

His laugh abruptly changed into a sanctimonious meditation. The two lights tried to pierce through the shadows on the ceiling to something the rest of us couldn't see.

"Theology? There now. You've done me a good turn. I've been trying to think of that word for a long time. Yes, of course—theology! Hell—isn't that part of theology? You are a priest, and you don't believe in Hell. You make me sick! I know more about it than you."

"Listen to me...."

"Listen to what? Hell—what is Hell in your theology? In mine, it is the land of farewell. Farewell to everything. Farewell. Eternal farewell. So then, do you know what they sing in Hell?"

He started to play again. I believed, at that moment, in the power of a word, the spell of a melody. He stopped and said, "That's what they sing, without stopping! Everyone has his guitar. Everywhere, night and day, you hear 'Farewell . . . farewell.' They are all crouched over, like me, and they strum their strings with fingernails that never wear down. You see the picture?"

"You are hungry. Lie down. Try to sleep. Tomorrow there will be a little sun, and you will start to believe that one day we'll get out of here...."

He laughed again. This time I saw his teeth and his gums. I have seen something like that before—on a dead man.

"We'll get out! We'll get over it! That's all you know how to say! You're all would-be romantics, phonies who say they are dying, and who would get dysentery if they really saw it coming. You must be nuts, because, even if we do get out ..."

My heart contracted. This twenty-two-year-old corpse is going to talk from his grave. A dead man talking is horribly truthful.

"Yes, even if I see my Provence again, what difference will it make? Hell will start all over. Hell will go on. A worse Hell than this one ... Hell, with the illusion of freedom. Here, you can stand it. This is Hell, but it is normal, legal, not a Hell that hides its nameplate under the wistaria. Here you know what it is. Like it or lump it, but there's no cheating. That's what it is.

"Back there, if we come out of it, as you hope, without any reason for hoping, your Paradise will be Hell and your Freedom will wear chains. You understand that, don't you? No— you don't want to. You are all chasing rainbows. You think all you have to do is open a door. As easy as that. And suddenly you'll be happy, in Paradise.

"I can tell you how long your fun will last, exactly one second, just time enough to put your foot on the steps of the train. Then, at that very second, you will have your revelation. You will shout, 'There, at last. It's finished!' Finished ... what? Right afterward you will need to hear my guitar again. You will call me to sing you my 'Farewell.' You will no sooner sit down on your benches of Paradise regained, than you will start insulting each other. And your religion won't do a thing to stop it. And when you have all gone back to your cozy little bungalows with tiled roofs, surrounded by other bungalows with curtains and central heating, you can ring your church bells! They will come to your church, your Christians, but remember this, I'll be there too, and I'll strum my strings. That will be worse than all you've seen so far. Your Christians will gorge themselves like dogs. They will tear each other's skins and flesh with their teeth (as they always have) and

126

then with their mouths still red, they will go and eat your God. You will be happy. Because you don't understand the first thing about all this, because you refuse to understand it any better, because you are so used to seeing that blood that you take it for dewdrops from heaven. Farewell, my friend. Farewell to everything. It's all a bad job, even your Gospel and your theology. Unless . . . unless they devour you, too. That's the best thing that could happen to you and to society. You would howl. They wouldn't hear you at first, but if you howled long and loud enough, they would take you a bit more seriously, and that would prevent them from dozing off. . . . You understand? That is the only hope; let the curés go through Hell themselves—otherwise they'll just go on making us believe—not in God, you're kidding—but in some phoney romanticism. Only, the curés, they always manage to come out on top. They are sacred. Perfect. Hands off them. What a disaster! They watch other people croak. They watch the big fish eat the little fish; the elegant ladies (worse tramps than the others because it's easier for them) sit on their padded seats; the just men tremble, and the innocent take the rap. All is well. Everyone is where he belongs. No one grumbles. They sprinkle their holy water on this caricature of the Gospel, on this Apocalypse, on this Hell. It falls nicely on Satan's chops, and they are as pleased as Punch. They laugh right along with the others. Everything is O.K., everything is just right. Long live God. Religion is making progress . . .

"And you are fool enough to imagine that this slut of a war is going to change anything? You read in your books that war makes men good? It will be just a little bit worse, unless it gives us the right to make you howl for a change, you and your whole corporation. . . .

"Get it, or don't get it, I'm going to play it again:

"Farewell Venice of my Provence . . ."

In the barracks, the murmuring rose a tone higher than before.

"You hear them . . . They are the ones who never change the record. What do they need to convince them—your brothers?"

From the other end of the barracks, the officer in charge shouted, "Lights out! Then maybe we won't hear him any more. He'll go to bed. . . ."

He looked at us all. "Yes," he said, "my pretty little damned souls. Lights out. What do I care? I can see better in the dark. . . ."

I didn't wake up after this dream. I found it intact in the morning. And I think that the reason it stayed so clear in my memory is that in that barracks, one winter evening, there was a reality which hasn't yet consented to die. . . .

January 2nd

The Dean and I have organized our mutual life smoothly and without questions.

I think it was the discretion he sensed in me—and appreciated—my obvious inability to probe into other people's private lives, that made him decide to accept a refuge under my roof. He will talk to me if he thinks it useful; he will talk about whatever he thinks might be useful. What more could we have to reveal to each other? Hasn't everything been said, almost without words? I am not making any plans. He is in God's hands and stands before his own conscience. He is my guest. I want only to stand at his side like a gentleman and a brother. He understood this perfectly. Sometimes he confides in me:

"My most painful cross was the absence of true affection and trust among priests. For many years I didn't even know which one to choose as my confessor. I have lost faith in them. That is our tragedy. They lack candor. Their preoccupation with saving souls, which is noble in itself, makes them forget to practice the humbler human virtues, and leads them into a labyrinth of half-truths, ruses, and civilities supposedly profitable for . . . Heaven; their smiles are those of examining magistrates, to which I prefer the most violent anger. It is a pathological state. Some of them have become smiling robots. They are insanely devoted to that professional smile—which they call Christian Joy—though it doesn't fool anyone except the simple-minded and the bigots. Fifty years ago it was perhaps acceptable, an integral part of the role, like the clerical bands and the shoes with buckles. The wars and all the other hardships we have endured have sobered us. Souls aren't made resolute by these acrobatics. People want a priest to be a strong man, dependably built, like a house well constructed of stone: they are sick of plaster and wallpaper."

On this score, the only difference between us is in our emotions. His ideas are exactly the same as mine, but I no longer suffer as much from them as before. I am resigned to them, which may not be any better. And although I abominate these attitudes as much as he does, I put up with them. Another difference is that I don't generalize. All priests are not alike, thanks be to God.

He has the bedroom, and I sleep in my office. We don't give any thought to our private lives. We don't exercise any control over each other, either outwardly or secretly. Our life in com-

129

mon is without complications: we recite our Hours in the morning; we have our meals together and we sometimes talk over things that interest us both. We serve each other's Mass. We have already developed one custom: we say a few words of Scripture aloud to provide our spiritual nourishment. I have noticed (without drawing any conclusions) that he attaches great importance to integrity of heart. He said this morning after we had recited our breviary: "Yes, God is good to Israel, to those who are pure in heart." Yesterday: "Light has dawned for the just man and joy for the righteous in heart."

The housekeeping problem is solved: my "old woman" has taken it over. I didn't ask her to. Neither did the Dean. I have the impression that he knows her well. That is enough for me. That evening of the Dean's arrival, before she left us, she said, "I will be here tomorrow morning at eight. Don't worry about anything." Since that day, she has been coming. My house has never been so well kept.

The question of what we will live on disturbs me. I am poor, and he came with no more than his breviary and his cassock, which is no longer new. Presumably he won't go back to take anything from his house at the moment. We have only my modest salary and the Mass stipends, which are not inexhaustible. This cannot go on forever. I don't give it too much thought. Most of the time we drink water.

Yesterday morning after we had exchanged affectionate New Year's greetings, his eyes grew somber. "Happy New Year! Yes . . . Vacation is over tomorrow. You know what I mean?"

"Don't let it worry you. There will be two of us to receive them when they come."

"Two? . . . Are you so sure?"

I took him into my office. At these moments when no answer is the right one, I usually say just the wrong thing. This comes from the fact that I want so much to find a way out, that I am willing to use any means. My imagination doesn't follow fast enough.

"I am going to read you a dream I had the other night."

He sat down. His composure amazed me. When I had finished, he said, "Is it a dream or a reality? Did you actually know that young visionary?"

"Yes."

"And did he really say those things?"

"In almost those very terms . . . perhaps even more violent ones. It wasn't the only time. And he wasn't the only one who talked that way. Being prisoners had one distinct advantage for all of us: it was a moment of truth that lasted five years."

"It left its mark on you—a frankness which nothing can dismay. . . . And you saw that whole scene in your dream?"

"Exactly as I reported it. It was his truth."

"His truth," he replied. Then apparently without any connection, "I am going to show you a copy of the letter I sent to the bishop. You may do whatever you wish with it. Since there are—two of us."

He stood up, put his hands in his pockets and went out, repeating, "His truth, his truth. . . ."

A few moments later I got up, too. It is so mild these days, so calm after all those storms, that I can hardly bear to stay in the house. I had thrown my coat over his shoulders when he first came, so I went out in my cape, and walked toward the sea.

The air was transparent. Before me the waves played with the sunlight; each drop was a diamond flaring up, then snuffed out. Millions of drops shimmered together, offered themselves to the sun, accepted the shadow, rebounding in the rays. A light breeze came from the sea, from far off, warm, moist and bearing the scent of seaweed. Of course, it was neither the wind from my mountains, nor from my plains, nor from those landscapes of long ago where my eyes fed on an infinite variety of colors and forms, and drew comfort from them; but at this moment the sea seemed familiar, the waves' caprices seemed like the games my leaves played in the woods, this beach was a land whose yield was simply of another kind—not grain harvests or grapes, but something which bore its own seed, which I might come to know and perhaps to love.

I was in the midst of these reflections, this admiration, this prayer, when I saw him, right at the sea's edge, far in the distance—motionless—an apparition, a question, a personification of loneliness. His back was turned to me. The wind blew his coat about him. What was he waiting for? Whom was he questioning? Why were his eyes held by the uninterrupted leaping of the jeweled spray? Nothing gave me any clue to his secret. At a distance it is impossible (at least for me) to produce the kind of contact in which silence carries a message between two people.

But at that instant a link was forged in my mind between the distant presence of that man and a memory of my days in captivity. Was it an uncontrolled effect of my dream of the other night? This time it wasn't a dream, but a conscious, living memory, accepted, instantly and knowingly in juxtaposition with the scene before my eyes.

It was simple enough: once I had seen a man facing another such immensity. . . .

He was, we used to say (but how, in our prison camp, could we have known?) a Serbian general. We noticed him from inside our camp, alone on that plateau without frontiers, stretching eastward without end. He was digging a trench. What was it for, and where did it lead? If he was supposed to dig it all the way to the end, out there into the infinite, the life of that one prisoner would never be long enough. It was a labor of the damned. Another Hell, a Hell without a guitar, but still with its eternal farewell.

One afternoon I was appointed to go with some fellow prisoners to the cemetery with the body of a captain, killed, for some obscure reason, by a bullet fired from a watchtower.

I calculated that we would pass quite near the lone prisoner, and I resolved to take advantage of the opportunity to speak to him. Of course, it was strictly forbidden. Sentinels, with loaded guns under their arms, kept their eyes on us every minute. Could I manage it?

On our way there, the circumstances were not favorable, but I had a chance to take a good look at him. He was in his hole, standing straight, frozen in a tragic posture of deference and powerlessness. He seemed very tall to me, well over six feet. His overcoat was unbuttoned, dirty, ragged at the shoulders. Eyes (again!) as deep as wells, a mouth like a saber-cut. A skeleton covered with skin which a gust of strong wind would knock over. It was enough, however, for me to perceive that he was a man of nobility, distinction, refinement, sensitivity. Certainly he was not an ordinary man, and it was therefore quite possible that he was a general. I also deduced from those indefinable signs which we use as criteria that he was not French. I was dismayed, because, even supposing I succeeded in speaking to him, he might not be able to answer me.

On the way back, I had a little better luck. Eyes can't hear, and it happened that my guard was quite a distance from me. In that guarded fashion—employed by all the prisoners in the world—of talking without turning their heads or slowing down their pace, I said to him, "What are you doing there?"

Quick as a flash, he straightened up, strained his fleshless body toward the sky, looked straight in front of him across that endless plain, and in perfect French, hammered out this reply: "I am waiting for vengeance!"

A second later, he bent his back again and returned to his labor....

Tomorrow I will read this page to the Dean.

Part III

The Questions

Part III

The Questions

LIFE HAS reclaimed me, snatched me up, seized me bodily. Once more it is inflicting its torments on me, taking particular care not to ask my opinion. Life is to blame; it is no doing of mine.

Will I have the time and the desire to speak of the past? Things have happened so fast. This time I have given up thinking that I will ever be able to settle down into a situation without any risks.

Last night I read the Dean my story of the prisoner. Was it the wise thing to do?

"I saw you on the shore, and that old memory suddenly overpowered me. I am not asking you whether the comparison is accurate. I think it is false. It was an association of images. You see how our minds work. It is disturbing. Images come to us which we haven't even had time to call up. They cling to situations, but they don't explain them. Then ... what are they doing there?"

He listened to me as he always does, in deep silence. His silences surprise me every time. Finally he said, "I think you're wrong about the association of images. Images don't grow by spontaneous generation. Take that one of yesterday which is bothering you—who hasn't been at one time or another, for

137

an hour or a second, the twin of your Serbian general? Even John the Mystic called down the fire of heaven on the heedless cities. What else can we call that desire of his but vengeance? No one is completely noble, utterly disinterested, entirely pure. Perhaps last night at the very moment when your Serbian general came before your eyes, I, too, was thinking of the fire of heaven. Everything holds together. The most ephemeral thought engenders a world, and that world can be beautiful or ugly. I was at least thinking this: that whatever you may say, there can never be two when it comes to suffering. That is why I sometimes have to be alone. Your prisoner was alone too, you can be sure. In communion with all the prisoners of those times, you may say. No, in communion with his trench, which was endless, and that vast horizon, as confining as your barbed wire. Christ was fearfully alone. Do you think we can succeed where he failed?"

What have I got myself into?

Such reasoning, no matter how sound, always upsets me. You can't build anything with it. You just line up words until you think you have exhausted the subject. Then you notice that you are right back where you started.

I answered, "Each of us suffers alone, it is true. It is the law. It is too commonly held and experienced to be an error. It is the path of salvation or damnation, according to whether it makes us warm or cold. But what of love? For love to exist, there have to be at least two . . ."

His lips parted. Joy, welling up from within, shone in his eyes. "Well, then, for love there will be two of us. It is more difficult . . . and I am still searching for a definition of love. . . ."

"We'll have to see, from day to day," I said.

"From day to day," he repeated pensively, "and there are so many yet to live through, and they will be hard ones."

"Back home in the early spring," I answered, "when we plant the barley, the wind is often sharp and cold. You shiver,

138

and have to cover up. But still not a day goes by without your feeling a breath of warmth which strays into that relentless wintry blast and somehow mysteriously remains there without becoming chilled. Before a peasant has a chance to straighten up, it has caressed his cheek and passed on, but it is enough to make him stop and smile in anticipation of violets soon to bloom. After all, love is perhaps just that. . . ."

He was standing, with one closed hand leaning on my desk, and he had been gazing at the opposite wall. I saw his hand relax slowly, and he turned to me. "Well, then, tomorrow I am going to take my whiff of spring, because tomorrow, I'm going back. . . ." He spoke joyfully. Then his voice became more serious. "You are wondering where I am going tomorrow, aren't you? Don't be naïve. Last night when I looked at the sea, I knew I had to return to her. I thought I was through with her, but she has me in her spell. She is stronger than I, than you, than everything and everyone. While you were watching me there and thinking of your famous general, she spoke to me. I don't need to put a shell to my ear to hear her. She said, 'I remember you. You won't betray me twice. Come.' That was the word I was waiting for. One always waits for a word. . . ."

"I have to admit that she went to some lengths to please you —her Sunday best, her jewels, all her diamonds."

He had folded his hands; his face was serene; he sighed with contentment. The child in him spoke. I felt something of his pure delight, his rediscovered youth, his certitudes.

"So you understand me?" he added in a kind of transport.

"I feel the same exhilaration when I see my wheat fields. . . . When do you leave?"

"Tomorrow at dawn. On the *Marie-Jeanne* . . ."

"*Waves of the sea, bless the Lord* . . .! Wake me up at whatever time you like. I'll serve your Mass, and then you can go back to her!"

After he had gone to bed, I went outside for a few minutes. I felt like singing. The tide was coming in. The stars were mirrored in the sea. That enchantress didn't frighten me any more. I gave thanks to her and to God.

I COULDN'T SLEEP. My heart was tight with anguish. (How many times will I have to use that word?)

The old nun who taught me my catechism used to advise us to say the rosary on such occasions. It never worked for me ... and besides, should one say the rosary to put oneself to sleep? Use the rosary as a sedative?

Toward midnight, I got up and went out. I wanted to see the stars and the sea—less the stars than "her," as he says. Since he loves her, I must love her too, or else she will be a barrier between us rather than a bond.

The weather had changed rapidly. Great black clouds had formed. There were no more stars. The sea had come up as far as it could, almost to the edge of the path. I could scarcely see it; I had to guide myself by the sound. That, there was no mistaking—no other sound is like that of masses of water surging forward, crashing, receding and withdrawing to gather force again, never vanquished, never wearying. ...

Was I going to be afraid again?

I had to love the sea, so much the worse for me, I had to love it.

But what can I love in it? Why does he love it? It isn't so hard to love, but it is hard to find the reasons for loving.

O Lord, help me ...

140

My parish is sleeping. All the lights are out. I am at the heart of night.

Tomorrow, no—this very morning, he will go. He will go because she has bewitched him again, put him under her spell. It is a good thing; he will be happy. I can see him boarding that boat. He will be able to forget. . . . I wish he could sail to a desert isle and never come back. How long can he forget? Two weeks have passed since he left the canton. Their silence is coming to an end. Peter will have put out to sea, but what of the "fisher of men" in Peter? What of the other enchantment . . . the Church?

The Church? Best not to think of it. There are times when you have to stop thinking, forbid yourself to think, when it is night all around, as it is now, and the Church is no more than this invisible sea, indecipherable, unintelligible, only a voice...

Could the Church be just that voice alone, that call in the night, under a lowering sky, that invitation, that sign, that hidden power, that turning point, that love?

Better not to think of it—but I am thinking. . . .

For the word (one always waits for a word, he said last night) that word has been pronounced and the image was drawn from the sea. Peter didn't mistake it; he could not. Jesus said to him one day, "Put out into the deep," and Peter obeyed.

Into the deep (*in altum*) even into the heart of the wind, the heart of the storm. But he understood the word, and he tried to put out into the deep. No one followed him; that is, no one got into the boat with him. He found himself at sea, all alone. You don't play bridge in a small boat on the high seas. The others stayed home at their bridge table. They didn't understand. They said, "He is mad. That isn't what the Gospel means." For them, the Gospel means peace, order, their kind of order. The Gospel is discipline, their kind of discipline. It means marching to their tune, the priest leading. After all, what can he complain about? They appointed him top sergeant; he is leading their parade. It is such a good arrangement that if by chance he doesn't respect their itinerary, they set him back on the right path. They have ways of doing it. Infallible ways. Out into the deep. *Duc in altum.* But aren't we there already? A turn about the town, a toast of honor, everyone smile! The priest did a good job. His colonel is pleased with him.

I hear, ". . . the honor of the priesthood and my fidelity to my vocation are at stake."

If there were a frontier marker, I would sit down there, searching and searching, waiting for an answer. I would say to Him, "What is left of Your Gospel? What have they made of Your priesthood? In all honesty, faced with this massacre of Your plan for the world, could he remain? Let him go out on that boat then . . . Of course, it isn't exactly what You meant, but out there, on that great rolling sea, he will have the illusion of a palpable contact with Your Word. Out there You will explain things to him. Do You believe that he couldn't go on? You have to make things clear to us. But if I might give You a word of counsel: don't make the explanation too complicated; don't let it be far from what our eyes see, what our ears hear. Be good, be mild, or be savage if You must, but be clear. . . ."

They are going to condemn him.
They have already condemned him.
Why? Simply because he had had enough of playing top sergeant. Would You have consented to twirl a baton and lead their parade? Is that what Your Church is supposed to be? If not, then he was right to leave. To whom does his con-

science belong? And, if not on his conscience, on what will he be judged one day before You, Son of God, crucified so that our consciences might speak? His choice was simple. I understand him all the better because I have been through the same thing. I stepped out of the parade in another way, it is true, through the door of obedience, as hard as that obedience was, but that is only a question of nuances and of understanding. My intentions were identical, my doubts were similar to his. What was our choice? A child in catechism class couldn't make a mistake. It was between You and that caricature of a Church; between playing bridge and Your *Duc in altum*; between Your Gospel of fire and theirs, made out of marshmallow; between the freedom to love You and the slavery of serving them; between our loving submission to Your Word and our servile compliance with their decisions. What would You have done? What would St. Paul have done?

He left, You see; he left. All alone, of his own accord. He shook the dust from his feet and abandoned them. He couldn't go on. His time had come, as he said. And they have turned in their report, respectful, detailed. Nothing is missing, except their portrait. His is there, in several copies, so that no one will fail to recognize him.

And Your answer, God of Heaven and also God of earth?

You don't answer. You don't answer me; I understand that. I ask for an answer just on principle. I am not cast down by Your silence. My faith doesn't falter. Is silence Your answer? Then I shall have to take stock of this silence and try to find at the bottom of it, in the very depths, the word for which he is waiting, for which we are both waiting; the inaudible, unformulated word, incomprehensible except on one's knees, alone, before those two pieces of wood that form a cross, before that gallows, before Your "yes."

I can't see anything now. . . .

Yes, you did answer. There is the rain. . . . The night is a little darker. . . .

And I hear people say it is easy to be a priest!

It would be impossible to describe his gait, his gestures, the expression on his face as he went down the path toward the little port. Right after his Mass, sensing his elation, I asked him what passage from Scripture he was taking with him. He confided: *"Flores apparuerunt in terra nostra. Tempus putationis advenit."* And I prefer the Septuagint rendering: "the time of song," not "the time of pruning." As far as I know, you don't prune trees when they are in flower.

It was raining. The sea was rough. He had put on sailor's clothes, a sou'wester covered his head. "What a fine day," he exclaimed, "what a beautiful day!" He pointed to the sea.

I hardly counted any more. He jumped aboard. The captain motioned to him. I gathered that he meant him to take the wheel. He took hold of it with a practiced hand; he caressed it, smiled at it.

The *Marie-Jeanne* sailed first, bowing gracefully to left and right. The other fishermen followed after her, but she was already far out. I think they wanted him to have the honor of going first.

Tonight I don't feel like writing, or rather like describing anything. All my landscapes are interior. Last night's anguish has returned. I always feel, in moments like this, the childish desire to look for truth at its center; to take it out of its case no matter how tightly locked; to look at it, eat it, wallow in it, live in it, accept all its fires—but let it be at last, O God, the Truth! No, his flowers didn't appear in my land this morning, and I don't feel in the least like singing. I am suffering. And yet it isn't my fault. I am suffering for him. Is he really happy, or has he only let himself be drawn into a game of pretend?

The time has come to resist. These discussions with myself are sterile and depressing.

My old woman came at eight o'clock on the dot.

"I bought a little less bread," she said. "Just enough for the two of us."

I would rather she hadn't spoken, and she sensed it instantly. One question was bothering me, and I asked, "Is the Dean on such good terms with the fishermen?"

"But . . . he is one of them. They didn't adopt him, they acknowledged him."

I don't really like to draw women, even intelligent ones, into my problems. And yet . . . "And what did those worthy fishermen think of his departure from the deanery?"

"Monsieur le Doyen is a good priest," she answered. "Not a soul here doubts it. He is frank, loyal, transparently sincere, and everyone knows it. A man! Here, Monsieur le Curé, there are a great many poor people. The Dean's decision surprised them much less than you think. Things are simple for them: if the sea is wild, they don't defy it. They know we can't fight the elements. The Dean stayed in the canton for fifteen years, and if he left, it must mean that he couldn't fight any longer. What could be wrong in that? You took him in. Your parishioners respect you for that. Naturally they wouldn't know how to tell you, but you may take my word for it."

"And is that your opinion of the matter, too?" I said in a neutral voice.

145

She began doing the housework. After a long while, when I had already taken up my breviary, she said, "Although I never told you so, I was brought up, like you, in the midst of fields, flowers, and flocks of animals. That has its importance. Perhaps my hopes were too high? As a result, I suffered a great deal and doubted even more. God keep me from taking pride in my sufferings or my doubts. But from them and from my contact with the darkness, I learned this: the furrow of our convictions forms in us slowly, and the seeds grow there only as the seasons pass: just saying, 'I wish,' does not cause the wheat to ripen."

"He spent fifteen years of his life sowing without any success."

"That is not where his problem lies. Where his real problem was, he was absent."

I trembled inwardly.

"What gives us the right to judge?" she went on very softly. "It is a waste of time. Sometimes one would think that you aren't a peasant any more. Today he is on the sea. Let him alone; leave him to the joy of rediscovery. The sea has opened its arms to him again, as to the prodigal son. It will speak to him better than we could. If I dared, I would say that my only fear this morning is that your anxiety may have arms, too; long arms that reach out and touch him. For pity's sake, let's not confuse things for him."

"But how do you see the . . . solution?"

"I am almost ashamed to give you my opinion. That word 'solution' frightens me. The solution—what solution? As though we held it in our hands!" She spoke more firmly: "The solution is God. Do we want to replace Him with our searching and impose our opinions on Him?"

I was the one to feel guilty. I remembered what I had written because I thought it was true: "I want only to stand at his side like a gentleman and a brother." I felt wretched. She continued, smiling, "The solution? It is for you to love him and for me—to serve him. And then, to trust in his sincerity."

She went back to her chores.

The postman usually passes at about eleven-fifteen, while I am teaching the catechism class, sometimes even later. He gave me a letter for the Dean from the Bishop's office. I decided not to give it to him when he returns. . . . Tomorrow.

He returned at sundown.

We didn't talk much. He had his whole breviary to recite.

TODAY DAWNED very gray. A pallid day with a sad-eyed, tired, sick expression.

My first surprise was the obvious piety of the Dean during his Mass. His joy of yesterday, his enthusiastic response to the call of the child reborn in him were not diminished. That day on the sea had been an enrichment for him. He had always celebrated piously, to be sure, but this morning there was something warmer. He gave me the impression that he could have celebrated like that on his boat, in the midst of the waves, and that they would not have distracted his mind from God. Yesterday, then, he was sincere and completely himself. He wasn't playing at happiness. God and the sea, his beloved, combined in the harmony of a soul singing. God and the sea, not intermingled, but not excluding each other.

The strong personality of this man has broken the spell of textbooks, theories, and formulas; of pure, just, and disembodied ideas. Or he has suffered enough to be purged of them. He has arrived at the border of the Gospel. His maturity and balance would allow him to enter, if he were so inclined,

147

with assurance and sincerity. His presence, closer to Christ, wouldn't seem like a ridiculous fantasy there.

I have forbidden myself to watch him. But I can't help seeing, understanding, and accepting the offering he makes to me of his spiritual youth and his strength.

Will he be able to go further? And where to? How far? Would he want to? What does "going further" mean to him now? Where are his frontiers? At what precise spot will he decide to stop? Has he set any limits within himself? Utterly vain and futile questions! There he is, on this day, returned, unharmed, and, it would even seem, enriched after this new baptism. Revived for the next stage of the journey. What will it be? God knows.

But one thing I do know, as surely as I know my "Our Father," is that he will have to have serious reasons for taking any step, and no one in the world will get the better of him without first presenting credentials written in blood. That is certain now. Rank will not be enough.

After my Mass, I prayed for a long time. When we had eaten breakfast, I gave him the letter.

"Has the postman come already?" he asked. "Oh, no, this came yesterday. . . . That was good of you—you were afraid it would make me lose sleep."

He held the letter in his hand, in no hurry to open it. He got up, went into the classroom, and came back with a basketful of fish, which he had hidden there last night.

"It was a real miraculous catch," he told me joyously. "The men want me to go out with them again; they are convinced that I brought them luck. They won't have to ask me twice!"

Just to make conversation, I said, "The sea didn't look very comfortable."

"What are you saying?" he replied, amused. "And how badly you express it! I guess I'll have to teach you to talk their language." He added, mischievous and smiling, "I'll take you out there, on a really stormy day when God is at the helm. . . . Oh, yes, suppose we open this letter."

I was very—inadequate: I said, "You know that there are two of us."

He answered, serious and slightly ironical, "In circumstances like this, one is sufficient." Then he caught himself up. "No, even the Scriptures tell us: a man alone is too solitary, and in times of trial, a man alone can easily veer toward despair, or toward pride, which is its blood cousin. So set your mind at rest: I accept once again, and I thank you. However, you ought to know something about my frame of mind. My mother always told me that I was born during a terrible storm. I believe it, because I came into the world marked with fear; I have been haunted by it all my life. I have been afraid of everything, of the slightest things. I have always put on an act of being brave, but it is not so easy to free oneself of fear, since it is one of the most powerful tools of our educators.

"Then one day, not so long ago, I found a way out of fear, all by myself, with God's grace perhaps. It is this: We must not confuse fear with the sacred. We must believe that we are living under the New Testament. The confusion is easy, it is human, I think it is widespread, but it is wrong. I discovered one day that fear is never the work of God, never! He has exorcised fear. He has separated these words which from the beginning of time men have coupled: holy-fear. Since the Redemption, either we haven't grasped the first thing about it, or else our age-old fear of the sacred has been transformed into trust. Fear is no longer a necessary, useful, or even advisable medication for the diseases of our souls. Fear is a mistake. At least that is what I believe; a frame of mind, a direction decided upon after serious reflection. I would be lying if I claimed that that ancient fear, the hideous companion of my childhood and almost of my whole life, has completely left me. But I don't believe in it any more, and that is a great step forward. It took a long time!"

149

I ventured, "Of whom then should we be afraid?"

"That 'should' is excessive. Let me ask you something: is it Christian, Christian according to the Gospel, to be afraid of God?"

"He said, 'Fear not . . .' "

"Several times over, and never the contrary. So 'should' we be afraid of others? And on what could we base such fear? Their superiority? Their rank? Their intelligence? Their skill? Their bank account? Their audacity? In a word, on what they possess and we lack?"

"It would be foolish, of course."

"Foolish and unworthy of a man. What is left? Their diplomas? Why should a doctor in theology give me goose-flesh? Their holiness? That isn't a bugaboo, it is a challenge. So, who have we left out?"

"Ourselves."

"Yes, ourselves. Our conscience, that is, in the face of the living God! Now St. Theresa of the Child Jesus wrote these words: 'Even if I were weighted down with the worst sins in the world, I would run and throw myself into my Redeemer's arms.' You know the passage. We have only to seek God in peace. Since Christ's agony in the Garden, there is only one valid fear, His fear, the real fear of man helpless and in torment, the fear neither of dying nor of living . . . but of not reaching the heights to which the Voice summons. . . . He overcame it. His *'in manus tuas'* on Calvary bears witness to it. But here we are launched into what? Words. . . . Ah, yes. This letter."

He opened it, read it, held it out to me:

Dear Monsieur le Doyen,

We were painfully surprised by your decision. We hope that, with the help of reflection and prayer, you will reconsider your attitudes. If you were to persist in them, you can readily understand that it would do serious damage in the diocese to the indisputable principle of episcopal authority, whose origins are perfectly well known to you. Your letter does not explain anything. The reports which we received subsequently are not, unfortunately, of a nature to set our mind at rest. However, the fact that you have sought and found refuge with one of your colleagues reassures us.

You have always been a good priest. We therefore count on your respect and love for the priesthood. They will inspire the noble resolutions which you must prescribe for yourself.

Yours sincerely in Christ and Our Lady

P.S. Sober reflection must already have persuaded you that one doesn't leave one's parish on a rash impulse.

Our lives are very nearly identical. The coincidence of these situations is a fact. What is strange is that when I search my memory for the bedrock of my convictions, when I grope along the grassy banks of the past to touch the branch to which I clung so as not to lose heart, my recollections become vague. I have already forgotten, or almost forgotten. I retain the poetry of things, and never the prose, so often badly written, of my difficulties and my griefs. I remember my happy moods.

And so I have to rediscover everything, live from day to day at the side of a man whose force of character is beyond question, whose good faith is indubitable, and who doesn't seem particularly in need of help from others. It is a security and a hope. Was I ever as strong as he?

Help him?
Help him do what? ... Take his place in the ranks again?

Keep step again—with his present beliefs intact? Make, as they say, honorable amends? It would mean misunderstanding his humility before truth and his loathing of cowardice. With what can they reproach him? With having left his work as a priest without his superiors' consent? (That is exactly what he did, and it is serious in the eyes of the law.) But it was because he could not in conscience carry on any longer without failing in fidelity. His scales tipped in favor of fidelity. Is that a fault?

I have to have it clear in my mind: the tragic part of his situation lies in the choice, which he considered urgent, between two of the promises he made at ordination: one made inwardly when the chalice was given to him; the other, also sincere and loyal, of obedience to the one who ordained him, and to his successors. Is conscience involved here? Many would say no, either because they believe—as a result of godliness or reasoning—that there is true harmony between the two; or because they simply take the easy way, remaining ignorant of the conflict, or overlooking it. For him it was yes. Between this yes and this no lies the mystery of the Church.

And so he is alone.

A lonely man, as alone as I am, uprooted as we both are from our families, which have rejected us.

A lonely priest, more alone than I, since I am still attached to the Church by the bonds of my submission to its hierarchical authority, and he has, in fact, broken those bonds.

Is such solitude rare? In any case, can there be a more bitter and desperate solitude? When I think about it, my heart, although unaccustomed to sympathizing, is touched and aches. Onto what Paradise or what Hell does this door of dereliction open? Is this the price of—the reward for—his passion for truth?

Who will ever be able to say?

I gave him back the letter, which he tossed carelessly on my desk.

152

"After physical labor," he said calmly, "work for the mind. I shall spend the rest of the morning reading."

"What are you reading?" I asked him. (Was I indiscreet? I try so hard not to be.)

"Newman. I took the collection of his *Thoughts on the Church* out of your library. I like this man's faith, his delicate sense of nuances, his courage in the face of truth as his conscience reveals it to him, and especially his tolerance of others."

He was about to leave when our old woman came in, with a basketful of potatoes in her hand. She greeted us, and then asked the Dean pleasantly if he had had a good day yesterday.

"It couldn't possibly have been better," he replied, "and look, I thought of you, and of us, too." He showed her the basket of fish, with which she was delighted.

Then she volunteered, "Yesterday while you were out at sea I had some news of the canton. I learned that Monsieur le Chanoine did not accept the responsibility with which you entrusted him. It seems that when His Excellency begged him at least to take care of the catechism classes, the Sunday Mass, and the visits to the sick, he replied that the spiritual needs of his nuns prevented him from assuming any additional duties. I think that the good folk would not have been very disappointed if His Excellency hadn't asked the young curé from over the way to take charge of your parish. No doubt he had no choice." She added, "It seems that that is only a temporary measure."

The Dean remained silent.

She opened her basket to show us what was inside. "Here is something that won't cost you much. They are from my garden."

"You have a garden?" I asked her.

"A very big garden, Monsieur le Curé."

"As soon as the weather is warm, I'll go and spade it for you. . . . No arguments! I am an old hand with a spade."

Her eyes lifted for a second to the Dean.

"That young priest is not very well liked. They have already christened him the 'breezy curé.' I hardly know him myself. I saw him here once, on Christmas Eve. He was on a motorcycle. But since he will be there only a short while, they will put up with him."

She left us then, and the Dean went into his room.

But I want to tell about the rest of our day ...

In the afternoon, after a nap, which is a physical necessity for me, I invited the Dean to join me for a walk. We took the street, which is very narrow. We were walking down the middle of it, which forced a car, approaching from the rear, to stop. It was an enormous car; it took up the whole street. I turned around and saw the Colonel's wife at the wheel, the Colonel beside her, and in the back seat the Canon and the young "breezy curé," the same one who had visited me on Christmas Eve. The Dean didn't greet them, and he surely would have gone on with his walk without waiting for me if the car hadn't been blocking the way. We were squeezed into a doorway and couldn't get out. What could we say and still say nothing?

The Canon broke the silence. He was honey sweet. "How we do run into each other! Delighted to meet you. We have trapped you nicely. We couldn't have done better if we had tried."

Faced with our dumb silence, he added, "We are leaving for Lourdes, by way of the coast, to enjoy the scenery. A short week of prayer and excursions. Once in a while one has to get away from one's cares. That is our young colleague's opinion."

The Dean didn't reply because he was determined not to. I didn't reply simply because I couldn't form the first syllable. The Colonel's wife looked at us. Her eyes had a disdainful, haughty expression. She was savoring something—a vengeance or a victory—and she was anxious not to miss any part of the meal. Finally she turned toward the Canon and said in a loud voice, "What were we talking about, dear Monsieur le Chanoine? Oh, yes, that bid of three no trumps you innocently made me lose last night. Let's see. Oh, yes, it was the second finesse. . . ." And, laughing, she put her foot on the gas.

"That really is going too far," I said to the Dean. "What about the catechism classes? And the sick? Who is the nearest priest to the canton now?"

He answered in a nasty tone, "My friend, first, the priest nearest to the canton is—you. Second, to be technical—I might add that in society (and ecclesiastical society is no exception) everything is a question of terminology—what is called 'abandonment' in some cases is called 'fidelity' in others. Luckily, faith isn't a question of terminology."

Some children came up to us and he spoke to them with tenderness and great gentleness. He spent a long while hearing about their childish joys, their work, their games. I had fallen back a few paces so that these youngsters wouldn't have to choose between us. Then he asked them whether their fathers would be going fishing the following day. When the oldest ones said yes, he asked one of them to let the owner of the *Marie-Jeanne* know that he would go with him.

We didn't talk much. But when we returned, I saw that he was pensive and hesitant. Before we went into the house, he said, "Will you do me a favor? Will you let me take over now and then, whenever you like, the Christian formation of those youngsters?" He said it timidly.

"Decide for yourself," I said, "the number of your classes and the days."

He answered gravely, "Thank you." And then, in his usual manner, after a pause, "You understand . . . the spring doesn't want to dry up. I realized it yesterday, out at sea. It wells up and doesn't know where to flow." He went on joyously, "The Gospel is so beautiful! And who will preach it to them if we don't?"

A phrase from Jeremiah came into my head. I recited it to

him in the voice of a schoolboy: "The babes cry for food, but there is no one to give it to them."

"Yes," he answered, "yes, but let's not get emotional. Jeremiah was not one for emotion. If we spoke like the prophets, our eyes would be gouged out. I asked you to let me do that just to—to keep myself busy."

It would be better to begin relating today's events at the end. Still, I don't want to change my method too much.

The Dean left at dawn, as he had the first time. I wanted to accompany him to the port, but he refused, so we said goodby in front of the church. He pointed to the sky and predicted a good day, "Because," he added, "the weather will be fine."

And, indeed, it is fine weather, but will it last? The sun is almost hot, though spring isn't here yet. And there is no sign that it will arrive any sooner than it does at home. I would be happy to feel its first warm breath against my cheek, the way it comes at home, between two puffs of icy wind. . . . It is a mistake to go into exile in middle age; one is too old for changes. I heard someone say that vine-pruning time is approaching. At home we usually prune in March.

Everything lacks variety here. Sometimes I wonder whether I'll be able to hold out. My guitarist must have been right. These disagreeable impressions make their way in my head, and it alarms me, because I am sure that I do nothing to encourage them. They simply take hold of me. I wonder whether one day I will discover that they have taken complete possession.

156

But what upsets me today is my own cowardice. I feel happy to be alone, without the Dean....

That man took fifteen years to make up his mind, but he won't change it now. The Bishop thought that he left his parish on an "impulse," but nothing is further from the truth. He had meditated over this decision for a long time. Our conversation the day we met on the plateau didn't determine anything, didn't precipitate anything; the time was already ripe. Perhaps all it did was allow him to choose a friend. In that (if my thinking is correct) there was a disposition of Providence ... perhaps? But he would have left the canton even if he hadn't met me. To go where? Anywhere ... depending on the way the wind blew....

And so I am a coward because I am tired, I am exhausted from this struggle and these eternal misunderstandings and contradictions which, in the Dean's case, brought him to the parting of the ways. I am a coward because I consent to believe that it is futile to resist, since twenty centuries of evangelization haven't changed anything. The weight of ill will, egotism, and blindness in our world, which we call Christian, crushes even the strong. And if the strong fall, if the strong give up, what will the weak do?

Those thoughts are tainted with paganism. They go against the grain of the Gospel and the Redemption, intelligently and humbly understood. But weren't even the saints, more often than we think, tempted to lose heart?

And is that why today I feel this kind of low-grade happiness, a base and vulgar joy (made to my measure) because he is not so near to me? He isn't here with his questioning, his drama, and his tragedy; I can breathe freely in my peace, my tranquillity, my success at having achieved finally an ordinary life, in which I may even come to terms with exile, since it is the price fixed and agreed to for my protective obscurity. After so many struggles, so many efforts, so many failures, I fit this role of a zealous priest, now defeated and sidetracked. I am harmless now. I will do good, in conformity with the law, and from now on St. Paul will waste his words preaching to me that the law is dead. I will cultivate my garden. . . .

Now, when I hear people condemn bureaucracy in the priesthood, I do not get angry. How else can a priest of middling intelligence spend the rest of his life? He is in the system, and no matter what he does, the system will win out over his wayward enthusiasms. A priesthood which in principle is lower middle class implies and demands this conclusion, and is bound to end up in this premature old age.

Today the Dean's absence makes me feel relaxed. I wallow in complete conformity. I bask in mediocrity. I live by the system. In a moment I will piously read my breviary. Then I will teach a class in the catechism, scrupulously following the textbook. I can talk about God for an hour, drawing on a whole arsenal of clichés, without actually thinking of Him for a single second. Who can say I am not orthodox? "I came to bring fire upon the earth. . . ." Those who believe that end up like the Dean. I don't want to be for Jesus Christ against the system.

If this black mood continues, it won't be long before I trot over in my best soutane and obsequiously beg the Colonel's wife to teach me to play bridge. The lost sheep will return to the fold, and the peace of Heaven will be my inheritance!

I was indulging in these disillusioned considerations and reflections, when a Dominican Father knocked at my door. I didn't know him. He introduced himself very civilly and declared (I was grateful for that) that no one had sent him. He came from the capital of this *Département,* where the Dominicans have a residence. He had heard rumors of what he called the Dean's "adventures." I didn't like the term, but I noticed that, on the lips of this jovial, friendly, and courteous man, it lost almost all irony and malice. I invited my guest to sit down and offered him the best thing I have, a glass of the wine I keep for Mass. He was perspiring and very thirsty, and he accepted it with pleasure.

He launched into a monologue immediately, all the while watching me attentively, with sympathy and with the evident intention of convincing me. (I have noticed that priests from religious orders always look at secular priests in a "certain way." I must try to explain this phenomenon.)

"I have heard," he began in a rich and slightly preachy voice, "what befell Monsieur le Doyen. Believe me, my dear and respected colleague, when I say that I was astounded. I have known Monsieur le Doyen for many years and I pride myself on having been, indeed on being still, his friend. I preached a mission in his parish about five years ago. You will understand, therefore, that I am very familiar with it. The Dean exhausted his strength on it; he employed remarkable gifts of intelligence and will there in God's service. He didn't obtain extraordinary results, but who among us works miracles? He was loved by the common people. The others considered him a harmless idealist, a dreamer. His approach to them was almost always unsuitable, even harsh. He was always right in principle, but in practice he was usually wrong. You know that that is a fault people find hard to forgive. He made enemies, but if a priest has nothing but friends, does that prove that he has preached the Word effectively? And because of the shortcomings that go with a strong character, he was not in favor with the diocesan authorities either.

"Did all these difficulties put together justify what some people are calling his 'flight'? As a matter of fact, that is an exaggeration. I call it his escape, a term more exact, and possibly more severe—I favor precision, especially in these excessively delicate matters. The Dean made his escape, and that is what grieves me. He escaped because, in spite of serious studies and extensive knowledge, he lacked the thing that crowns all learning, even Scriptural learning: a solid Thomist background. God knows that he was familiar with St. Paul, that he followed his teachings. But he hadn't assimilated St. Thomas! *In medio stat virtus.* (Real strength is that which is found at the meeting place of two opposing currents.) That is the axiom, the explanation of our forbearance and all our courage. *In medio.* Not too much, not too little! The highest wisdom. The *ultima ratio.* (The final argument which carries the point.) The *videtur quod non* (in Thomist debate, the exposition of the opponent's arguments), the quintessence of truth in our practical behavior. What priest, religious or secular, could ever imagine that St. Thomas might be mistaken? St. Thomas is always right."

My Dominican visitor was magnificent in his candor and sincerity. In his simplicity, too. He could have gone on for an hour, two hours, without losing the thread. I didn't dare interrupt him; it was he who questioned me:

"Are you a Thomist, at least?"

"Good Lord," I answered, "how could I help but be? I studied his philosophy for two long years, and isn't our theology——"

He didn't let me finish. "Two long years, you say! Two years that were too short, Monsieur le Curé. What are two years of Thomism? You have to spend a lifetime at it."

This kind of affirmation always means that the speaker is about to bring himself into the discussion. He was no exception. "I have read St. Thomas eight times, all of St. Thomas, with my pen in my hand——"

This type of proof exasperates me. I interrupted, "Is it permitted, Reverend Father, to oppose St. Thomas and St. Paul? By opposing them, I mean set them face to face."

He was triumphant. "St. Thomas facing St. Paul! What a pity that our master thinker was born so late!"

He then launched into a long dissertation, to which I didn't listen. I think he meant to prove that the Church was the poorer because these two geniuses never met. St. Thomas would have introduced more subtle distinctions into St. Paul's thought and all of the difficulties in the Apostle's writings would have been happily resolved.

I attempted a breakthrough. "St. Paul," I said, "was not much more politic than our Dean. His manner of expression is often more conspicuous for violence than for sweetness. He didn't convert the Pharisees of his time. . . ."

My guest had an answer for everything, but he didn't answer everything. That conversational trick which consists in seizing on the last words pronounced by one's companion somewhat diminished my opinion of him.

"Convert!" he answered. "Convert! *Quid est et quid significat?* (What is that, and what does it mean?) The primary matter is not to convert others, but neither is it trying to escape!"

"And suppose that one can no longer hold out where one is? Suppose one feels that the priesthood is ineffective, even a mockery? Suppose the Kingdom of God cannot take root there? What do you advise in such a case?"

"The Angelic Doctor answers you once again, *in medio.* Take one's stand *in medio.*"

"The middle road between what?"

"Who said anything about a road? I am referring to a frame of mind which must be acquired."

"*In medio*, then," I replied, "between anger and patience, between the Gospel and the Pharisees, between the Cross and Herod's palace, between yes and no! But, Reverend Father, it is written, 'I would to God you were either hot or cold.' You know what is in store for those who are lukewarm?"

He seemed discouraged. He stood up to take his leave. I said, "Why do you want to go? Search and find—in my case, in the case of total incomprehension—the middle ground. Either give up your turn at escaping, or admit that the Dean was right."

My words saddened him; nevertheless I went on, "I have been reflecting on that *in medio* for years. But there are some men—and I am one—who from lack of imagination or intelligence, or strength, or because of their mental make-up, or some unchangeable trait of character, can never stand up straight *in medio*. They either aspire to holiness and move toward it, or else they consent to something that seems to them to diminish and downgrade them. No doubt I am misinterpreting the Angelic Doctor. I have always been of the opinion—and the Dean a thousand times more than I—that not believing in the light, not advancing toward it, means entering into darkness. There is no middle-ground solution there. Prefabricated formulas crumble to pieces when the winds of choice start to blow. For many years, I drove a car, and the time of day which I always considered the least pleasant for driving, the most dangerous and also the saddest, was the twilight hour when night is encroaching upon what remains of daylight. You can hardly see anything, but the headlights are of no use as yet. *In medio* between day and night! Well, any driver will tell you: Give us day or night, but not twilight."

He took hold of himself again and pronounced the "word" I had been waiting for: "And what did you do then? Did you stop driving? More likely you struggled on in that failing light, and your own inner light guided you."

I was about to agree with him, when in came the Dean.

That man takes up the whole room. As soon as he comes into a place, his presence transforms the whole atmosphere. He was wet, dirty, carelessly dressed; his hands were sticky with fish scales—and he was happy!

He threw his sou'wester down on a chair and kissed my Dominican on both cheeks like a child greeting his father.

There was no question of continuing the conversation. The Dean spoke in exclamations. The Dominican was won over.

First he smiled, then he laughed out loud. And, as though by enchantment, the Dean, in complete control of the situation, let his soul speak:

"If you had seen the sea today, Father, and if you had been rocked all day on that boat with me! I feel sorry for you! You pray to God in your choir stall, your head in your hands. That is called abstracting oneself, I believe. It is a matter of taste. For me, prayer has to be"—he searched for a second—"it has to be everything! Everything—the sea, the sky, the wind, the waves, the risk, the slippery deck, a gull passing or following me, the seaweed we cast off, the fish struggling, a rudder, a net—everything, I tell you, and in the midst of it all God holds my hand. It wouldn't take much to toss a man overboard. You come out or you don't. You are better versed in reading the Scriptures than I, so I give you this verse of Psalm Eighty-four. It has been ringing all day in my head. 'I will hear what God proclaims.' Well, He has told me all sorts of things today."

The Dominican was on the verge of tears. He turned to me and said, "There at least is something that isn't prefabricated." And he added, to me, in a low voice, "When Monsieur le Doyen understands our story of the driver..."

I HAVE borrowed a spade; it is a strange shape, flatter than those at home. Here there is no earth to turn, only sand. How I love to spade the earth, cut into it, lift it, turn it over!

It is still amazingly mild, soft weather. The wind that comes from the sea has lost all its flavor; it takes forests and mountains and wheat fields to make the wind bold and vigorous and full of life. Here it doesn't lack power, but it lacks youthfulness. It lacks fragrance. It carries only one odor, which in the end is flat and slightly sickening. I don't want to malign it, but I can't forgive it for not being my wind from home.

I have made a discovery.

This garden isn't very big and it is surrounded by walls. On the side facing the little path and the sea, the wall has crumbled; you can glimpse what is going on outside, and on a clear day, you can look out to sea. In the corner opposite the entrance gate (this is my discovery) there was once a cabin. Not really a cabin, but a sort of niche covered with branches. The former proprietor, doubtless dead (I will ask my old woman) left there, well hidden from view, away in the back, a few sticks of wood, some dry grass and straw, a hatchet, four or five tools—everything you ordinarily find scattered about in a gardener's shed. In that dry grass and straw, he left even the imprint of his body. There it must have been that he rested, smoked his pipe, took his ease.

I went into this hut and glanced over its contents. I would have stayed, but I was ashamed to rest without first having worked. As soon as my limbs were a bit weary, I returned there and took "his" place.

No one sees me; no one can see me. I sank down into the hay, which has no fragrance because it is old, into the debris of straw, between the sticks of pine. At last I was alone, free. Free from what? From whom? And why this question? Neither from God nor from the priesthood, which were never chains for me. Free from everything else. Even my body relaxed. I breathed easily. . . . My chains, all my chains had fallen. An angel could have come, and his appearance wouldn't have surprised me. It was my house-in-the-meadow, my enchanted domain. I need so little and I have it all. The wind made the roof-branches tremble. The sun slanted into a corner. I didn't look at the sea. I looked at my spade sticking into the ground, waiting, and the weeds which I was planning to bury. . . . I let myself dream of staying there, living there, dying there. Is that romanticism? Nonsense. Not to have to watch myself any more and not to have to say "Be careful!" Here I can find my ants, my spiders, my roots, my field. All that is missing is my dog. I will ask my old woman to lend me hers. I won't tell her why. How could I explain it? We always lie a little. On rainy days, I will say I am going out to gather snails (are there any snails here?) or something like that. I will teach her dog how to be my dog; how to hide under my coat with just his muzzle sticking out; how to get dry; how to listen to sounds; how we can keep warm together; how to look at me, guess my thoughts. It is all settled. She will consent.

I have found my home, my hermitage, my retreat, my secret, my escape, my Temple. There in front of the door I will plant narcissus, tulips, hyacinths, jonquils; then pansies, daisies; in summer, petunias. The wind will be perfumed when it comes into my house. I will plant a tree, too—but what kind? . . . No, not a pine. . . . And there will be room for a climbing rose! I will fasten it to the thatch.

In the meanwhile, let me enjoy this complete happiness, without a flaw, unmixed, limitless. The Dean talks to me about his sea. My ocean is here. Let me just burrow down into this hay, "wedge in" as we used to say, let me settle into these scraps of Paradise. . . .

God! God in that? . . . Don't make me laugh. God isn't in books, formulas, theses. Some people have put God into aspirin tablets. One takes Him in homeopathic doses, according to them. God is here. The door of my cabin opens onto the infinite. God's joy is rooted in this human joy. And here I am, my God, with all the complexes of a child of the poor. . . .

The Lord's are the earth and its fullness; the world and those who dwell in it. . . .

The heavens declare the glory of God and the firmament proclaims his handiwork.
Day pours out the word to day, and night to night imparts knowledge;
Not a word nor a discourse whose voice is not heard;
Through all the earth their voice resounds, and to the ends of the world, their message. . . .

The Lord is my shepherd; I shall not want.
In verdant pastures he gives me repose;
Beside restful waters he leads me; . . .
The earth is full of the mercy of God.
Though my father and mother forsake me, yet will the Lord receive me.

Both melodies, both songs, both joys, both cries intermingle.
All I can see now is the beauty of things. . . .

THE DEAN cast his stone into the still water of the lake. Since then the rippling of the water has not ceased. He is the one who is right and I am wrong. . . .
First of all, what would I have done in his place? Nothing. I would have been incapable of doing anything. All my life I have been indecisive, changeable, inoffensive, a man no one fears, and whom no one likes very much, because basically I am a coward. I see the truth; I wholeheartedly embrace it. I cry out; I suffer for it; and then in the hour of battle, I desert

it. I refuse to discuss it with other men. I have spurts of inspiration; I take up my tools and outline a project, but I don't finish it. In my studio full of odds and ends, I have piles of unfinished sketches. There are hundreds of them. The quiet man and the obedient man in me understand each other. They sit on the same chair. They look; I look; life goes on. The same as yesterday. I haven't changed the slightest thing.

I am disgusted with myself . . . and being a priest doesn't make me any the less disgusted. My superiors aren't responsible for that. Men like me don't change the world. They find it ugly; they accept its ugliness. They die in their "hut." The body is picked up; . . . a few shovelfuls of sand, and a week later the sand has flattened out all by itself. The wind blows over the grave, ironical, indifferent, content at not having to slow down its pace. No mound is visible. And the chariot moves on to the same smooth rhythm. "The just man perishes and no one mourns. The godly are carried off. . . ."

In the name of obedience, out of respect for obedience, because I couldn't or wouldn't or didn't dare to be defiant, what have I become? A *petit-bourgeois,* not rich, to be sure, very poor, but aside from that, untroubled. As empty as a village buffoon. It is true that I was humiliated (and not just a little), that I suffered (very much), that I bled (a great deal). Apparently, to go by the formulas, I am a sort of martyr of obedience, that is, an individual whose life was active and who was cast alive into those humiliations, that passion, that bloodshed. . . . I accepted this semi-retirement, and You will see, my God, that soon I will find it rather pleasant. So much the worse! . . . So much the better! But if obedience is the absolute and only objective form of truth, the ones to be pitied are not those who obey, but those who command. On the day of truth, they will bow their heads.

The Dean couldn't obey to the very end. In the struggle between obedience and conscience, his conscience won.

That's fine. It is clear cut. But then he fled.

Taking flight means giving in. Giving in is not daring to stand firm; it is being weak. It means giving arms to authority after laying down one's own; it means compromising the cause which one wanted to uphold; it means recognizing the existence of authority and reaffirming, negatively, the principle of obedience. It is an extremely risky anticipation of the future based on two doubtful hypotheses: first, the "self-righteous" will come to understand, which means that they will change their ways; second, the authorities will be forced to reconsider their formulas. Now, both of these hypotheses are more than doubtful; they are unsound: the self-righteous never give in, and the authorities refuse to modify their viewpoint when they are against the wall. Authority never bows to force. Ecclesiastical authority very rarely repents, and then only when faced with glaring proof of absolute purity of intention. But by that time, the one who brought about this revision of judgment cannot benefit from it, because he is dead. A flight like the Dean's doesn't affect the authorities. The Dean has dug a hole in water. Running away doesn't mean choosing to die, it means choosing the manner of one's death. Now it is well established that this is not advisable. Socrates, who was offered a chance to escape, and who could have done so without too much trouble, preferred to die according to the law. That was more than two thousand years ago, and we recognize that Socrates was right. He set an example for all of humanity, which needs models. He would have fallen less gallantly if he had chosen where he would fall, for centuries of human thought agree that to die in the night of obedience means dying in the light.

If that is true, and it would seem to be, the fact is that we don't even have the free choice of our own death. . . .

I am up to my neck in theories, and I detest theories. Especially abstract theories. I am plunged into them by a force which I feel I haven't the right to resist. If I was wrong myself, if it was a mistake to accept this semi-retirement, is it sure, in the light of these considerations, that the Dean was right to decamp? . . . I see the thread, but I can't quite get hold of it.

In the army, and that is no recent development, one obeys first and protests afterward—providing one still has the desire, and supposing that this so-called passive obedience hasn't already destroyed the individual. It is brutal. And men being what they are, how can it be any the less so? Men aren't usually led and kept under fire by gentle persuasion.

But in the Church, and for the priest, there can never be a question of pragmatism. From the humblest curé to the summit of the hierarchy, purity of intention is absolutely imperative. The priest must be pure, pure in the Gospel sense. Transparent. That means at the very least that he must not give in to any emotion. Priests, as well as their superiors in the hierarchy, don't always live up to this ideal, but the principle is imperishable and it always reappears from the ruins accumulated by defeated wills. The whole edifice can crumble, but it never crushes this principle, which somehow comes safely out of the rubble and sets itself on top like a banner.

On the other hand, in the Church, as a result of the slow and inevitable evolution of minds, the time of so-called passive obedience seems to be dead. Priests are free men in this ecclesiastical society, where freedom, emancipation, and consent of the will are the key words, the justification of all the rest, and passive obedience is now considered unworthy of them.

In the Dean's case, did this purity of intention, of mind, of will, this purity of orientation, exist? Does it still exist?

I hold that it does.

I remember his sermon. Here, for the record, is a copy of

his last letter to the bishop, the one he wrote on Christmas Eve:

Your Excellency,
For several years now—at least four times in person or by personal letter—I have respectfully solicited the favor of a transfer. Without clearly indicating the reasons behind your refusal, you have failed to grant my request. I thank you for the confidence in me evinced by these refusals.

On the other hand, you have, or so it appears (certainly it is the popular interpretation), continued to support all those in my parish who, on the pretext of serving the Church, inhibit my functioning as a priest.

I do not presume to judge your intentions. Your conscience, I am sure, is clear. However, I consider myself obliged to make certain decisions for myself. Since I am no longer able to preach the Gospel without exposing it to serious distortions, which would damage the very thought of Christ as the Church has always interpreted it, I hereby respectfully advise you that I am leaving my parish. Acting on my own responsibility, I accept in advance all the consequences of this irrevocable decision.
                                   Yours, etc.

So then, my God, You who have permitted us, through Your prophet Isaiah, to discuss things with You ("Come let us take counsel together"), would You show me where in the Dean's soul there were any hidden shadows? I am—You know it—the opposite of a hairsplitter. I don't play at being a "Don Camillo," and neither does the Dean. I don't blame the bishop. I respect him. I don't exculpate the Dean. I am too fond of him. I will wait as long as necessary. Take Your time. When You judge that I am ready, speak to me.

Things aren't improving in the least.
This morning I was in my study, the Dean in his room,

when someone knocked at the door. I opened it and received a priest who was all smiles and friendliness, but who didn't introduce himself. He launched into long speeches about my health, my getting settled, my parish, and even my former diocese, with which he seemed quite well acquainted. I could hardly get a word in before his monologue was off again in artfully balanced cadences which communicated chiefly his desire to please without committing himself. He had a colorless accent acquired by constant efforts to make it inoffensive.

He was rather tall, still young, but with an emaciated face lined with premature wrinkles. He had long twisted hands in whose hollows I divined a peasant ancestry, visible and mute. He leaned over, straightened up, stalled for time, and kept the secret of his visit wrapped up in the thin stuff of his phrases. I didn't have long to observe him, because suddenly the Dean opened his door, and, addressing me without a glance at my visitor—already stepping forward to greet him, smiling from ear to ear—he said, "Be good enough to tell Monsieur le Vicaire Général that I am out."

And he went back into his room.

I was between the devil and the deep blue sea, a most delicate and unpleasant situation. The comic element was uppermost, and I felt a great desire to burst out laughing. Can one laugh in front of a Vicar-general? I didn't try it.

My visitor didn't seem as amused as I was. He remained still for a few moments. His face grew serious, but not somber. He drew me over to the door, and lowering his head, he said, in a confidential tone, a bit sadly, and as though talking to himself, "He hasn't changed. Grace has not yet penetrated to him." Then, more slowly, "But we do not despair." He turned toward me, saying in a tone of indisputable sincerity, "His Excellency has asked me to thank you. By taking him in, you have accepted a heavy responsibility." I made a vague gesture which he interpreted as a denial. "Don't deny it. Providence is good, and you have helped." Then, more confidentially, and after making sure that the Dean's window was closed (we were outside by this time) he said, "God has His secrets." Then with a friendly and relaxed manner, somewhat put on, treating me as an equal, which I don't much like: "May I ask you what your plans, your hopes are? What is your method? You surely have a method. . . . With souls like his, grace and chance are not sufficient. . . ."

I could almost hear myself say, "A method, a method?" Then I understood that my reply would be the last word, that our superiors were founding their hopes on it, and that it would determine their future actions. I therefore continued with assurance, "Yes, I have a method . . ."

"Then we are saved," he said. "St. Ignatius, Monsieur Olier, St. Francis de Sales, Bérulle—all differed as to the means to employ in these cases, but they all agreed that one must impose a rule of life on the penitent; they all had a precise method of action. You would completely reassure us if you would tell us which one of these great reformers is your guide."

The earth opened beneath my feet. . . . I looked at the sea so as not to have to read the disappointment on his face.

I couldn't play the game.

I replied, "Monsieur le Vicaire Général, I—I love him."

I WENT OUT, without my cape, early in the morning. I left the Dean to teach the catechism classes, as I had the day I went to spade. The old woman's dog goes with me now. It is unmistakably the beginning of early spring, and it makes me feel young again. There will be grass, not as much as at home, but enough. The paths are already green. I begin to smell the fragrance of the meadows, the smell of a color. The pear trees, and the peach trees are in bud. The almond trees are almost in flower. The apricot trees will bloom this very night. They seem to wear a look of amused reproachfulness and discreet pride. I wrote at the beginning of this Journal, "It must be true that things have souls, for they speak to me and I hear them." These buds, full of good will, are trying to reassure me, soothe me, warm me, cheer me. They succeed. I touch them, especially the pear tree buds, as big as thimbles, and the peach buds, pink and cool. The pruned grapevines are weeping from all their wounds. I discover the damp corner where the periwinkles hide. Periwinkles! I had planted some at home in my garden. They were so prolific that I had to thin them out every spring. I hated to do it; they seemed to suffer. Here they are less hardy and determined. They are flowers one wants to caress; they seek the shade and thrive on the fallen leaves. They push up through them and absorb them. Soon there will be only a vast green and blue carpet, soft, made for strollers, who are surprised to hear a dry branch they hadn't noticed crack beneath their feet.

If I were learned, I would immediately change in all textbooks the classic conception of drama. According to these manuals, drama is the rending of the soul and heart, both at once, so unendurable that the man who experiences it has to take a stand, decide, choose imperatively between two equally compelling solutions. I admit that in fact that is drama, carried to the point of paroxysm. But according to what I feel this evening, after the shocks of today, drama is something else as well. Drama is something humbler. It is daily occurrence; it intrudes and slips into our lives like an invisible and permanent presence; it is life itself. A sentinel on the alert, the explanation for our changing moods, our mute anxieties, our eager preoccupations. It doesn't arise only from our good or bad qualities of character or from differences in temperament. It comes from without, and we have to struggle with it. We have to fight free of it, triumph over it. We have to wait, too, and see which way the wind blows. Those are the hardest moments.

I ought to have realized this forty years ago. We don't grow old fast enough!

Today—what could be more commonplace?—after my nap, we were talking. The Dean is helping me to know my parish in a deeper way, an indispensable undertaking for any conscientious priest. His contacts with the children led us to talk about their parents, whom he knows better than I. One little boy seems strange to me. His parents moved here five years ago, but they weren't originally from this parish. The Dean thought it necessary to draw our old woman into the conversation.

"Who are his parents?" he asked her.

"They don't have many friends," she said, "and they don't talk about themselves much. The father has a job working for someone else; the mother has all she can do to bring up her five boys. They are poor, but they have seen better times. They haven't made a success of life. They have come down from a better social position, but they are careful not to publish the fact."

"How do you know?"

"What does it matter? I can guess more than I am told."

"That little boy is sad."

"He has his reasons...."

"Listen to me," said the Dean severely. "I am not questioning you for my own amusement. I think that it would be useful for Monsieur le Curé and myself to form an opinion in the interest of this child. But feel perfectly free ..."

She made an imperceptible effort and answered, "The

174

mother is aristocratic and sensitive. An artist. She is Christian, too, in the sense of . . . fine-grained. She would like to spend her life with a man who is sensitive, attentive, cultured. But . . ."

The Dean shifted heavily on his chair. He heaved a very audible sigh. My old chair, which is missing a rung, groaned. Cross, as most priests are, more or less, when anyone brings up these inextricable problems of incompatible couples, he said, looking at the old woman, "But—that is not the case! Monsieur is boorish and sometimes coarse. This doesn't sit well with Madame, who is bored. . . ."

His violence upset me. He went on relentlessly, "And Madame believes that her life is ruined, that she ought to have exercised more caution (which no one prevented her from doing), that marriage ought not to be indissoluble. And the ones who suffer are the children. Their lives will be marked by it. But what does that matter? Madame sees her case, her tragedy, her trap"—he raised his voice even more—"her art —but of course, her art—her music moldering away in boxes, her painting, her poem, her landscapes, her melodies, her rhymes! Madame is bewitched by these stupid mirages . . ."

The old woman had resumed her cleaning. She was dusting, carefully moving things out the way. I noticed a slight pallor, an involuntary contraction of her face, a weariness in her features. She was smiling, nevertheless, that special smile of hers which comes from within, from her memories, her past, certainly from her heroism, from all that unknown and invisible world which is the source of her strength. She had taken into her hands the standing black crucifix from the mantle. She wanted to dust it, but she didn't dare use her dust rag to take the specks off the wounds of that torn body. She looked for a fine, pointed stick, covered it with a white handkerchief which she took from her pocket, draping it as piously as the priest does a communion cloth.

175

Her presence was becoming awkward, however. Awkward because of the Dean's words. We are so made that a cry, even unuttered, can be transformed within us into an unbearable humiliation. She was about to leave, when the Dean detained her.

"I am sorry," he said. "Please answer this question all the same: In the humiliating position in which this woman finds herself, that is, with all her youthful dreams ruined; in constant contact with this brute whose ways, whose manners, cannot conceivably change; for whom spiritual enrichments are impossible and unthinkable; whose lack of appreciation for his wife's gifts is unchangeable; who lives honestly, let us say, at her side, but as a stranger, a *moujik* looking at the Mona Lisa . . . this woman"—and his words passed like knots between his taut lips—"this woman . . . *what does she do?*"

The old woman turned around. I saw a flame in her eyes, I swear it. Her fervor, her conviction, her beliefs, her faith, her truth all welled up together from those subterranean regions where she keeps them captive, and sparkled like diamonds in her clear eyes. There was a sharp contrast between this light which she could no longer master, and her face which was still under her control. She smiled again, the smile of a sculptured figure at prayer. She was terribly pale. She bent her head slightly to one side; her hands were folded. She answered, "What does she do, Monsieur le Doyen? Well . . . she stays there. And when I pass beneath her windows, I sometimes hear her singing. . . ."

She left us, a pitiful, tiny human form, crushed, sunk beneath the weight of a truth too heavy to bear. She closed the door very softly.

My heart contracted; I asked the Dean the question which had been tormenting me for a long time: "But who can that woman be?"

He stood up wearily and leaned his two hands on my desk. "Have you read Léon Bloy?"

"Every line."

"Then do you remember, 'One doesn't enter Paradise tomorrow or the day after or ten years from today. One enters this very day, when one is poor and crucified.'"

He turned toward his room adding, "Those are the ones who force you to make the sign of the cross . . . and not the others."

Part IV

The Struggle

FOR A FEW DAYS, I will have time to write. . . . I am not especially glad of it. While spring is opening a roguish eye, here am I in bed, sick.

It happened the day after I wrote about the extraordinary scene the Dean made over that woman who was misunderstood. I had a dizzy spell during catechism class. It wasn't the first time, but it had never before been that serious. All I can remember is that I couldn't keep my balance and finally capsized in a fog which grew thicker and denser. Did I call out? Was I capable of it? . . .

When I came to, I saw that I was in the Dean's bed, and before I opened my eyes, I heard whispering. I could distinguish the voices easily enough: the Dean's, my old woman's, and one other that I couldn't identify. They were all in my office. They couldn't be sitting down, because I also heard the light shuffling of feet and the intermittent creaking of the old floorboards. This first impression was quite pleasant: an unexpected sharpness of hearing. I had never heard so clearly before. Then I realized that the unknown voice was the doctor's. This annoyed me. I have no use for doctors in their professional capacity.

The unknown voice said, "Good . . . good. It is a bit long,

181

but with what I gave him, there is no immediate danger. Let's see, it is noon. The pulse is strong . . . the limbs are pliant. . . ."

The Dean said, "I would like to see him regain consciousness. Taking care of a patient with no reactions seems to me like a guessing game. What do you think of his condition?"

I quickly buried my head in the covers so as not to hear his reply. I didn't know why I had fainted, but the doctor knew even less than I. And there he was formulating a diagnosis which was learned, definitive, unverifiable, and as is the case ninety-nine times out of a hundred, inaccurate. It was better not to know what he was saying. When I pulled up the covers, I felt pains in my left arm. I must have had some injections.

The doctor was giving useless and long-winded instructions to the Dean and my old woman, and I was left here in this room, where the light filters in through the old blinds, where I shall have to live (how long?) with my solitude. Outside it is a beautiful day. A pine branch is dancing between the sun and my window. I can see its shadow. It looks as though it were playing with the sun and trying, kindly, to distract me. I wish I could rest without falling asleep. Now I am afraid of sleep. Perhaps it is the physical effect, the shock, as they say, of fainting. What were the precise reasons for that long spell of unconsciousness? The doctor and my friends were looking at me, and for me they weren't there! I was another being, in another world, a vegetable world. I was no more than a plant breathing. The most painful moment is the one when you sink down, when you slip, when all the branches crack. . . .

Outside, life goes on.

I hear steps on my little path, the sound of sand crunching underfoot. Fast, small steps. Some boys on the way to school. The sun is going to travel toward the wall. Soon it will light up the ugly, discolored wallpaper. Then it will disappear. But it won't have set. It will be that fleeting hour when in sanatoriums, hospitals, in all the sickrooms and prisons of the world, the angel of twilight sings his sad refrain. I promise myself to be brave; I won't give up.

How long does it take to think of so many things? The ray of sunlight has hardly moved. And things from other times come to mind, things from back home. I will retrace those memories. Write them down. I feel the child in me coming to life again. I crossed my hands under my head, the way I used to do. I look into blank space. For a few days, this Journal will serve its original purpose. I will forget the Dean, the self-righteous parishioners, all the bishops in the world. God will be mine.

I notice again with surprise and pleasure how acute my hearing is. The air between sounds and my ears has been filtered; sound has become more subtle. I feel light, set free from my body, liberated, and on the march toward another world.

The three in the office didn't sit down. The doctor seems to be pacing back and forth, his hands behind his back, no doubt. He has set his useless bag on a chair. Suddenly he is stripped of learning, of his physician's shell, the heavy stratification of his medical-school years. He is the man, the parishioner—who knows?—perhaps the Christian. The Dean isn't walking, or I would hear his heavy steps. At first they probably looked at each other in silence, as people do after a long absence. They searched for each other with that blade of a look which cuts beneath the surface. My mother used to say to me, "I don't like it when you make those little eyes! It means that you are hiding something from me." I think that the Dean is making "little eyes" and that beneath his dark lashes a spark is alight. They have lost interest in my illness.

The doctor speaks first. His voice is veiled, muffled, coming from the chest; worried, sad, bearing a man's disquiet, as he says to the Dean: "We are waiting for you back there! Nothing goes right . . . that is an understatement! Everything is going wrong. The services are hurried through; there is no sermon. The children have no religious instruction. The sick often die without the sacraments."

So the struggle has begun. . . . For me, since I can see nothing, since I can only hear, two voices seem to rush from opposing sides toward a barricade; they will clash; they will raise a cloud of fire! Power of the word! Harmony, enchantment, triumph or defeat of man. . . . What will be left that truth can claim as its own? Which of the words pronounced will take root in a soul? Which will grow, which flower? What harvest, tomorrow, will that seed yield?

The Dean's voice is that of his last sermon (but it will surely change). Calm, austere, firm, somewhat sharp, and without a break: "You know why I left. Don't you know better than to presume to tempt me? Do you take me for a child? What do you put into your side of the scales? Abandoned souls? Children for whom the bread is not broken? Is that all? . . . For fifteen years I broke that bread. Why don't you bring me the—conversion of the Pharisees?"

"However true all that may be, for fifteen years you were there."

"What a lack of imagination! I was there . . . and were things any better? And when the broken bread dries up on the table, when the one who breaks it has to see that happen, and do nothing—has the problem disappeared? What do they want now? If I came back, what would they sink their teeth into? Do they want bread or do they want me? The Gospel, or the apostle's skin?"

"The apostle also must be devoured . . ."

The Dean roars: "Words! words! More words which are an abuse of confidence! More calculations in your engineer's algebra! Slogans which do no more than hide your emptiness and your ashes! Your basket is full of stale fish! That is the

184

way they talk in the canton between two bridge games! Do you realize it? I know—and I don't need you to remind me—the apostle, too, is food; but so long as a priest is no longer the master of the pastoral teaching in his own parish, second only to the Church; so long as ambiguity exists between the absolute freedom to preach the Gospel purely and the shameful servitude of having to round off its angles to please his parishioners, the pastor will be eaten alive, that is sure . . . in *their* sauce! They won't devour him like savages, and his flesh will only fatten their complacency! They miss me, you say. Ah, yes, they miss me. . . . Who do they miss? The slave or the free man? Those people have to have slaves. Is it God, in them, calling me, or Satan desiring me? Do they expect that through me God will make apologies to them?"

A surprising thing has happened to me: in my mind his argument still holds; it is still valid, but it seems less tightly knit. A little air passes through. What can have brought this about? Something I read the other day, perhaps: "The person who deserves the name of saint is the one who can love with detachment, whose love has become so pure that it casts no shadow." This saying has entered into me by some secret path. It has burrowed in, and won't leave. Even if I cast it out, the hole it has dug would remain, the place where it crouched, where it curled up and slept for a while, and from which it has now been roused, a frightened creature, goaded by a cry.

Love with detachment.

Love without casting shadows.

What shadows?

The doctor continues: "Christ encountered the same difficulties. The Pharisees of our time (even though I may be one) are hardly distinguishable from those who condemned Him. Did he run away?"

"I am not Christ."

"Who are you then?"

This is the crux of the situation. . . .

The Dean pauses, as though mustering strength. He answers slowly, "Who am I? That question, Doctor, is not new. It is not your invention. That is the question people ask, the one they throw in the priest's face when they have run out of arguments. You think it will carry the day, don't you? Is a priest going to falter before words of this sort? With these three or four words, astutely used at the right moment in the conversation, like a rock dislodged and rolled down on his head, one can easily crush a priest's vanity and make him give up his stubbornness!"

His voice has become muffled. (What can I liken it to?) It rises from the depths, from a chasm; it is like those white mists which ascend from the base of the mountain to storm the heights.

"And you," he continues, "who are you? What are you worth? You? What are you doing for the Kingdom? If I am a priest of Jesus Christ, aren't you His disciple? And back there, aren't all those lonely people disciples of Jesus Christ? And if, by virtue of our belonging to the same Christ, we were all working together for the same Master, what sense can be made of your criticisms? With what Gospel tint can we color your paganism? And this priest who lived among you, whom today you dare to call Jesus Christ because he challenged your compromises, because he refused to play your game any longer, to whom did you liken him yesterday? Doesn't it seem strange that then he was not less Jesus Christ than he is today? And so you, the disciples, left Jesus Christ alone, in solitary confinement, in that jail to which you had the keys, in that carnival where you used Him as a banner. You blindfolded Him and said, 'Prophesy who struck you.' For the honor of the Holy Name of Christ, I would like to believe that you are talking without deliberation, and that it was not Jesus Christ

186

whom you saw in me in those days. Or else, since you haven't changed, since you are only spouting hollow phrases at me, let's inquire who you really miss back there in the canton? Is it Jesus Christ? You have nothing else to sink your teeth into then? Is He the one you want to devour? And are you annoyed that you can't call the Sanhedrin together in your living rooms any more, over your sad cups of tea of an evening?

"Who am I? . . ." The Dean repeated. "Here, listen to Jeremiah."

From my desk he has picked up a worn volume, the Bible. It is the one I have had since my seminary days, in whose pages I have never ceased searching for God. His voice takes on a formal tone; he reads the text respectfully, careful to give it the whole stage:

" 'The word of the Lord came to me thus: Before I formed you in the womb I knew you, before you were born, I dedicated you, a prophet to the nations I appointed you. "Ah, Lord God!" I said, "I know not how to speak; I am too young." But the Lord answered me, Say not "I am too young." To whomever I send you, you shall go; whatever I command you, you shall speak. Have no fear before them, because I am with you to deliver you, says the Lord.'

"Be good enough, Doctor, to listen to what follows:

" 'Then the Lord extended his hand and touched my mouth, saying, See I place my words in your mouth! This day I set you over nations and over kingdoms, to root up and to tear down, to destroy and to demolish, to build and to plant. . . . Be not crushed on their account, . . . for I have made you a fortified city. . . . They will fight against you, but not prevail over you, for I am with you to deliver you, says the Lord.'

"And later on, speaking to the unfaithful Israelites [it is still God speaking]: 'Return, O rebellious Israel, for fear that I turn away my face from you: and make you into a waste place, an uninhabited country.' "

187

And in a changed voice: "That is what they asked for, Doctor, those Pharisees back there."

The doctor's silence oppresses me. I fix my eyes on the figure of Christ above my bed. I forget that I am sick; I hold my breath. O Lord, don't let the thread snap. A breath can break it. Don't let them kill that small Hope which has furtively slipped between them, which is listening to them and waiting. Don't let the doctor speak, if his words are to be harsh. Don't let him smile if his lips are to look like the Colonel's wife's or the Canon's, sarcastic and self-satisfied. For then the Dean will suddenly fall silent, or he will say without transition, "It is a fine evening," or "How do you like your new car?" or else—and it would be terrible—"And what is the news of my math professor?" Then my frail spider's web would be torn and my Hope would be crushed to death.

If only I could get up, look him in the face and say to him, "Now is the time for greatness, Doctor, greatness like Jeremiah's. Will you, can you attain that height? Can you hold out your hand to him, over the tops of oaks and pines, as high as the stars? If you don't grow in stature now, if your forehead doesn't touch the sky, if your hand now stretching out to him (perhaps) doesn't brush against galaxies, don't let a single word pass your lips, or the breath which forms it, which propels it, will put out the eyes of that watching infant, Hope."

There is nothing I can do. Once more, I can do nothing. I have to go on seeking. For forty, fifty years now, I have been seeking, always seeking. . . .

The doctor speaks clumsily. I am thankful to him for continuing in the tone of one who is speaking a piece. "Monsieur le Doyen, in the Bible there are others besides Jeremiah. There is also St. Paul. 'How then are they to call upon him in whom they have not believed? . . . And how are they to hear, if no

188

one preaches?' Faith, then, depends on hearing. Now, Monsieur le Doyen, back there, the Word is dying. . . ."

It was a mistake to choose this battleground, where the Dean is a master. "Let me continue the quotation, then," he said, "your incomplete quotation. 'But I say' says St. Paul 'have they not heard? . . . Their voice [the Apostles'] has gone forth into all the earth and their words unto the ends of the world.' And at the end of this tenth chapter, Paul also quotes a prophet, Isaiah: 'All the day long I stretched out my hand to a people unbelieving and contradicting.' Paul also says, 'For am I now seeking the favor of men, or of God? . . . If I were still trying to please men, I should not be a servant of Christ.' "

They haven't moved forward, but at least they haven't broken the thread; they won't break it now; so my small flower of Joy, named Hope, can breathe again. They didn't quite get through to each other, but let them say what they please, my flower of Hope will live from now on. . . .

"I must leave you now, Monsieur le Doyen," the doctor said. "It is past time for my office hours."

The sun has slipped over toward the wall. This stability of physical laws has always been reassuring to me. The tempests of my inner universe seem a bit absurd in the face of this calm and serene obedience of things.

My old woman brought me my broth mixed with red wine. This was an old remedy of my mother's. The bowl was a bit wobbly on the plate, so the old woman sat down close to the bed to ward off possible disaster. I relived my childhood memories; my heart was touched. How simple life is! A few gestures fill it. Do we have to have our strength diminished before we can appreciate its unity? Perhaps all men should fall sick, all at the same time, so that they would consent to love one another.

To love one another! I have often thought about it. I have preached many times on this evangelical theme. The words lose their meaning from being repeated, exploited. Another phrase came to my mind as I was drinking my broth; where I read it I don't know: "The day that your heart no longer burns with love, all around you others will die of cold." An idea, even a pure and just and objectively correct one, is always cold. Air has to pass through the lungs to be warmed. Ideas ought to go down to the heart. I have tried to make this a way of life. Unfortunately, a disappointed love drags along in the soul a whole lifetime, like a poison you can't get out of your system.

And yet . . .

Shall we close all those boxes of ideas we call books? Destroy all the archives? And even if they were to burn in vain, relight this fire over the cold ashes? I have loved. The world didn't get even lukewarm; men haven't pronounced a single gentler word; the wolves continue to devour each other.

My heart pains me. It pains me when it beats uselessly, when it is forced to be just a pump for blood, an instrument, a muscle. Then it beats for nothing, and it complains. That complaint of the heart is the worst thing in the world, worse than an illness, worse than a cancer, worse than death, worse than dishonor. Whoever, for whatever reason, plunges a man's heart into the desert of love is guilty of the gravest of crimes. Beyond that nothing exists. It is the lowest of crimes, and that is why men have never invented a punishment for it. It breaks the scales, it crushes them. But I am searching, searching, although it is painful to search. I continue because it isn't possible for a man's heart to beat for nothing. What does "beat for nothing" mean? Has an error slipped into our classical conception of love, into that psychology of heartbeats? Has a fleck of dust damaged that delicate machinery? Is there one digit too many in the addition? . . . And suppose

190

the heart were able truly to love for love's sake, without trying to make any impact, without thinking itself diminished if it didn't encounter any other person? If, like the star in the desert, it were able not to die while looking at nothing but the sand? . . . And if God . . . ? But let's not try to play Francis of Assisi. . . .

The Dean came in. I had finished my bowl of broth. My old woman stood up, straightened the blankets, and said, "Rest now. In a little while the trolley conductor will bring your medicine, and you will take it before you go to sleep."

There was a storm in the Dean's eye. He sat down, thrust his neck forward. "Those people in the canton have killed everything in me," he cried out to us—or to himself—"everything, even my youth. I owe my white hair to them (that doesn't bother me), but I owe them mainly, there"—he struck his breast heavily—"there, there, emptiness. Well, when it is empty there, a man is ageless; there is nothing left of him but a bundle of rusty scrap iron. You can melt down old iron, but what about a man? What crucible is there for him?" At that moment, he was capable of damning our souls and his own. "Hell," he went on, "Hell is just that! Your guitarist . . ."

What stopped him was, I think, the attitude of my old woman. She turned her waxen face toward him, that medallion illuminated by the lamp, that face of a more than earthly vision, of freedom, of abundance of joy. She must have passed beyond all suffering, beyond all deprivation, into those serene regions where the desert flowers. She was, at that instant, my answer. But how, why was she that answer? She didn't speak. She herself was the word, the only valid word, the one and only living word.

After a few seconds, which were eternity, the Dean rose. His features wore a new expression which I hadn't seen before. I didn't know which of the two to look at, so I looked at the fading rays of the sun. At last he spoke. His voice had become calm, soft, slow. It was still questioning, but so polite and deferential that there was scarcely a trace of anguish left in it.

"Madame," he said, "you—yes you—after all the trials which have been inflicted on you, after your calvary, how old are you now?"

I could see her hands slowly open, in a gesture of offering, empty hands holding out riches. "Monsieur le Doyen," she said, "I will be just twenty . . . this evening."

I AM NOT recuperating very fast. I had to face the fact that I've really been very ill. As soon as I made up my mind to it, I became a docile patient. I can keep this Journal if I write slowly. My ideas are clear. I think; I meditate, as they say, especially at night, for one can't drowse away three or four hours of the day and expect to sleep all night.

The Dean keeps me company. He talks to me about my parish. He has trained the youngsters who come to catechism class not to make noise. I hear only their footsteps on the sand, like the sound of the sparrows' wings in the leaves. The Dean made a little writing table for me, which fits over my bed very well, at just the right angle. He walks softly. When he goes, his smile and wave of the hand stir my heart.

I am going to write without following the exact chronological order of events. In fact, nothing out of the ordinary has happened that I know of, except for one serious thing which was not the Dean's doing. Unfortunately, I am afraid it has strengthened his resolutions.

It was yesterday afternoon: I had recited my breviary and I was dozing. The Dean must have been sitting at my desk.

An hour before, we had decided to read the Bible together for a few minutes each day.

"You will choose the passages yourself," he said, "and we will read the Book in a way we have never done before."

"How?" I asked him.

"When the verse or the word spoken has meaning for you, you signal me, and we will close our eyes and meditate on the text."

"Then let's begin with the Hundred and Fifth Psalm, and we will close our eyes forever after reading the third verse: 'Rejoice, O hearts that seek the Lord!'"

He smiled, and I went on playfully, "But what will happen if our tastes differ? Shall we close our eyes together all the same?"

"For my part," he answered in the same gay manner, "only one thing worries me, and that is that my capacity will be less than yours."

Cars stop in back of the house; we never hear them coming. To reach my door, one has to go along the path which leads to the sea and passes my little garden. A knock on my door woke me. A man whose voice I didn't recognize came in.

The Dean barely returned his greeting, which instantly put me on my guard. Then, without any preliminary civilities, in a very annoyed and firm tone, he added, "So you are making the call today? Does that mean that your young colleague is sick?"

"It must be a doctor," I said to myself, "not the one who came first, but another." My curiosity was trying to get the upper hand, but the Dean's words, and even more the manner in which he spoke them, forcefully suppressed it.

The doctor was at no loss for a reply; he had it ready. "He is busy this afternoon. He asked me to take his place, which I agreed to do all the more readily since it would afford me the pleasure of seeing you again, my dear Monsieur le Doyen."

That was enough for me.

I know that voice. Such voices are all and everywhere the same, as though there were only one, as though they had all taken the same public-speaking course. But this one had reached perfection through long practice.

It was the undulating, supple, superficial, slightly sneering, self-assured, enveloping, irresponsible, and, for some, irresistible voice of all the Mephistos of the world since first the serpent spoke in the Garden. The voice of the one who spoke to Him in the desert after his forty days and forty nights of fasting: "All these things will I give thee, if thou wilt fall down and worship me." I know it so well! That "My dear Monsieur le Doyen," so friendly, obsequious, cunning, falsely humble, almost tender, almost affectionate, leaves me no doubt: the Devil in person has entered this house.

The Dean answered, "The pleasure is all yours, then. But perhaps you want to see my patient?"

He came into my room. It was indeed HE. Mephistopheles!

Intelligent, to be sure, and his eyes show it. Small eyes, watchful fox's eyes, which in one second see, evaluate, weigh everything. Eyes which register many images at once, then carry them to the brain, which sorts them as fast as an adding machine, classifies them, compares them, and keeps only those which will be useful for lying. A heavy body, a purposely countrified gait, clumsy and good-natured, the body of a shrewd, crafty peasant, a cattle trader, who turns on his charm, hesitates to commit himself, approaches, withdraws . . . a body which participates completely in the subtle game of persuasion, which will stay at the auction as long as it has to, until the animal is sold at the highest price and the buyer congratulates himself on having been cheated.

After the deal, body and soul depart; the one bundled into the other, both snickering, and they go off into some dark corner to count their loot.

Of course, it is he. That was all we needed!

194

I didn't interest him much. He looked at me from the door-way, with his practiced eye: something of the physician, more of the cattle trader, the two intermingled. He stepped forward, but behind him my old woman made the floor creak. He turned about, like a hunter surprised by his prey. His eyes became hard, evil, ironical, and suddenly uneasy. Venom was about to spurt from his lips. "Oh, so you are here! . . . But I see that you can be found everywhere where priests need your —devotion!"

He stressed the word "priests," and the word "devotion" was not the one with which he intended to finish his sentence. If we hadn't been present, he would have delivered his prepared insult. She stared at him without replying. Their secrets confronted each other in silence. A storm of memories whistled between them, in gusts. I read in the doctor's eyes what is called hate; in the old woman's, strength. There can be no doubt: she has suffered at his hands. It was the confrontation of victim and torturer. He has not broken her. He will not break her. From a long habit of self-defense and of prayer, she folded her hands on her breast. This silent dialogue impressed even the Dean, who did not make a move. He waited. Actually, what were we doing there, he and I? I saw the doctor's jaws contract, just enough to be noticeable: Apparently he never loses his self-control. When she saw that his anger was going to be futile, that before this man's diabolical power she would again be victorious, she assumed the docile tone of a conscientious and attentive nurse, and said, "I followed all your colleague's instructions, Doctor. Our patient seems a little better. What shall I do now?"

He had lost the first battle. He turned his eyes quickly away from the old woman's. They had been so firmly riveted there that I felt a physical sensation of unsnapping. He was sure to try to get back his own. How? I was soon to find out. He looked at the prescription filled on the day of my attack and pursed his lips. A grin appeared. "Our patient is better! Well, then, he must have a strong constitution."

Then, calling the old woman to witness, "He absorbed all that?"

"Yes, Doctor."

"Then he must be as strong as an ox! Is it possible? That young fellow is killing the whole canton. . . . Yet people flock to him!" And he added sarcastically, "He is young—that explains everything."

The Dean was leaning against my bed. Obviously he could have answered him. It must be that he wanted to avoid a clash.

"Here is what I think of this prescription," the doctor continued. He threw it on the floor. "From now on kindly use what I am going to prescribe."

I am of such a nature that in moments when my mind ought to be tense and paralyzed with cold, I perceive the funny side of things, which restores my balance. I said, "Before you prescribe, Doctor, perhaps you might examine me."

He replied dryly, "I know what's wrong with you. He told me and his diagnosis is usually correct. I said 'usually.' In your case, a first-year medical student couldn't have made a mistake. It is on paper, afterward, that he goes wrong. . . . Now, keep to this."

I am the patient. I have some right to talk back. "This dosage or the other one," I said, "what difference does it make?"

He didn't jump. He calmly screwed the top back on his fountain pen, and answered me in a joking tone, "Occupational disease on your part, dear Monsieur le Curé. For you, a prescription is like the penances in confession; they depend on the confessor. . . . I have heard tell, however, that the severest confessors don't always have the best penitents. There are some priests called the Fathers of Mercy, aren't there? They never cure anyone, but they don't kill them either!

When I was at the Jesuit school, we always liked to go to a professor, as old as the hills, almost completely deaf, and always indulgent." He added ironically, "If, as you teach, confession is not an invention of priests, the superior must have had sound reasons to let him—operate under those conditions. He was not unaware of them, as you can well imagine."

He laughed loudly. His whole body shook.

Was I going to be spiteful? The intention was there.

I had no time to arrange the words in my mind to make them acceptable. The Dean, noticing my efforts, smiled. In a moment he was going to need all his wits. He was keeping a cool head. I was only a pretext. He knew that with this man, it is hard to have the last word. The real game hadn't begun. The circus hadn't opened its doors.

The doctor went right on, "You are hardy, dear Monsieur le Curé. Peasant stock, of course, like me. Strong as oaks! From Burgundy, or Berry, no doubt? Your accent isn't from the Midi . . ."

I have at least one skill. A minor one, I admit, common and ordinary (I don't take much pride in it): I can put a quick stop to indiscreet questions. Since they are indiscreet, they don't deserve any better!

"Don't waste your time guessing, Doctor. I was born on a train. . . ."

"Then I'm not surprised that you have dizzy spells," he returned, disappointed, but sporting.

That is enough by way of introduction.

Shall I have the heart to write it all? If I am weary of it, it is because I am tired and disheartened. I will just have to make up my mind to it: this individual, the very prototype of baseness, hypocrisy, destructiveness; this Pharisee, just like those Jesus knew, unchanging, I will encounter everywhere. Everywhere the same and everywhere invincible.

School is out. I can hear the children laughing, shouting, shoving. The sea is high. The waves crash, recede, pause, then hurl themselves against my garden wall again. It is already dusk. Today the sun's rays didn't visit me; the birds didn't sing in my pines. In my room, the dull light of a cloudy day is fading, spending itself, blending into the invading night, like a lamp being extinguished. Everything is becoming substance-less, indefinite. Everything is disappearing, escaping, slipping through my fingers, emptying itself of life, of blood, of strength, of joy. All is silence, except for the waves, and their voices.

The doctor went out of my room first, slowly, heavily, his massive shoulders bowed. In his huge hand, against that well-built, mature frame, his medical bag seemed like a tiny, ri-diculous toy, and he gave the comical impression of a railroad engineer bringing his son a small toy train in a box. The Dean followed after him, his nervous gait slowed down by this Rodinlike living statue of Mephistopheles—thinking. I wasn't going to be able to see them. Once again I would have to re-construct the scene from the sounds I could hear.

I will record only the essentials.

The doctor's voice was purposely inoffensive. "So," he be-gan, "you have deserted. . . ." He didn't laugh; he clucked. Then he went on: "Of course, of course, your reasoning is sound. But if everyone followed it, no life would be tolerable and we would all have to decamp! Where would we go? Do you think I am treated any better? And you yourself, were you tactful with me? I just let people talk, and life goes on. What have you to complain about? You were the only curé, but there are three doctors . . . which doesn't add up to prac-ticing medicine; it is a race, on foot or by car. Whoever gets there first wins. My patients leave me, then one fine day they come back. It doesn't even bother me any more."

The Dean replied, "If you are here to speak for my parishioners, may I ask you to skip the preliminaries?"

The doctor was silent for a moment, no doubt pretending to look around him. He continued, "Well, look at the spot you're in. I'm not here to pass judgment, but what kind of shack is this to live in? Gypsies are better off. And the food? I'd just like to see what you eat! What income do you have? A curé doesn't ask for much—agreed—but poverty doesn't mean want. How long can this go on? You can't tell me that this dreary 'little hole,' as the Colonel's wife calls it, will sustain you for long."

"So, then?"

"So, then, afterward . . . in two weeks, in a month?"

"My question had another meaning which I don't think escaped you."

"Don't get yourself worked up. The people of the canton aren't bad, they're stupid. All of them. Take them all—one after another. I'll spare you the list. I don't even make an exception of that matinee idol, the pale one—no need to say which—who wears a cape. Respectfully, I include the bishop, whom you have put in an untenable position, caught fast and hesitating as he is now, between you and them. . . ."

Did the Dean try to answer? If so, the doctor cut him off. "No, the argument is not where you place it. There is no intellectual or religious question to debate. . . . Oh, my! You really believe there is a metaphysical conflict!"

His voice became insistent, honeyed, the singing accent of the Midi adding its own spellbinding quality. "Your parishioners aren't asking themselves any metaphysical questions. Not a single one. You were playing Simeon Stylites on your own austere platform—the faith, the Gospel, your priesthood. And while you were practicing learned restorations, at your feet, comfortably fixed, they reveled in gossip, bridge

199

parties, big money; they even tossed your words back and forth like a ball, laughing; they used your Gospel as a salve, and your person which—admit it—they need! as a fetish, and that is also something to consider! When savages have lost their fetish, they are terribly unhappy. They would do anything to get it back. You didn't realize that—you still don't.

"You didn't take advantage of your opportunities; you didn't play your part. Those people would have been your slaves if you had shaken your rattles more adroitly, if you had pronounced your incantations in a way that would scare them a bit. It would have been so easy—and it still would be! You made a fool of yourself, like an actor who apologizes for being what he is, and says, 'Don't be frightened, I am not the leading man here; I am only an extra. We are all poor sinners together.' What a joke! John the Baptist believed it before you. Isn't his example enough for you? They cut off his head! And afterward? Afterward, you're a dead man, and that isn't worth much. Think it over. Life is too short, and although a little religion is necessary, the time of the Polycarps and the Blandines is dead and gone. If you want proof, just listen. . . . Imagine that the little Father of the People, ruler of all the Russias and a remarkable organizer, you must admit, of those vast and profitable enterprises, the prisons, the concentration camps, and so forth—just imagine that Comrade Stalin were to show his face, less than that, a hair of his mustache, at a street corner in the canton—let's add a little spice—during Mass; well, all your so-called faithful (what a vile word) would scurry out of there like rabbits, and when you turned around for your *Dominus vobiscums*, the empty pews would yawn back at you. The next day they would all apply for their Party cards. The day after that they would come to take you away and hang you. . . . And the worst of it is, dear Monsieur le Doyen, that you really agree with me. This is nothing new to you, and still you hang on to your theories."

How can the Dean let him talk so long without interrupting? I heard again only his eternal question: "And so?"

"So? . . . Don't take yourself for John the Baptist. Follow my example."

"How is that?"

Almost persuasive, and with disarming candor, the doctor answered, "How? Stop thinking of the canton's people as the sick; think of them as clients. That would still be giving them too much respect. It doesn't prevent me from taking care of them. It wouldn't stop you from hearing their confessions. It would be somewhat—corrupt. All right. But at last it would be efficient, and what more do you want? They have flayed you, put you on the grill, like St. Lawrence. Good! What you won't admit (and it's pure pigheadedness) is that they are longing for you; they are dying to have their fetish back, and they are waiting for you. They aren't waiting for you as God, whom they have never wanted (don't be simpleminded), but as their own god, their necessary little god, a bit of a sorcerer; or to talk like the books, their recommendation to the real God in whom they don't believe, but with whom you would be their link, in case by some chance He might exist. They have lost their peace of mind. Put yourself in their place. Your absence torments them. Of course it does. Since you left, I have treated a great many more liver ailments! Your shadow no longer passes among them. Just yesterday evening I heard this at the Colonel's house: 'But tell me, my dear, whatever possessed him? If he needed a little extra in the collection, he had only to say so. We would have made the effort! We would still make it if he came back. . . . Could you make head or tail of his last sermon? I couldn't. He didn't even act very angry. Before, he used to get madder than that, but he never left. The worst is that the bishop seems just a bit displeased with us. I went to see him the other day, and you know, he received me, but just barely. Can you imagine?

After all we've done for him! Let's have it out once for all, and get it over with—such a trumped-up affair! What more were we supposed to do? What could we dream up to please him? He doesn't play bridge. Well, so much the worse. We'll invite him, and he'll have to make the best of it.' And so on. You see, my dear Monsieur le Doyen, if you wanted to create a stir, you've succeeded. They won't do any of these things once you are back, but let's be reasonable—starting with you! When you hear their confessions, you don't really expect steadfastness from them . . . your absolution falls right on their . . . good resolutions of the moment. But . . . Is something the matter? You look pale."

"I need some air. I am going out for a while. Thank you very much. . . . What do you think of our patient?"

"He can get up for a few hours tomorrow. In a week he'll be on his feet. Watch his diet and his blood pressure."

They went to the door and exchanged good-bys.

The Dean came back into my room. It was true that he was pale. He dropped onto a chair near my bed. He didn't raise up his head; he seemed ashamed. I thought of the day when he put my coat over my shoulders, and I said, "That's not what matters."

"What? . . . Do you agree with him then?"

"What matters," I told him, "is that after that long walk in the shadows, your lamp needs oil. Give me the Book. I will read it, and you close your eyes."

" 'Peace I leave with you, my peace I give to you; not as the world gives do I give to you. Do not let your heart be troubled, or be afraid. . . .

" 'These things I have spoken to you that my joy may be in you, and that your joy may be made full. . . .

" 'If you were of the world, the world would love what is

its own. But because you are not of the world, but I have chosen you out of the world, therefore the world hates you. Remember the word that I have spoken to you: No servant is greater than his master....

" 'Amen, amen, I say to you, that you shall weep and lament, but the world shall rejoice; and you shall be sorrowful, but your sorrow shall be turned to joy. A woman about to give birth has sorrow, because her hour has come. But when she has brought forth the child, she no longer remembers the anguish for her joy that a man is born into the world. And you therefore have sorrow now; but I will see you again, and your heart shall rejoice, and your joy no one shall take from you....

" 'These things I have spoken to you that in me you may have peace. In the world you will have affliction. But take courage, I have overcome the world.

" 'These things Jesus spoke; and raising his eyes to heaven, he said, Father, the hour has come! ... But now I am coming to thee; and these things I speak in the world, in order that they may have my joy made full in themselves. I have given them thy word; and the world has hated them, because they are not of the world, even as I am not of the world. I do not pray that thou take them out of the world, but that thou keep them from evil.

" 'Just Father, the world has not known thee, but I have known thee, and these have known that thou hast sent me. And I have made known to them thy name, ... in order that the love with which thou hast loved me may be in them, and I in them.' "

He closed his eyes, his elbows leaning on my bed, his head almost disappearing in his big, knotty hands. At the end of each verse, I let a long silence follow. My voice, which I concentrated on keeping impersonal, filled the room completely.

203

I can't explain how. It wasn't the Sinai desert any longer, but the incomparable sweetness, the immense plenitude of a triumphant spring. It was a chant, light and airy, whose melody was unusual in that it was scarcely audible; it didn't reach us through our ears, but through the marrow of our bones, through our veins; it gripped us from within, spread to our hearts, eyes, heads, to our hands which clasped of their own accord, with human warmth. At that moment, those notes touched that hidden depth of our souls where only the Devil —or God—finds an audience. The depth of our secrets. . . . Never have I understood so well that man does not live by bread alone. . . .

But what was the Dean thinking? Was he thinking the same things I was? Did he experience the same emotion?

When he realized that I wasn't going to go on, he said, without lifting up his head, "Yes, but turn to the last page of John the Evangelist. The one who touched Him. I want to hear the last cry. . . ."

"His last cry," I said. "His testament was in that cry . . ." and I read, beginning a few lines before the end: " 'And let him who thirsts come; and he who wishes, let him receive the water of life freely. . .' "

"No, no," he said. "That is not his last cry!" He lifted up his head; his hands were clasped, and he said urgently, "I am waiting."

"His last cry," I said, "the cry of a man like us, is 'Come, Lord Jesus!' "

He stood up. His fists were clenched, and he stared at the wall. My bed lamp left his head in shadow. He stretched out his arms. "You see," he said, "you hear it; you are a witness: John himself called Him!"

And then, praying: "Come, then, come! I can't—hold out—any longer! Come!"

204

IF ONLY I hadn't agreed to getting up late and celebrating my Mass at nine-thirty, like a middle-class priest, I would think myself better already, and everything would be forgotten. I am still quite weak, but I am no longer dizzy.

What has been worrying me these past few days is our poverty. My savings are almost all gone. The garden still hasn't produced anything. We have pooled our resources, so the Dean must be aware of the critical state of affairs, which can't go on indefinitely. My old woman is thinking about it, too. I can understand why. But it seems that, in a case like this, decisions can't be made until the very last minute. I was born poor, and I have lived that way. Shall I one day die destitute? Shall I be unable to keep up the sacred duties of hospitality? Oh the slavery of poverty! . . . If the Gospel didn't exist, I would be capable of grinding the rich into mincemeat! What a scandalous idea!

The Dean and the old woman were talking together yesterday morning, and I heard him say, "If I could only—oh—not change water into wine, because water is good enough for us—but multiply the loaves once a week! Unfortunately, the time of miracles is past! . . . And it wouldn't be right to ask 'them' for help."

"Who do you mean by 'them'?"

"The diocesan administration. . . . They would answer very politely that I have only to go back where I came from. The temptation would be too much for them, and who in those circumstances would refuse to taste the forbidden fruit?"

"What forbidden fruit?" she asked, surprised.

"The lack of inner purity, the temptation to take advantage of the chance to teach me a lesson! They aren't God, you know, only men. If only I could go fishing, I could bring back enough fish for three or four days. There would be that much gained, and I wouldn't live here feeling that I am a burden to him. But, you know him: if I leave him, he won't recover, because he'll worry about his parish being left alone. That fishing—it was what made me agree to stay here before his attack, and allowed me to accept his hospitality. He adores fish. To leave him because we are in need would kill him. Ah, the poor will always be poor! And when I hear people say that they are in God's hands . . ."

She didn't answer, and the Dean went out.

It was time for my herb tea and pills. She came to me and I said, "He is worried, isn't he, and you are, too. How many days can we hold out?"

Her face was serene and trusting. "I read the paper that comes around your pills," she said. "They are supposed to calm you down and make you sleep. Take them now and rest. I hope you dream about that poor widow saved from hunger and disgrace by the prophet Eliseus."

"Who taught you that story?"

"The priest who taught me my catechism. I can recite it by heart."

" 'Now a certain woman of the wives of the prophets cried to Eliseus, saying: Thy servant my husband is dead, and thou knowest that thy servant was one that feared God, and behold the creditor is come to take away my two sons to serve him. And Eliseus said to her: What wilt thou have me to do for thee? Tell me, what hast thou in thy house? And she answered: I thy handmaid have nothing in my house but a little oil, to anoint me. And he said to her: Go, borrow all thy neighbors' empty vessels not a few. And go in, and shut thy doors, when thou art within, and thy sons; and pour out

thereof into all those vessels; and when they are full take them
away. So the woman went, and shut the door upon her, and
upon her sons. They brought her the vessels, and she poured
in. And when the vessels were full, she said to her son: Bring
me yet a vessel. And he answered: I have no more. And the
oil stood. And she came, and told the man of God. And he
said: Go, sell the oil, and pay thy creditor: and thou and thy
sons live of the rest.' "

I answered, "Eliseus the prophet has been dead for a long
time now."

She said, "Were the rich people of those times any better?
They wanted to take away her two sons in payment!"

"Where do you see any progress?" I asked her.

"Did you go hungry today?"

"I don't like to be given advice...."

"And how right you are," she returned, amused. "Will you
at least allow me to advise you to sleep in peace?"

"And while I am asleep, my vessels will be filled with oil.
... This odious dependence of the French clergy poisons their
lives and paralyzes their action. We are the playthings of the
rich, and believe me, they know it!"

"I don't believe that you depend on the rich to that extent,"
she replied. "You depend on the poor, and the wealth of the
poor is immense."

On these words, she left me. I fell asleep with the familiar
weight of anxiety on my heart. I don't remember having
dreamed, not even of the poor widow.... When I woke up,
night had fallen. The Dean wanted to keep me company. He
was melancholy. He tried to act gay, but he didn't succeed.
My dog came, too, and settled down near me. Before going
home, my old woman came in to say good night. We were
gathered together like a family. My bedside lamp cast a wan
light.

I am writing this on the same night, under that same lamp,

in a solitude which is less dreadful because scarcely an hour ago, and without any other miracle than a Presence, according to the promise, we forgot that we were poor.

We didn't speak. The Dean was sitting on the only uncomfortable chair, in the attitude of someone who is listening and receiving. His mouth was slightly open and his lids lowered. My old woman was leaning against the dressing table. Her hands were joined in front of her. She seemed to me the poorest of the three of us, and if she had been dressed in rags, we wouldn't have been surprised. She brought to mind Léon Bloy's definition of the "poor woman": "She has even understood, which is close to the sublime, that Woman exists truly only on condition that she be without bread, without shelter, without friends, without husband and without children, and that it is only in this way that she can force her Lord to come down."

As I lay with my hand on my dog's head, I realized that softly, like dew in the hot months, joy was refreshing our souls. Only the waves encroached on our silence with the sound of their vast, regular breaking. Then, I think everything died down to make way for the inner voice. First it cut off, or rather destroyed, the mundane roots of our worries, and held out to us, in this receptive state, freedom of choice. That truly existed. We felt ourselves become light; we were inwardly happy and in direct contact with peace. I know that I tended to resist a little, suspecting it of being an illusion, but this half-refusal had no effect, and the silence discouraged my fears. From then on, it seemed to me that a path opened before us which I had never explored, a wide open path filled with a light which was not from the sun. It came from above, below, all around, everywhere. It came from us too, from within us, and we pressed forward, the bearers of this light.

It brought to mind an image whose symbolism I used to admire, but which now struck me as false. It used to decorate

208

the cover of a pamphlet for Young Catholic Worker groups. It depicted boys and girls running joyfully toward the sun. In our light everything was more intimate and to me seemed to be more true. I don't say that those young people were wrong to believe in the light and to march toward it, holding each other's hands; but their sun was too much like our everyday one, which, bright and pleasant as it is, doesn't prevent tears from being shed. It sets, night enfolds the earth, and men's teeth chatter. The light of our new path came from another source, from farther off, from nearer by. That light comforted us and it became more and more intense until, following from branch to branch, parted by an invisible hand, we arrived, refreshed, in an immense clearing. Then we understood that this was the place of rendezvous.

I will not describe the spot because it is not humanly possible to do so. I have never believed in that Mohammedan Paradise where happiness is carpeted with moss. We ourselves were the coolness, the oasis, the well, and the palm tree. The setting was not important and I would never be able to remember what it looked like. All carnal feeling was absent. Joy radiated from us. We were the blossoming and the flower. I never questioned my impression that the manifold blessings which were ours came from Another, and that that Other, whom we did not perceive, was Jesus Christ. He did not pass by us like a rich man distributing alms; He did not sit on a throne to command attention and oblige us to bow down ceremoniously. . . . We were in Him and He in us, and it was He who, without inspiring fear, without confounding us or changing us, took in us the place of our hearts and sang with us the symphony of His Joy.

I was very much myself and yet different. In fact, everything was the same and yet transformed. My alarm clock ticked on without counting time. The waves kept time to our mood, but their hostility and their indifference had given way to a harmony, akin to our own, blending in, familiar and heart-warming. The wind still played the role of wind, not to destroy and frighten, but to revive the flame of our lamp with its breath. My dog had dozed off near me, something he rarely does. The silence did not foster any hidden egoism we might have. With incredible precision, it served to link our thoughts, our prayers, our astonishment. I wished the doctor would come back with his toy in his hand; his great shoulders arched with malice; his small, mean eyes; his baseness of soul. . . . It was unthinkable that he would not be vanquished, that his sneering would not be drowned out by our music.

A whole lifetime in one second. . . .

When I reread these pages, they will seem trivial and ridiculous, simply because such realities cannot be expressed. With a shred of talent, one can write about anything else. Not an experience like that. I remember my surprise—to touch with my hand what I had been desiring to possess for years without ever believing myself worthy of it! For after all, who were we? Not saints? Then why this grace? Why this path, this clearing, this answer? Why, in spite of our poverty of soul, this laden table? And how was it that we had only to feel empty, to be at last filled?

My old woman spoke first. "I am going now," she said. "I am very happy. Good night. With your permission, I will go to the canton tomorrow to do some errands. But I will be back to prepare the noon meal."

My dog opened his eyes. He went with her to the door. Then he came back and sat down in the same place and didn't take his eyes off me.

The Dean said, "It is past time for you to rest. But let's be realistic and try to see whether it was an angel or a demon who raised the veil. I am the opposite of a mystic. You are like me. I prefer struggle to peace, seeking to having found. And whatever happens, either the whole world has received this Visitation, or tomorrow we will have to do battle once again...."

"That is true," I replied, "but if our armor is stronger ... if our eyes are clearer ... if our hand has a firmer grip on the sword of truth..."

He went on: "God never intervenes in our lives without a precise reason. And usually (this law is taken from the well-documented history of the saints) when He makes his presence known, it is because a new Cross is being fashioned somewhere."

He picked up the Bible. "Here," he said, "for once open it without looking. Francis of Assisi and Ignatius Loyola opened it that way and the truth they gleaned made saints of them. Follow their example for yourself, for me—not to be like them, not to tempt God—just to see ... I don't know why, but this evening I would prefer the New Testament to the Old. Perhaps because it is closer to us."

My heart was pounding as I said, "The Bible isn't a fortune-telling book. What significance do you attach to this?"

"Open," he said peremptorily. "The Word is one of peace. When it disturbs us, it is because (to use a young people's expression) we aren't on its wave length."

I opened the Book toward the last pages. My finger fell on the middle of a page. I read the reference: Epistle of St. Paul to the Philippians, Ch. II, Verse 5. "Have this mind in you which was also in Christ Jesus, who though he was by nature God, did not consider being equal to God a thing to be clung to, but emptied himself . . . becoming obedient to death, even to death on a cross. Therefore God also has exalted him and has bestowed upon him the name that is above every name, so that at the name of Jesus every knee should bend of those in heaven, on earth and under the earth——"

He interrupted me: "Good," he said. "I wish you an excellent night. But you have to get up earlier tomorrow and test your strength a bit. As for me, I will go out fishing as soon as you allow me to. Soon, I hope."

With those words, he left me.

I GOT UP earlier, with an intense satisfaction at getting back into my habitual groove. The Dean was seeing to all my parish duties, and it was unthinkable that anything would be neglected. I therefore could spend my time as I wished.

After my Mass, the sun seemed inviting, so I went out for a walk, and encountered this early spring, which I half expected, but which nevertheless surprised me. At home, I used to know all the signs of the seasons' changes.

The buds have already burst on the vines, and tiny leaves have come out. They look like the curled fists of a newborn baby. In a few, more open than the rest, I searched timidly for the promised miracle and saw the tiny fruit taking shape. If God gives it life, I will admire its blossoming again, the humblest and the most fragrant flower of all.

I felt completely cured.

The petals of the fruit trees have fallen. The wind doesn't blow them, it draws them up. They catch on a blade of grass, tarry in a fold of earth, then flutter to and fro, jostling and skipping until they come to a puddle, which they cover with a bridal veil.

I am not used to the ways of my pines. I will never learn them. They aren't like anything I have loved in days gone by. Here and there at the tips of the branches, I see an odd kind of burgeoning. I am grateful for their fragrance, even though the scent strikes me as useless.

And the sea, below me—is it spring, or an effect of light perhaps peculiar to this day?—it isn't blue, but white. A great milky, marble surface, striped with dark lines which quiver strangely. In the distance the sea fades into the fog, also completely white. The horizon is indistinguishable.

We ate at noon, after the catechism classes. Cold boiled leeks in vinaigrette sauce, fried fish, cheese, bread, and water with a drop of wine. For the past two weeks we haven't had coffee because it costs too much. I have started smoking a pipe with an excellent tobacco which someone gave to the Dean, who doesn't smoke.

After that I went to take a nap. I needed it: my legs were starting to tremble, but I didn't mention it.

I must have been asleep a long time, when the sound of conversation woke me. I recognized the voice of the priest who had visited me after my first sermon at the deanery. It was a soothing, kindly voice; a bit monotonous, not seeking to impose itself; honest, respectful of the thought of others, and as undogmatic as possible. He was saying, ". . . that portrait of a man. There is no such thing, Monsieur le Doyen."

"All the same, ever since men have been thinking and writing, they have been attempting it."

"True, and the result has invariably been disappointing. They oversimplify, and always reach a dead end. To arrive at the truth, one cannot take a straight road."

That man thinks exactly as I do, I said to myself.

He went on: "The absolute exists only in God. If we are pilgrims hoping to reach it, we have to be willing to put forth painful effort, traveling down a thousand byways. It is wonderful to draw maps, to say to the faithful, 'Go this way, and no other!' I am suspicious of all those geometricians of the Kingdom of God. A compass, a pencil, a ruler. A key statistic, to justify the theory, and there you have men who are satisfied and bothersome. . . ."

The Dean laughed, not loudly; rather self-consciously like a convert being taught the Our Father. His companion, waiting for a reaction which was not forthcoming, moved his chair, then filled in the silence with, "At least that is the way I look at it."

He was just rising to leave, or so I imagined, when the Dean detained him. "It is the way I look at it, too," he said. "Still, we didn't reach it as easily as all that. When will this path branch off from our ancient convictions?"

"Every man has his enlightenments and his grace. We have only to keep from resisting them. Every honest priest is led by them at first to a deep respect for souls, to tolerance, and a practical consideration of individual situations; otherwise a priest can become a good technician, but in him love is lacking. When his heart beats at a regular pace, he has found tranquillity, but he is a hundred miles from orthodoxy, for to be orthodox is to love, and loving is not tranquil. I can confess this to you, at the risk of appearing naïve in your eyes: the thing that led me to the understanding of the mystery, and of God's plan for the world, was the vision, which I had to have spelled out for me, of the Poor Man. For me the Poor Man is the supreme Witness, the torch bearer.

"You know that for five years I was vicar in the capital of the *Département*. How time flies! You were not yet a Dean. I often encountered poverty there, but never more totally embodied than in the silent and humble person of a certain vender of National Lottery tickets. Winter and summer, in all weathers, always wearing an ageless overcoat, he stood a few feet from our church door. He had only one arm, and although he had two legs, one of them, the left, which appeared to be boneless, served only as a counterweight to keep his fleshless, crooked body in precarious balance. He never sat down. From time to time he leaned against the wall. He had no accordion and he never held out a beggar's bowl. He didn't talk. He

214

waited, without calling attention to his wares. Don't think that he may have been mad. The expression on his face and in his eyes convinced me that he was not.

"What had happened to him? Who was he? Where did he come from? No one knew. And perhaps you will say that no one cared.... That would be an error. But he would have discouraged a saint. Several times, many times, I tried to speak to him. To put him at ease, I bought a lottery ticket from him every week—one that never won. A waste of effort. If I said to him, 'Are you cold?' he replied, 'Yes.' Or if I said, 'You won't make a fortune in this business,' he answered, 'No.' I tried, without success, to find out where he spent the night. One day I said to him, 'Do you live alone?' . . . 'Alone?' he replied. 'Alone? I don't know.' I said, 'Allow me to help you.' His reply: 'I manage by myself.' That was the way it went everytime.

"Toward noon, he would take a chunk of bread out of his pocket and eat it neatly. Then he left his station for a few seconds and, walking like a puppet, went to drink from the fountain, then he returned to his post.

"People passed him by without seeing him. They were used to him. They didn't look at him any more than one looks at a wall. They avoided him as one avoids an obstacle; they detoured around him; that was all. A landmark. Or else they took one of the tickets displayed on a little folding table to which they were secured by a rubber band. They paid him and he said 'Thank you' politely. They went on their way, and he picked up the money and slipped it into a little drawer which was always open; he was careful not to bend over too far for fear of losing his balance. Then he went back to his waiting.

"When it rained, he covered the board with an old oilcloth; as for himself, he weathered the storm stoically. I don't think he was daydreaming. His eyes were not fixed. He was aware of his surroundings. Neither sad nor gay, always himself, a man among men, lost in the crowd, intrepid witness of its passions, its fevers, its restlessness and its joys. But detached from the world by his poverty and his absolute powerlessness to imagine being rich.

"I think he loved us all. He loved the Christians or semi-Christians who came out of the church after the services, even the powdered and painted ladies who displayed their vanity at the eleven o'clock masses on Sundays; the stenographers who, at the same hour every day, forever late, brushed past him exchanging the latest gossip; the young mothers in the afternoons, pushing their pink and blue baby carriages; the lovers with their secrets; all of them, myself too, thin as a rail at that time, anxious and idealistic. Because he had to concentrate on his center of gravity, he didn't turn his head, but he saw us and would have known us, I am sure, just by the sound of our footsteps.

"What was his universe like? Into what deep well of beatitude or despair had he sunk his heart? Toward what suns did his eyes turn, seeking light? Or did he already possess it, captive of his desire? Was it his reward, his nourishment, his ecstasy? Did he remember his past, his mother? Had he, on some distant day, ever sat at a family table, or in that clumsy hand which gathered pennies into the table drawer, received little certificates of merit from one of his proud sons? Did he know joy, the kind that we wait for, for which we hunt, and of which we sometimes catch glimpses in the thick forest of maturity? And his loneliness? . . . I often wondered what to think of his loneliness: An enormous burden? A weight on his heart? A constant darkness? An ocean of silence? Or perhaps a door open to the dawn, chains broken, a star, ultimate victory, victory over everything, over everyone, over others and himself?"

The Dean was silent. In the short moment of silence during

216

which our guest put away his memories, I got up. Desire stiffened my resolution to enter into the monologue and transform it into conversation. Say anything, but make it move forward! His story was true, but what meaning did he give to it? I had read recently that our younger generation "tries to fight language as Jacob fought the angel. They want to take it by the throat and make it confess." In spite of my age, I am of that generation. He is going to have to explain, I said to myself; he can't leave me with this pleasant and empty impression, like a hungry man in front of a good meal which he has no right to touch.

He was extremely courteous. What is more (for me it is the most important thing) he was sincere in his show of friendship. I said to him briefly, to make the connection before his images faded away, "I listened to your story. . . . It is a shame to have it end like that."

He understood my impatience, and to destroy whatever emotional overtones it might have, he paused before replying. Then he said, "My story isn't finished. And if it has a happy ending, it is no doing of mine. I am absolutely certain that I had no part in it.

"One day, a freezing winter day, my ticket vender didn't appear. I was surprised, as one is surprised by silence when one is used to a certain noise. Without conviction, and to reassure myself, in cowardly fashion, I blamed the cold for his absence. The day went by, and he didn't come. It was a Saturday, as I recall. He was absent the next day too. The people coming to Mass saw his place empty, but they were in a hurry to get home because of the cold, and didn't ask any questions. On Monday morning, after my Mass, our old chair attendant beckoned to me. I immediately sensed that she had news about him. She said, 'The old ticket vender is very sick.'

" 'But where is he?' I asked her.

"She told me the street and house number. The street was

one of the finest in the city, in the residential section, and the house was the most luxurious of all. I had never been inside because I didn't want to vex the curé, who reserved for himself the right to call on such parishioners. The notion passed through my mind that the old fellow had been play-acting, the saddest and most despicable act of all, sham poverty.

"'All the way up, to the top floor,' the chair attendant told me. 'When you see only three doors, you open the one on the right.'

"I rushed to the place. The concierge saw me go by with my satchel of holy oils under my cape, and nodded her head. I went rapidly up the wide stairway. The walls were lined with marble. You have surely seen those immense doors which have, at the level of your hand, a yellow plaque with an intricate lock. No latches, no doorknobs. Doors with secrets. But the farther up I went, the less luxurious it was. To get to the top floor, there was only a rickety wooden staircase. I knocked on the right-hand door, heard a faint moan, and I opened it.

"It was a kind of large attic, with no ceiling, unfurnished except for an iron cot at the end opposite the door, a three-legged stool, and in a corner the folding table which held the lottery tickets. Perhaps it was just an impression, but I had the feeling that it was colder in that room than outside. Between the roof tiles, a fine powder of snow filtered in and formed parallel white lines on the floor.

"I had to kneel to talk to him. And what could I say? What could one say to this man who had remained silent for so long? He was breathing with difficulty. His hands were burning. I wanted to pull his threadbare overcoat up under his chin, but it was his only covering, and if I pulled it up, his feet would be left exposed. I was about to take off my coat to cover him, but he held back my hand, and said softly, 'Don't bother.'

"Then he looked at me and smiled."

The priest stopped talking. He took off his glasses and I saw him wipe away a tear. My desire to make him tell had disappeared.

He continued, "I will never forget that smile. It was not like any other, except perhaps for the smile of a stone Angel, or that Romanesque Madonna in her chapel in Auvergne. All other smiles are grimaces compared to these. A smile like that remains with you all your life. You have touched Heaven. You have understood everything. It opens onto mystery; it doesn't leave you outside; it plunges you into it and you don't feel heat or cold or anything at all. You stop traveling; you have arrived. I hung on to that smile as iron clings to a magnet, poor and rich in my turn, subdued and supplicating; asking that this man not die, that I might stay there forever, that between us, to keep alive in me that apotheosis of grace, this man in his extremity might continue to look at the angels! There were his eyes and his lips, and I knew then that they were the key to everything.

"He said, 'I am sure that I will go to Heaven.'

"His lips barely moved, but from then on, anything was possible and I believed him.

" 'I am sure of it,' he added, 'because, the day before my first Communion, the priest told us we would go to Heaven if we recited three Hail Mary's every day. Now, every day of my life, I have recited fifty-three, my whole rosary. . . .'

"I heard his confession. I anointed him. I was going to administer the last sacrament, but he held me back, saying, 'It is too late.' Then, painfully, 'Every morning for the last fifteen years, when the bell rang, I called God into my heart, and He came. . . .'

"Did he understand that I was waiting for some message from that Beyond where he had pitched his tent for so many years? He turned a little toward me, murmured, 'All men are good. . . .' and, still smiling, he died.

"There," said the priest, after a long pause, "that was all.

The only person at his funeral was the chair attendant. I went with his body to the potter's field. He had his secret. No one knew it but me, and now you. . . ."

He stopped again, then repeated, like an echo, "All men are good."

The Dean stood up, wearing the rather frightening and impenetrable look he has on solemn occasions. I waited for him to speak. He began to pace the room. Sometimes he shook his shoulders and stamped harder on the floor.

This couldn't go on. Speaking in his place, I asked our visitor this stupid question: "And since then, have you really believed that all men are good?"

His face took on a playful expression. "I believe especially that you ought to get out of this house, both of you, leave this parish for a little while, and breathe some different air. . . ."

Almost harshly the Dean replied, "I have always respected you deeply and for that reason I permit myself to inform you, even though it is not commonly done, that before long we will be as poor, the two of us, as your ticket vender. So please don't insist. Yes, I am dying to get out, as you say, and go almost anywhere. But since men are not, as far as I know, as good as your poor vender held, the pleasures of travel are not for us."

And he added ironically, "I think I have a vocation to be a ticket vender, a vocation to be a gypsy—as your man, in his fashion, was a gypsy. That way I would have the time to recite fifty-three Aves every day, and to die—smiling. What do you think?"

"That I am a boor. I am going now. I'll come back tomorrow."

"Tomorrow," replied the Dean, "I am going fishing."

"The day after, then?"

Suddenly the Dean's anger subsided. "In that case," he apologized, "come and have lunch with us. There will be fresh fish. I must be a bit more of a boor than you, and it doesn't help to bite my tongue. A good mullet will fix everything. I'll get one, you may be sure. But then—I am warning you now—all three of us will hold a press conference, right here. I need to have someone listen to me and answer my questions."

I HAVE TO resign myself to leaving some things out. I can never write it all. I regret it, but my days and nights would never be long enough. Since I started keeping this Journal, everything has taken on more importance and interest for me. Nothing is insignificant. Without wanting to, without knowing it, doubtless without being able to help it, men have transformed the world into a vast stage where, for better or for worse, they play their parts. All men. Every day, the play moves a little further toward its climax. If, then, there is a valid philosophy, it consists in setting out signposts to guide the action. They are not always useful; they don't help everyone, but they are valid for the majority. Any other philosophy is senseless. Freedom which has a direction is still freedom—and when could man boast that he lived freely any other way?

It is this onward march of humanity toward its goal which we ought all to write some part of every day. And suppose that every ten years, for example, one could sort out that tremendous accumulation of data? It would indicate progress. Who would ever have the time? A team of angels in Heaven must specialize in this work, the only work that makes sense! We advance, we stop, we obey the signals, or else we wander off the track of our own accord. And those angels place their little flags all over the map of the world.

Yesterday the Dean put on his sou'wester. The *Marie-Jeanne* is laid up for repairs, to the great distress of the owner. The Dean went out on the *Stella Matutina*, the fishing boat which best meets his personal conception of what a boat should be. "Not too new," he told me several times; "handled the old-fashioned way." I didn't ask for details! Out of caution, because of the cool morning wind, I didn't go to see him off. When he hung up his amice, he said, *"I am poor and downcast ... my God, do not tarry!"*

I replied, somewhat mischievously, but very sincerely, "Put it in the plural!"

Was he afraid that he had given himself away? He replied, a bit irritated, "Not one iota of it should be changed. You may apply the text to yourself if you like, although I don't know what could trouble you on this fine spring morning. You'll have the whole day to look at your flowers." He added, as though reciting a phrase learned by heart (why did he add that?), "All men are good." Then, a bit too playfully for my taste, "As for me, I have to bring back a basketful of fish."

He turned on his heel. He made a prolonged and prayerful genuflexion in front of the altar. I heard the door slam as he went out, forgetting to hold it.

Solitude....

His solitude and my solitude....

My old woman said the responses for my Mass from the nave, which was still dark. When I turned around, I could hardly distinguish her kneeling figure.

The enigma! Always the same enigma! Always this wall against which men hurl themselves. Even here, at the altar! I think I would have preferred to be alone. I would have taken a whole hour to celebrate that Mass. But what answer would I have received and in what corner of my heart would my ineradicable romanticism have taken refuge? I have struggled too long to give in now. God is Spirit....

But does God take into account that I am not a spirit? *My God, do not tarry.* But He does tarry; He does. He does nothing but. Where does He find so much time to waste, and is He playing at making us waste our limited span as well? For centuries upon centuries men have been waiting for Him. I am waiting for Him in my turn. The Dean admits that he is waiting for Him. It is our turn in the waiting relay.

In the afternoon I went out.

I was very pleasantly surprised at the kindly reception given me by my parishioners and the children. They were all happy to see me. The children's joy was as clear as a mirror; the women's was mixed with concern.

"Did you suffer much?"

"Heavens, no."

"But what was the matter? They told us it was your head . . ." And their eyes searched for signs of a head injury.

One of them made bold to say, "Be sure you take good care of yourself. Are you really comfortable in your house? Do you need anything? We need you. Don't worry, Monsieur le Doyen will teach the catechism classes until the children make their first Communion. You ought to rest."

They made me aware of the fact that I had been dangerously ill. I must be better now, since I had a desire to stir things up. I certainly succeeded. "The Dean," I said. "The Dean won't be here forever!"

I read consternation on their faces. But fishermen's wives are incapable of remaining at the level of mute consternation. They had to talk, all at once, and I record here at random what I heard in that tumult of exclamations:

"What do you mean? . . . Where would he be better off? . . . Maybe he feels like going back there? . . . He was right to get out of there! They had a good curé—they should have known how to hold on to him. . . . You two get along together. . . . And first of all, he ought never to have gone there,

223

he isn't a landsman, he is only at home on a boat. . . . He is too frank for them. They lie, those people, as easily as they breathe. Oh, we know them, only too well! We see them every market day, coming to look in our baskets, and you should just listen to them! No one is spared! They have forked tongues, like devils. . . . Let them ask his pardon! Yes, ask his pardon, but believe me, they would rather leave their children without baptism. Those people have nothing to apologize for; they're perfect, aren't they? . . . They're too rich. With their money, they have everyone bowing down to them. No, not everyone! Not us, and not the Dean. He told them a thing or two. Good for him! And now, let them cry! If all curés talked like that, we'd be better off. He hasn't set foot there since. He ought to leave them like that for four or five years. It can't make them more heathen than they are already. . . ."

One voice rose above the tumult: "They aren't all like that."

There was just a half a breath's pause. "Not all like that? No, luckily. But what good does it do the weak not to go along with the strong? What did the weak ones do to defend him? I ask you. They loved him, of course, but like snails. As soon as some bigwig showed his face, there was nobody there; they all went back into their shells! And they are surprised that there are no more priests. They kill them all. Is that a life for a man? Their priests are worse off than their errand boys. God knows it can't go on like that. . . . Jesus will have to come back. . . ."

One voice, the same as before, added, "But the bishop— couldn't the Dean's friends have gone to the bishop? He is a fine man, that bishop! We saw him when he came for the Confirmations. He has a handsome head, and he's a good talker. He says the right thing. Only, he probably doesn't know the whole story. . . ."

A woman whose children are in my catechism class replied seriously, and alone this time, "The bishop? I can tell you about that: he is surely a decent person, but he doesn't know

224

how to get rid of the bigwigs. He listens to them too much. When will he ask us our opinion? Of course, we don't know how to talk the way they do, but it is better not to talk so well and not tell so many lies."

She turned to me, suddenly remembering that I was there. "You can tell that to the bishop. Tell him to come and talk with us...and with our men! All the men here love the Dean. Today he went out with my man on the *Stella Matutina*. Well, I can tell you my man is proud! He is almost glad that the *Marie-Jeanne* broke down. That way, he can have his Dean all day long, and right now, the two of them are probably telling each other things you wouldn't know about, but I do, I know about them. When the kids are in school, he lets it all out. I just have to listen. My word of honor, he would give his life for the Dean. And he is fond of you, too, because you aren't complicated, because you stood by the Dean, and also because you love our kids—and even if you don't know anything about fish. You are two real curés."

I attempted to say, "What is going on in the canton?"

Another woman, waving her arms and coming toward me replied, "What is going on is that they are trying not to let it show, but they are really upset...and that doesn't make him go back. The Canon was born exhausted, and he won't die of exertion, word of honor. The young priest has his motorcycle. ...Oh, they got what was coming to them! And the ladies ask for news of him, on Mondays in the market, pretending not to ask. I put my hands on my hips and I say 'He is well off where he is. His head is back on his shoulders. He doesn't have to put up with you any more. If he wanted to go back to you, we would bar his path. Forget it, my pretties! Go ask the Canon to hear your confessions—for whatever good it may do you! Aren't you ashamed!' They turn their backs on me. I lose their trade, but I don't care because I give them what's coming to them!"

They all laughed.

I realized that I was now surrounded by them, and couldn't get out. The owner of the *Marie-Jeanne* came to my rescue. He was passing, with a gardening tool on his shoulder. I followed him.

I got a few grunts out of him which might have meant yes or no. His path was on the way to my old woman's garden. I resolved to push on until I reached it.

As GOOD as his word, our neighbor came back this morning.

After lunch, I wanted to do things right. I invited my two colleagues into my office, saying, "Let us retire to the drawing room!" and I served them some excellent coffee on a little table (my last middle-class luxury). My old woman, in a spotless white apron, brought in a bottle of that fine old brandy from back home. Our guest was a man of discrimination and humor. The Dean was very relaxed. Their mood was such that I hesitated several times to enter into it for fear of weighing it down with my verbal clumsiness.

They let me doze for about ten minutes, then woke me up with the invitation to take a walk. The weather was still fine. The sun was hot. The sea was gently rocking. Along the port the fishermen had stretched out their nets on great posts to dry, I suppose, and to be mended. The Dean showed us how it is done, a very tricky process. My fishermen were wearing no more than their trousers held up by a rope or an old belt. Bare feet, bare torso. They smoked incessantly. As we passed one group, I heard them ask the Dean, "Coming with us tomorrow?"

He shook his head no.

226

A man said, "Too bad," and he pointed to something out there, whether the waves or the gulls, I couldn't be sure. The Dean, with a sweeping gesture toward the sea, replied, "Yes, tomorrow there'll be some action."

So there will be stormy weather tomorrow. How can they tell?

Walking on the sand tired me, so I said to the others, "I won't be able to follow you much longer. I sink in. Let's take the path through the vineyards."

"It will be a climb."

"I'd prefer that."

Halfway up, at my request, we sat down. Our guest said to me, "So, you aren't quite sound yet! . . . In a couple of weeks you will be better; everything will be all right!"

It was the wrong thing to say, but without thinking of what he had suggested two days before, I gave in to a mood of absent-minded daydreaming, and replied, "I will be better, yes, I will be all right when I have breathed the air of my wheat fields and seen my mountains."

He replied, "Then I am delighted to think that you won't be sick much longer."

The Dean made a gesture of annoyance . . .

I mustn't stay up too late writing tonight; I will have to gloss over some of the subtleties of emotion. I never felt the limits of my strength so much before.

The Dean insisted on having his "press conference," which had slipped my mind. He initiated it adroitly, very intelligently, while I, feeling quite myself again, was filling my pipe. Our guest was talking about the discontent of our fishermen over the difficulty of competing with the big modernized fishing industries, and the Dean took up the debate, saying, "Yes, oh, yes! If we could paint the world on the dark walls of some Sistine Chapel, a hundred times as big as Notre Dame, our fishermen would occupy a tiny panel of that immense fresco, and everywhere you looked, to the right, to the left, above, even in the sanctuary, even in the Canons' stalls and perhaps even on the Cardinal's throne, what would you see? Rebels. Their ranks are growing; the walls of Notre Dame wouldn't hold them. The whole sky would have to be painted over, after carefully blotting out the stars.

"Children rebel because they weren't able to choose their fathers. Wives, because they were defrauded, although they chose their husbands. Workers are in rebellion against their bosses, and the bosses against their workers. Priests against authority. Old men against their rheumatism. Everyone, against everything. And those who keep it to themselves are not the least determined. I once knew a sick man, a multi-millionaire, who had a room in a private hospital looking out on mimosas; he had two nurses, two doctors and a priest at his beck and call; the telephone was at his bedside, his banker visited him every morning from nine to eleven; he had lady callers, books, and his cats. . . . I never saw a sorrier spectacle! An earthworm cut in two! Which received Holy Communion every morning. I still have a terrible recollection of him. The demons in hell are not uglier.

"Of course, you won't fail to point out that all men are not that bad. Let's understand each other: it is sometimes good and proper, sometimes dangerous, to seem to be in rebellion. For a priest, it is at least imprudent and—unseemly. We ought, because of our state in life, to give the impression of an in-alterable inner contentment and a peace of soul without flaw. This isn't very conducive to honesty, but it is a fact. It is false, in my opinion, to pretend that in our times men, and even priests, express themselves freely. Thought is always captive. But never so much so as at present."

OUR VISITOR (smiling): I have the impression that you are a free man.

228

THE DEAN: Before men, yes, I think I am. Before truth—that's another question. But seeking it is a liberation.

OUR VISITOR: It has taken years for us to understand. I mean the fact that the rebel is not a scandal or a surprise or a mystery to us. He is man divorced from the sacred. Rebels all together constitute society so divorced. Even unbelievers admit this and teach it. So we don't have to look any further: everything that lies outside the bounds of the sacred can only be in rebellion. Therefore——

THE DEAN: Therefore, what name can we give to rebellion within those bounds?

OUR VISITOR: It no longer bears the name of rebellion, but is called "act of thanksgiving."

Silence from the Dean. A gesture of impatience. He starts to stand, to cut off the conversation, then changes his mind.

THE DEAN: The consequences of that seem ominous to me. If that's the way things are, let us open our breviaries, and recite Vespers and Compline, since it is time for them, and go back home content! No more problems for us. We are bathed in holiness and therefore in beatific thanksgiving. And no doubt it is because our fishermen don't say their rosaries properly, or don't say them at all, that their business is failing and that competition is making them discontented. By all means, let us turn to prayer. Let us become holy, and make others holy! And all rebellion becomes, for them as well as for us, purposeless, a futile pagan attitude, a bit ridiculous, even, and in any case opposed to God's plan for the world. Let's have done with philosophy! I profess an equal indifference to pure ideas and to slide rules. Formulas, both of them. The fact is that life is action, and it imposes action on us whether we like it or not. And action means taking sides. And taking sides in most cases means rebelling. I notice that the world is moving—in rebellion—away from thanksgiving to God, away from canticles, and sometimes in blood and tears and as a logical result of the failure of the sacred, toward an order which holiness was capable of formulating and describing beautifully, but which those consecrated to it didn't have the courage to bring to being in the flesh. That is where the drama lies. Do you admit it?

OUR VISITOR (sadly): I admit this: that tears and blood are necessary wherever the world lacks saints. And I admit that in consequence the state of rebellion is not always without effectiveness, and that the rebel can also in his way push humanity toward its goal. I admit that the formulations of which you spoke ironically, with some justification, are, even in the Church, mediocre excuses. I admit the failure, not of the sacred, but of most of those who pretend to live within it, while, in reality, they are using it only for their idol worship. I admit even this: that rebellion is the only resort for a priest who hasn't the courage to enter body and soul into the sacred, and that his rebellion, truly sincere, honestly lived and fully accepted with all its consequences is a thousand times better than a caricature of patience.

"I admit," he continued, "that behind the closed face of the rebel there is often real detachment, evangelical contempt for self and therefore a form of asceticism. But if the soul of a saint so much as brushes past me, all my systems collapse! I return to my starting point and suddenly I begin to believe that only a saint can spread joy. The sincere rebel commands my admiration, and there my tribute ends. . . . But if by God's grace I breathe, even for a second, the same air as a saint, I don't have to speak to him, or question him, or even admire him . . . my heart begins to beat and your Sistine Chapel lights up all at once! In this sudden projection of grace onto rebellion, the rebel is distressed, questions himself, doubts his own truth, hesitates, discovers that he is naked, like Adam after his first crime, and goes to hide himself in the foliage, trembling like a weathercock on his rusty pole. The rebel can only destroy; he leaves a trail of ruins behind him. Was it only to destroy, even in the name of justice, that God made man? Was it to pile up ruins that the Son of God consented to the Cross?

"I know all the objections you can raise. The Church? Yes, the Church, founded by the One who placed the seal of holiness on all human rebellion—is the Church free from that will to power which snatches man out of the spiritual and plunges him alive into the universe of rebellion? I never doubted the purity of the Church's evangelical inspiration. The Spirit which guides it led the Innocent One to Calvary, that is, to mute acceptance of the worst injustice, so that rebels like ourselves might know that a door is always open onto Thanksgiving. It is the same Spirit. We are not in a position to judge those who sometimes seem to make Him their servant. Who of us is without sin himself? I think that, in our time, the Church has need above all of a little collective humility; that it is suffering from complacency and from a supersensitivity which are out of place in the Redemption which the Church purportedly carries on. I think that it ought to put more trust in humble people, even in rebels, and show more alacrity in punishing the Pharisees, even the outwardly docile ones.

"I think that the theology of sin has to be rewritten; we must start by rereading the Gospel, with astonishment. The authentic interpreter of the Gospel is not the moralist, but the saint. That is why, moved also by the Spirit, priests—you, me, all of us—are in a panic at the idea of being cowards! Fear, the holy fear of distorting the Message, of serving it up in the bland sauce of self-righteousness, and of being judged unfaithful because we lacked audacity. I am convinced that God blesses all those brave men who identify themselves (and at what cost!) with the letter of the text. However, after hail storms have destroyed so many already-meager harvests, God would like these men to do something more. They have up-rooted the useless stalks; they have knocked down the rotten tree—well and good. But shouldn't they build something in its place? Has the rebel, strong enough to destroy, suddenly become too weak to build? It seems so. For no one can build unless he enters into the sacred, and that means clearly that sanctity is beckoning us...."

He spoke without gestures, looking far out to sea. He searched for words two or three times, without impatience. In front of me some ants were transporting pine needles ten times as heavy as themselves. My dog, who had followed us, rested his head on my knee. I petted him, to look occupied.

The other two were sitting down. Everything was calm. The wind brought us the odors of the beach. It was clear from our visitor's manner that he had no intention of convincing us. He is far above the level of amateur apologetics. He wasn't debating against anyone. He was unburdening himself, ex-pressing himself, justifying himself, or condemning himself. When a man has that kind of respect for other men, acknowl-edges that he is weak, and doesn't take another by the hand for fear of leading him astray, one hears this kind of strange monologue, without knowing to whom it is addressed, or whether it conceals suffering, desire, or acquiescence. Every-thing would be the same if this man were to cease being pres-ent, provided this song of the soul were still offered up, and this sound of water trickling beneath the moss still gave evi-dence of an invisible spring.

From the moment the Dean had mastered his anger, he had become passive. He looked drowsy. He made little piles of pine needles with his stick. Once in a while he would stop and listen, as though he were expecting someone.

Our guest continued in a lower key: "Yes, in the middle there are the cowards, unworthy of the angels' respect or the devils' scorn, those whom Dante was surprised to meet in the entrance to Hell. He quoted the terrible verse, *Coloro che visser sanza infamia et sanza lodo.* (The cowards come and go, less substantial than smoke.) We could ignore them if they weren't the ones who generally trouble us the most, with whom we can do nothing, and who do us harm because in the hope of raising them up, we submit to the terrible temptation of descending to their level. But it is hopeless, because with them, there is no end to the descent. They have a genius for falling lower and lower. And besides them, what is left? Those two forces, those two weights, chains, anchors, pendulums of the world: men divorced from the sacred, and saints. We have to choose and accept the risk . . ."

Had he reached the end? It was clear from his manner that he would have spoken that way if he had been alone, and that he no doubt often did so.

"The risk, the risk," he went on, "that profitless risk of breathing their breath and keeping faith, living in their world, yet living in a different way. . . . The hardest part of it is that one must not consent to cross the frontiers of the sacred, not go over to their side, when it would be so easy; not to deliver the Gospel over, to lie at their feet like a sick child. If once that line were crossed, they would go to Mass more readily, since the priest at the altar would be their accomplice, and, according to the contract, Christ on the cross would be their property.

"They are the same everywhere. But you have to have experienced it! Who of us has not been stunned by his own worthlessness, his emptiness, the abyss of this risk; who has not been shaken by the wind of their insults? 'The day will come when they will kill you, thinking thus to glorify God. . . .' "

That man, I said to myself, is a brother. . . .

He held his head in his hands, his elbows resting on his knees. "You have to have been through it. You have to have

233

felt that devil's claw digging into your chest. It knows how to grip your heart, and come out covered with your blood. I must have turned as white as a sheet, and then they were almost satisfied. Not quite . . . for they wanted me to cry out, 'Have pity!' By God, I didn't give in, and that will always detract from their satisfaction. Who won? Not they!

"That was a long time ago, so long that I can talk about it now. At that time I was vicar of a city parish. Some of the members had planned their attack in advance. They belonged, or so they thought, to that privileged category of chosen individuals called 'militant Catholics!' It is risky to call laymen 'militant.' Young ones, all right . . . but old ones, like these? They get so self-important they think they are the Pope! I can still see the hall, the long table where I sat at one end. I can see them, my murderers. Three or four hundred years ago, they would simply have stabbed me in the street. A man was quickly dispatched in those days. Today we are more refined; we use words, a new vocabulary, more cutting than in olden times, words that kill.

"There were five or six men and women; two nuns, a young one with a face like the Blessed Virgin, and a very old one— not malicious, rather on the borderline of innocence. The others, who had got wind of the plot (and hadn't told me about it, naturally), looked at them and looked at me, sideways, without even moving their heads. They were supposedly meeting to discuss the program of a parish celebration . . . but nothing was further from their minds. I had hoped to inspire them with a religious spirit, but after the president opened the meeting, I had scarcely time to say my piece, when I was interrupted by his insults. Everything was grist for his mill: my Sunday sermons, my devotion to the public school children, 'who aren't our kind, and receive their religious instruction in the parish hall on Thursdays,' my patience with those who lived outside the Church, my tendency to mix sinners with the undefiled, my mistakes of all kinds, which put me

234

in the class of secularists and compromised 'their' good works in 'their' parish! A renegade, that's what I was, a renegade!

"What I hadn't grasped was that I was only their guest, by a great favor; their guest at the end of the table, and I had no right to speak, except to say Amen! It took me a while to realize what was happening. After about ten minutes, he stopped talking, and, stunned as I was, I was unable to answer him. All the more so because in his conception of religion, and his role as a 'militant Catholic,' he was right. I was guilty! It was true: I loved those youngsters from the public school; I preached without sparing anyone's feelings, especially those of practicing Catholics; I wanted everyone to come to church, and I perhaps mixed everything together, since I have never been able to separate the cockles from the wheat. Religion, for him, was something quite different. His indictment was objectivity itself, blinding objectivity. To refute it, one would have had to undertake a justification of the Gospel, exonerate Christ, and explain the meaning of that folly, the Incarnation! And what could one hope to gain?

"Two things happened that suddenly changed the direction of my inner reactions, up to then restricted to disillusionment: one of the nuns, the one with the Madonnalike face, found it fitting after this diatribe to thank 'Mr. President' for all he had done in the parish, *for the Church and for ... souls!* And one of the men, in whom, to tell the truth, I had had some faith, insinuated, noncommittally, that this *'exposition had been most opportune.'* No one contradicted this, which indicated to me that they all agreed. My situation was thus different than I had thought, and it was necessary and urgent that I take a stand, not before one individual who might be misled, but before these delegates of the Church in my parish. Otherwise error would be confirmed. Error is quickly confirmed in times of crisis.

"Then it was that I experienced the frightful temptation: I wanted the truth to be bathed in their blood. The temptation

235

of the fight ring! Suddenly it seemed legitimate to give in to it. To use their own arms and let the strongest win! The scandal wouldn't be any worse than the one they had provoked, and violence for violence, I would show them what stuff a minister of the Gospel is made of. What did Moses do when he came down from the mountain? Do the same. Yes, looking back, it seems infantile. With the confused intention of divorcing myself from the spiritual, I was ready to doff my cassock, and fight them. I am very strong, and anger gives me the strength of ten men. The only valid apologetics: punch, kick, ram them in the stomach. The women would run out screaming. I would strangle the others; I felt capable of strangling them one by one and trampling on their bodies. Moses had thirty thousand killed by the sword, and then the situation was clear: the One God was worshiped again!

"Yes, I thought of that. I would have done it. Which would have been more reprehensible: to consider the Church as that heap of self-styled apostles, or like Moses faced with the Idol worshipers, to avenge the Church by slitting their throats? Since they had never entered into the sacred and in order to force them to enter it, I considered coming out of it; the means were no longer important, the more violent the better.

"That was my temptation! The eternal temptation, the will to power, outside of holiness, outside of grace, outside of Calvary. . . ."

There was a long silence. Then he lifted up his head, placed his closed fists under his chin and said, "My God, my God, will you hold it against me? This temptation, the same that Moses, your Chosen One, knew—I didn't give in to it! But why, why—at the very moment when I was going to weaken, when the life of a priest was about to engage in vengeance to try to implant grace, at that moment when I was on the point of shouting, 'God wills it!' and 'In His Name I am going to smash your face in!'—why right opposite me over the other

236

end of the table, hanging on the wall, plain to see, did a great crucifix attract my eye? The kind of crucifix you see in people's houses: a stark white Jesus, hanging on a black cross. A machine-made Christ crucified, right out of St. Sulpice. A plaster Christ, mass produced, manufactured for sale, for the marketplace, for profit. A crucified Christ bought at a bazaar, hung up there for appearance's sake, commonplace, inexpressive—but He was looking at me. . . .

"I stood up then. I went forward in a sort of trance and knelt before Him. I didn't say anything to Him because I have never known how to start a conversation with God, and that evening I was more inarticulate than ever. I knelt there for a few minutes. Then I sat down again at my end of the table and the President began to outline 'his' program.

"Their ideas hadn't changed. I had kept within the bounds of the sacred. That was all. I had entered the realm of risk. I had taken the Gospel along with me. . . . All that happened a very long time ago, far from here—and I have forgiven them."

The Dean stood up slowly, like an old man whose joints creak. He dropped his stick. He leaned his back against the tree and held the trunk between his backward-stretched arms. His hands rubbed the bark nervously. He reminded me of those painted images of the martyrdom of St. Sebastian or of Christ on a cross without the horizontal beam. Perhaps he realized that his posture revealed his inner turmoil. He left the tree and began to pace back and forth on the path.

He spoke then: "So this proves it. The minute a priest expresses himself freely and truthfully, he displays open wounds. We are all in the same boat. . . ." He stopped walking up and down, and raising his voice, he added, "Do you have an answer to my question?"

"No."

"You must!"

"I don't have advice to give to anyone, and certainly not to you. I have talked too much. I have a mania for telling about myself. When I used myself as an example to prove my point, it was a bad idea. Let's forget all these troubles and go on."

He attempted to stand up but the Dean sat down beside him. They were now shoulder to shoulder. Behind them, sitting between two tree roots, I didn't know quite what to do. I felt indiscreet, unwelcome, and—forgotten. I felt humiliated by the situation, but I resisted such a vulgar idea. I prayed silently: "I will be happy, my Lord, if a little of your light shines this evening under this pine tree, without my having any part in it."

The Dean questioned him. To get an exact, clear reply, without lenience, quite pure, he made his voice calm, almost too calm.

"What do you think of obedience?"

Our guest answered him in the same tone, without a shadow of hesitation, "Obedience is the means God has put at the disposal of subordinates, every time they find themselves at a crossroad of life, to express their own thoughts to those in authority and at the same time to accept the thoughts imposed on them. For ever since Christ pronounced the words 'If it be Thy will,' there is no more blind obedience, whatever the textbooks may say. Christ did not obey blindly. Christ was a free man. In the light of the Gospel, blind obedience, the obedience of a slave, is a contradiction in terms. Christ knew why he obeyed."

"And when one doesn't know why?"

"Only the saints know. . . ."

"What do they know?"

"Not much, except that life is lived only once, and its fruitfulness depends on how much blood is shed."

"In that sense, the rebel lives life, too."

238

"I said as much. But the saints direct it toward Calvary. With them, one knows at least how to obey."

"What is sanctity?"

"No one has ever provided an exact definition of it. Theologians who by chance were saints took care not to answer that question as theologians. Sanctity invariably defies formulation. Perhaps a saint is one who, with God's help, has opened the door onto the unknown. He plunges in, without a parachute."

"That is still a formula."

"For the rebel, yes."

"What happens to cowards in this system?"

"Cowards don't fit into any system. They don't know—that is their intellectual position. It doesn't require much energy. Where there are no saints, cowards follow the rebel. They are drawn to him, as a feather is drawn in when you throw open a window. If a saint steps into the center of the ring, their game stops. They look; they are astonished, and they blame the saint for interrupting their dance. No, they don't follow him, but as long as they look at that saint and mutter to each other, they are not moving toward the void. It is a gain for the sacred. And if that saint stays there, *ne varietur* (unwavering), for years, in the end he makes a Christian civilization out of them."

"And what happens when the rebel confronts the saint?"

"That is a different matter. God knows."

"Tell me about sin."

"Sin is negation in its absolute form. But there is no such thing as sickness, there are only sick people. Whom do you mean? Mary Magdalene, Caiphas, or Judas? As long as the sinner doubts, he believes. As long as he hasn't consented to evil because of hatred for God, he is seeking God, even in evil. Thus he has, according to the famous formula, 'found' God. Sin is not a page in a picture book. It isn't a road. It is an attack

239

of giddiness. It may not be a goal, but it is still a summons. It can easily turn into hunger if its absence leaves one empty."

"The solution . . ."

"What solution? Let me quote Léon Bloy, who wasn't a theologian. You are more familiar with him than I . . . 'From afar she comes to cast into the artist's soul a bit of her peace, her mysterious grandeur; then she returns to her immense solitude, in the midst of streets thronged with people. There is only one sorrow, she said to him the last time, and that is not to be a saint.' "

They stood up, and I took my cue from them. The Dean picked up his stick. After this interlude of conversation, our lives resumed at the point where they had left off a while ago, like the pieces of a string cut in two and knotted back together. Nothing will remain to mark these moments of fulfillment, no witness, no proof, save for this knot.

Far off, on the path along the shore, a woman passed, stooped, crushed beneath a bundle of grass. I recognized my old woman. They recognized her, too. The Dean pointed to her with his stick. "There," he said to the priest. "You were searching for examples . . . You see, you see . . . someone always crosses your path . . ."

Our visitor did not reply.

OUR GUEST took the Dean back home with him yesterday evening; I think they had been planning it for several days. Before leaving me, the Dean went to speak to my old woman in the kitchen. He must have asked her to look after me.

And last night when I was fast asleep, after writing the preceding pages, I heard a knocking at my door. I was not

240

mistaken in my guess that one of my parishioners was seriously ill. I will never get used to this ministry of approaching a man struggling against death. I manage to control myself by God's grace. I appear calm, but I am deeply affected. I sit down next to him; I look at him. I can't help looking at his eyes, his mouth, his hands. I touch his forehead. We talk a bit, if he can still talk. In two hours, two days, two weeks, this man will see God. I have never frightened sick people. To a few I have even been able to give messages for "when you come before Him . . ."

I met the doctor, the young one, coming out as I went in. We shook hands. The sick man was still able to talk, low and very distinctly. He was eighty-six years old. Of course there was no hope. I stayed with him, waiting. He received the last sacraments as I knew he would, loyally, matter-of-factly. Historic words of people close to death appear in books, but I have never heard any spoken. His family was glad to have me stay until the end. Once in a while I prayed aloud. Some Hail Mary's. His lips moved. Then his legs swelled up and went cold; his fingers turned white, beginning with his fingernails. As the swelling spread, his life took refuge in the fortress of his heart.

I said to him, "Is there anything you regret?"

He turned to me slowly and answered, "Yes."

"What is it?"

"It is about three in the morning . . . I won't hear my cock crow."

Then his eyelids lowered. I put my hand over his heart. It was beating. Then it stopped beating. After a long while, it started again. The heart resists, then it gives in. . . .

He died before cock-crow.

Now *he knows*.

When I went home again, after laying him out, I went to the church, which I had unlocked to take the Viaticum. The sky was dark. The stained-glass windows were black. The wind had risen; the fishermen were right—a storm was brewing. The sanctuary light swayed, casting shadows. It lighted the tabernacle enough so that I could see to the left and right of the altar those votive offerings typical of sailors' churches: miniature boats, suspended from the ceiling by strings. . . . How many years have they been there? It took me a long while to get used to them.

Was what I was thinking a prayer? "My God, I no longer say, 'Let me see!' I have worn out my eyes trying. You have enough young people and poets to bother you with that request. When I am like that old man (and it will be soon) I will have all eternity to see . . .

"I no longer say, 'Let me know!' I have wearied my brain trying. I give it up. What is there to know? You exist. What more do I need? Is this the result of fatigue? So much the worse; I beg you to accept me in my weariness. For years now, a whole lifetime, I have tortured my brain to extract Your secrets from my darkness. I will do it again; yes, I will begin again. I think it would be right to try again. But just now, I don't want anything, . . . except You.

"I no longer say, 'Let me endure.' I leave that to those who set up your cross on velvet cushions. You endured on your agonizing cross until you were taken down. I have to endure there, too. Nails are strong, and a wrist pierced by nails holds out as long as it has to! The rest is empty words. If everything were cut out of so-called devotional literature except your body hanging from its three nails, there wouldn't be much left. . . .

"I say—for this is the point I have reached—I want to live and die a free man, so that I can offer You the soul of a priest struggling as You struggled. Free in the light! All my life I have shaken off chains! I want to be free, like that old man, to hear my cock crow at the break of day. The pride of being free:

242

to sink down into the dry grass of my hut
to weep, on my knees, when I hear the Ninth Symphony
to caress the foreheads of old men who are dying
to hang stars on my ceiling
to pick the flowers I like whenever I feel like it
to say yes and no with your acquiescence
to find my way, seeking your Face;
to obey with my eyes open without being forced
to prefer your cross to worldly entertainment;
and to love You, to choose You, to follow You without
bonds, freely, like a free man, like a free beggar, in heat or
cold, holding Your hand. To go where? Wherever you
wish. Toward the true, toward the beautiful, toward the
sun; in the wind, taking all risks; even to your Cross, providing I am not forced, but that smiling at me You say,
'This is the way.'

"Orthodoxy?

"The Church is not a vile troop of slaves. It is the opposite
of Hitler and Stalin, who represent Hell with its bolted doors.
The Church is the Church only because of its freedom. And
its field is vast and full of beautiful flowers.

"Have these thoughts brought me closer to You? The way
is hard and painful. Have I found truth tonight, or was I
closer to it a few weeks ago when I thought that a 'directed'
freedom was necessary? We never finish breaking our chains,
because we forge new ones in the freedom we have won. That
is orthodoxy, too: considering man as the builder of his own
dungeon. But at the very depths, in the deepest part of my
soul this yearning for freedom, this longing of the free man
pursues me and imposes itself on me. The truth is there. O
God, let me, let us all be free men; let us trample our chains
under foot as we march toward You."

The church door was torn out of my hands by the wind.
The lights of the village were out. I was afraid of losing my
way. I walked along touching the walls. My presbytery is only

a hundred yards from the church, down two little streets, and I reached it by groping my way. My roof! My roof again with its weak tiles.

I was no sooner indoors than the clouds burst. I had no lamp. I went up under the roof with a candle, crawling on all fours to see if there were any leaks. No, it would hold; I could sleep in peace.

That lightning-filled night was the night of that old man's passing. He couldn't hear anything more. He could no longer see that copper-colored sky lit up by the storm. Where he was, he didn't need the light from the lamp or the fire on the hearth. He was sitting at that family table where, as St. John says so beautifully, "There is no more weeping, nor mourning, nor tears, for the Lamb, the Shepherd, leads them to the springs of life."

I fell asleep at dawn. My old woman was careful not to make any noise. I celebrated my Mass very late, at almost ten o'clock.

I didn't come back from the church until time for lunch. The house was filled with the good fragrance of green peas cooking with onions and bacon. Everything was ready, and clean, and gay: the opposite of commonplace. I spoke about the weather; she spoke of my health, scrutinizing my features for signs of convalescence. I noticed how clear and deep her eyes are, and how little time they take to decipher signs.

"We saw you from far off yesterday," I said. "You had a heavy load."

"Yes, these peas, these onions, and some grass for the rabbits. The garden has finally made up its mind. I hope last night's storm hasn't done it too much harm. . . . I had a big load, but for once it seemed light to me. I am going to tell you something funny: as I came out of the garden, I met the old doctor——"

244

"What is the connection——?"

"The connection is that after I left him, what he had said still delighted me. Imagine—he was complaining bitterly about the hard times and his poverty, and he said . . . that he envied us! He coveted our poverty. It bothers him. He would like to possess that, too. He is jealous of it. It is something he lacks. He weighs it in his scales and it seems heavy to him. Once in a while God gives such people the grace of insight, too! Then they feel terribly poor and alone. But even then they go wrong: they start envying the riches of the poor."

I made no comment, so she went on: "Lies weigh more than a bundle of grass! Lies are heavy, and dark. And then an old woman bent beneath her misery perhaps seems attractive. At moments like that, I suppose they must feel the temptation to destroy, to lighten their burdens, to breathe, to come out of their darkness. But what can they destroy, since they haven't built anything? And they suddenly realize that they are beginning to grow old and their hands are empty? Empty hands are embarrassing. When they belong to persons who are supposedly important, they are also ridiculous. And so, for the first time, he didn't treat me with contempt . . ."

She was watching me eat. Her face had become even more transparent than usual, her eyes more limpid and her wrinkles nobler.

"What I said is rather commonplace," she added apologetically, "and not very learned."

Not very learned perhaps, but at that instant I saw that there is another form of courtesy besides that of words, another culture besides that in books, a distinction which doesn't depend on manners. I saw Truth as a very great Lady, whose image at that moment was reflected in that old woman.

The question, which I regretted as soon as I had asked it, escaped my lips: "Who are you?"

The expression on her face altered a bit, not from surprise, not from distress—more from sadness, I think, at seeing me so far from the obvious.

"Who am I?" she said. "Who am I?"

Her voice grew firmer, but lost nothing of its sweetness. She gave me an intense piercing look for the space of a second. Her hands joined on the table edge; she stood looking at the sea. "Who am I? I walk along all your paths and you have met me a thousand times. I have often spoken to you, and, as you do with all my kind, you thought you answered me. . . . Who am I? That is hard to explain, except by comparison."

She turned slightly toward me. "What if one day God speaks to you and asks who you are? . . . I don't hold it against you, but when have you and your colleagues—carefully chosen to bring us joy—when have you instructed us? When have you defended us? When have you preferred us? When has our problem, as you call it, ever been your problem? For twenty centuries your barns have been full, and the springs have flowed on your lands, and you think that you have done enough because you have spoken well. You are very good at talking.

"But in the end you have to plunge into the heart of things. Your life isn't just looking at the Colonel's wife, or the Canon, or that simpleton of a professor, or that colleague of yours who reduces the Gospel to the smooth working of his carburetor, or that old fox of a doctor who today for the first time seemed to be in love with my nothing. Although these people are hungry, too, believe me, they are not the center of the universe. They are only an infinitesimal part of that People of God for whom your hands were anointed. They aren't your reasons; they are only your pretexts. And because they bother you, because they are powerful, because they rule, and they cheat, you are willing to abandon the others on the fringes of the light! You complain! You are unhappy! You want to be approved and praised. I have done it. I told you, clear as day,

246

what I think of the canton. But, the Virgin be my witness, I have prayed, and I pray still that your eyes may be opened! Yes or no, are you willing to serve? Monsieur le Doyen walked out. His ideas were sound. All ideas of that kind are good. The Dean is a man. I've said that to you before. If it were not for him, I would have been strangled by these people. But it is not enough for him to be a man. He has to be a priest; he must be drawn to the Cross. Men like him are rare, it is true, but how can God forge priests of the kind he could be, except by using men of his mettle who lack only one thing: the ability to hear, above the sneers of the mighty, the call of the weak. The screen is not the Colonel's wife; it is the Dean himself. I fear—please forgive me—I fear that a wall has risen up between him and the Gospel, a wall of vanity.

"Or then, let's face the fact that in him and in all of you who preach it, the Charity of Christ is no more than a corpse. In that case, the Church is dead."

She added softly, "Unless the Charity of Christ is, perhaps, only pronouncing its first syllables, unless you are the first generation of brave men, artisans of truth; unless there hasn't been enough time since Calvary for you priests to reach full growth...."

Did she see me take my head in my hands?

She continued, "Yes, you are right, always right. Now you are sifting all my wretched words through the sieve of your learning, and nothing remains. You have the key, you have the power of opening the door or leaving it shut. But that Child in your arms isn't growing any stronger. You ought to let us take care of Him for an hour or two every day, like those foundlings for whom they always need nurses. You are too rich. You live in palaces and you teach Him to walk on carpets. He isn't made for that life; he needs air, and the paths where we pick strawberries."

She was silent a moment, then, lower still, she added, "The

mistake is this: Monsieur le Doyen is a priest only halfway, or a quarter, a tenth; not for everyone; not for us. And because he is afraid of the others, he makes us afraid of him. The truth is that the Church doesn't want to die, and that over and above the malice and the insurmountable stupidity of the powerful, the Bishop, whether or not he has a clear conscience, is asking obedience of the Dean, is offering him the means of being wholly a priest. . . . But what have I said? What can an old woman say? You wanted to hear it. Now you know who I am: I am a suppliant! And I am sure that one day that Child will become so active in his arms that he won't be able to hold Him any longer; and then he will let us have Him. . . ."

What could I say?

I got up from the table and went to the window. Dark clouds lowered over the sea, edged with great gold bands where the sun filtered in through invisible cracks. It took me back forty years to the war of 1914–1918. At that time I lived near an air strip, and on certain evenings when my father and I were returning home from the fields, a small white airplane would shoot up toward the sky. It would reach the sunlight and shine above our heads, climbing higher and higher until the sun disappeared, and it had lost the game. I was in an agony of waiting, saying within myself, "He doesn't realize . . ." and saying to him "Come down quickly; it's already night down here!" He would return, his motors shut off, gliding like a hawk. And in the almost monastic silence of that nightfall, before touching the earth, the wings would rock back and forth, while the pilot, whom I could have embraced, played the trumpet call of victory. The piercing and triumphant voice of that trumpet is still in my ears, and it came back to me beneath those low stormclouds.

But what would be victory, what would the trumpet call mean? Who is dreaming and who is awake? The same anguish . . .

Let me leave that sun to its flaming solitude, too high up now, too far off, escaping from me, and come down to earth, to solid ground. Let me leave those rays to the moon and not play the saint when I am nothing but a humble man. The old woman hadn't said these things in front of the Dean. She didn't dare. With two or three common-sense words, he would have put a stop to it. To me she confided her lament. . . . She is waiting. She is living in expectation of seeing him climb up in search of the sun. She approves him so as not to lose contact, so as not to become alienated from his drama, but she puts her hope in his heart. She is growing old in that hope. She serves us, watching for the moment when the Dean will once more seek out his path along the lighted fissures between those dark clouds.

My God, why did you tear me away from my vineyard? Why, You who are all-knowing, did you bring me to this place, where dreaming is impossible, where I have to choose between earth and heaven; where to serve You, I have to sacrifice You? I am absolutely at a crossroads. If that was what You wanted, You have achieved it. The Cross, this time, or the things of this world. Crucify You again, and myself with You, or avoid that slaughter and not know where my road leads. . . .

Face up to the words now that they have been pronounced. Remold my face. Break my mask—and I thought I was frank! Lose myself, as it says in their books, in order to find myself. Reduce myself to a minimum. Seek my axis exactly at the spot where the stars go out and faith lights up. Choose between the absurdity of faith and their sneers (including their sneers!). Be truthful or sneer with them—or perhaps not sneer, but affect a surface seriousness, a seriousness of convention and habit! Deny life in order to enter into Your life, into Your plan, into that delirium, that dream, even—but what is the dream and whence are its fleshly images drawn? I cannot deny life. You didn't deny it. What does the earth count for in this adventure? What substantial support can it give to our

thoughts and attitudes? Do the lines cross anywhere? All that
was, indeed, taught to me, and it may be that I received it
wrongly, or perhaps it was given to me the wrong way, but
the reasoning seems to me today to be a formless series of
ridiculous abstractions. It sounded good. It was sometimes
called John of the Cross, sometimes Vincent de Paul, or even
the Gospel. Now I am backed up against a wall, and these
abstractions are vain. You can't build anything with a trowel
full of mist. The recitation of a lesson learned by rote is a hor-
rible formula. It is I, myself alone, on the threshold of rebellion or of indifferent resignation, at the door of "let things
take their course," or knocking to gain admittance to that
unknown world of light and dark. If I knock, and if I enter,
the page has been turned forever: I will leave the Colonel's
wife and the Canon outside playing with their puppets, and
in the end I will perhaps love them, with that disturbing and
magnetic love of God. I will leave the question of whether
the Bishop's orders are paternal and responsible up to him,
but I will not be able to contradict them without doubting my
own good conscience and without consenting to discuss them
with him in a conscientious and loyal spirit of seeking.

Here I am preaching a sermon to myself—and I detest
sermons. Would it be honest to preach my theories to the
Dean? They seem all right when I am alone, but with him, his
terrible faculty for upsetting everything in a word or two
changes the complexion of things. I am like my old woman,
watching him and never saying anything. She has kept silence
with him for an uncommonly long time now. But suppose it
is true that the Cross is the pivot of the world? Suppose St.
Paul was not just hypnotized with words when he declared to
the Galatians that the scandal of the Cross cannot be voided?
He won't hear me, because he cannot renounce his responsibilities as a man. But let someone point out the spot where
the priest and the man join hands and move forward together

along the paths of truth. . . . Even if he holds the Child too tightly, he will never consent to leave Him in the care of his parishioners without safeguards. He would rather have Him live at a slower pace in his arms than see Him dressed up as an actor in their circus. That has always been my opinion, and it is surely his, too. We can't love Him as we should and deal Him out in small change. And if loving Him that way is wrong, He will explain it to us one day. Too late. But it isn't our fault. I am not God.

So I am back where I started. Nothing has changed; nothing is going to change. I am pacing like a caged beast, in circles. Rebellion or acquiescence? I know what rebellion is, but what constitutes acquiescence? Can the present satisfactions of that excellent priest be more tragic than his former sufferings?

I must be rambling a bit this afternoon. . . . If a theologian could hear me, or the Canon, they would double up laughing! They have given me to understand as much! . . . I have no "theological background"; mine was only a "late vocation." I was sowing wheat while the others were studying St. Thomas! I never fitted into the mold, and I will live and die a sniper, unregimented, always suspect and treated with caution for fear of my unpredictable outbursts. I am classed, catalogued; my records follow me wherever I go. I am just good enough to administer the sacraments—and then only to the simple-minded!—to hold a position without responsibilities, to sermonize on a few vague Gospel themes, a few scraps of half-truth in my invariably nonclassic manner. My candor leaves them cold. Everything is attributed to the excessive, disproportionate, superficial rantings of a self-taught man. I have no influence. In a word, I was never considered "fit for active service." I am retired without pension, listed on the administrative records of the reserves. . . .

251

And here am I alone, before the mystery of this priest and two beams in the form of a cross!

If only I could ask for advice!

My desire to do that was killed a long time ago.

One day I went to a theologian to ask advice on a serious matter affecting the spiritual future of a man's soul. I remember that his floor was waxed (I am always afraid to walk on waxed floors!) and that he was sitting in a leather armchair while I sat before him on a cane chair, in the idiotic position of a sparrow in a trap. He looked at me, his small eyes half closed behind old-fashioned glasses with iron rims and frames, which dug purple furrows into his temples. Under his eyes the skin was wrinkled, dark, and somewhat chewed-looking. His long hands, as white as marble, his thin fingers extended on the chair arms, remained absolutely still. . . . And he said nothing. He listened to me. And soon I found nothing more to say; my point of conscience, so intricately presented, seemed stupid to me. I wanted to escape, to be whisked away by the wind, to disappear through a trapdoor. I forgot why I was sitting there in front of him. Suddenly, my hands panicked. Should I fold them? Let them hang down? And then everything, my tongue, my eyes, my neck, my head, my feet—probably most of all my feet—my whole body began to tremble like an animal's. I stopped thinking; I was paralyzed, bloodless, cramped in my ideas, empty of imagination, reduced to the state of a disjointed puppet. Boneless, liquefied! . . . Still he said nothing! We remained mute, face to face. It could have lasted a year, and it might still be going on! At last I found the physical courage to stand up, turn in the direction of the door, take hold of the handle. I said, I think, "Good-by, Monsieur le Supérieur . . ." He stood up, managed a faint smile, answered my farewell with a courteous word, and bowing slightly, added in a suave, musical voice, "Be good enough, Monsieur l'Abbé, to have the prudence to send that soul to me."

252

My old woman said, "Aren't you going to rest?"

"Yes, but I don't know where. Not here. I'm going out."

Here, the clouds have permission to pass closer to men than they do back home. There, the mountains hold them up. When they appear above us, on the plains, unless they are heavy with rain, they haven't had time to sail lower. Here, when they come from the sea, as they did this evening, they don't have enough time to climb up, and they pass over our heads so near, so threatening, and so bold that they are quite frightening!

Back home there were two kinds of wind—the one from the earth and the other from the clouds. They didn't always agree; sometimes it would take them an hour or two, even half a day, to make up their minds to blow in the same direction. If the earth wind won out, the clouds could soon be seen to thin out, unravel, and melt, and the sky would clear up. But almost anything might happen if the wind from the clouds came down to earth.

I went out with my dog into the wind which drives the clouds and the waves in the same direction. My instinct, which in its discretion, its gentleness, and its insistence, furnishes me with a natural image of what they tell us of the action of the Holy Spirit in us (I wouldn't want a theologian to read that sentence) led me to the garden, to my shed.

I sank down into the dry, crackling hay. I found it hard to sleep, but closing my eyes, I let my mind rove at leisure in quest of images. I was back on a railroad station platform of several years ago. It was ten minutes before midnight. My train was due in five minutes. It was summer. I stood in the midst of a weary crowd, which was half asleep, sweating, patient. It was so dense that no family groups could form. I put down my suitcase, which was heavy, and leaned it against my leg to keep track of it. The pressure of the crowd pushed it away, and I forgot it for a few seconds. When my train came in, I stooped to pick it up, but it was gone. I had to go on without it, and I never got it back.

What prompted this recollection?

Have I become a traveler without baggage? That suitcase full of ideas I had acquired—is it perhaps lost like the other one, without hope of recovery? Is my train leaving while certain objects, indispensable for my daily life, have been stolen from me, and must I, this time alone, reconstruct one by one, in detail, each of my lost certitudes? How does one go about questioning one's subconscious? Why did mine lead me back to that station, under those light bulbs, to that moment when I was stripped of my belongings? What link is there between the past and the present? Should I go to the limit of these conclusions? . . . Where is faith sold, or a small hope? Where can one find the shop of some old dealer in love? Have I then been left destitute? My suitcase, I think, contained certain beliefs, a bit worn, a bit threadbare, which I used from the moment I woke up in the morning, and which always traveled with me. They were enough for me. Does my subconscious mean to warn me that I must renew them? At what price? Or perhaps the recollection is a warning from that oracular voice, that indissoluble mixture of nature and grace?

I can't fathom it.

Then I saw myself in that train. In my pocket I still had my handkerchief and my rosary. Everything else had fallen into the void. I felt that I had become the void. I was sitting opposite travelers with baggage, happy travelers, and I looked at the impressive pile of suitcases in the racks. What unappreciated riches! I had a desire to walk the whole length of the train, which I did. The conductor stopped me, and fortunately, after a long conversation, accepted the coin of my miseries.

I was very unhappy.

What a strange memory!

254

Or perhaps it is a premonition of future spiritual detachments for which this memory is preparing me? God makes himself clear only in the minds of saints. . . .

I didn't budge out of my hole. I love solitude, but I don't benefit much by it. I do better if I have difficulties to overcome, provided they are concrete problems whose outlines are clearly visible. These problems of human souls struggling with the good and the less good, in open warfare between day and night, weary me in the end. Voluntarily, this evening I reject the dialogue with the unknown. (But tomorrow?)

I went back indoors at nightfall, after reciting all of my breviary and going to sprinkle my old man with holy water before I bury him tomorrow. In his house everything was peaceful. His cock was perched on a pile of wood. His goats stretched their necks sadly through the gate of their stable. His wife and children were already accustomed to the idea that they had lost him. We talked a long time, of many things; we even spoke of him. Life goes on. The Dean, whom I was expecting, hasn't come back. I opened the Bible at random. There I read in the First Book of Samuel, Chapter III: "Now the child Samuel ministered to the Lord before Heli, and the word of the Lord was precious in those days; there was no manifest vision . . ." And I am going to sleep (if I can sleep) on the call of God to that child who slept in the Temple, near to the high priest Heli whose "eyes were grown dim, that he could not see: before the lamp of God went out. . . ."

IF, NOW that I am wide awake, I could retrace my thoughts of the night with clarity and freshness, my life would be considerably simplified. (I would almost consider myself an intelligent man!) I am writing this rapidly, just after getting up, before the funeral. And already a wall has been thrown up between the night and the day. I search painfully for things that once came easily to mind; my cerebral mechanism has resumed its slow rhythm. I drag my memories out of a block of marble, with my fingernails. . . . I can't reach the center of them.

What comes to the surface most clearly in the floating mass of last night's thoughts is the head of a clown painted by a friend of mine. That idea of the clown must be firmly rooted in me somewhere. My personal conception of the summit of tragedy, in its most desperate and poignant expression, is completely summed up in the clown. Has my subconscious mind, by dint of searching and making comparisons, drawn a parallel between that man all smeared with ochre and chalk and our humiliating and inextricable situations as priests? I trust it, and answer yes. And I don't feel any shame. The prophet Isaiah dared to present the Savior in the guise of an earthworm. I haven't yet dared to identify myself with that lowly creature which we step on and crush. But it isn't impossible that, in my mind, that earthworm also has a certain significance. Between my clown and me there must exist a secret affinity. In a few years, that puppet's head will stretch, lengthen, twist like a worm and let itself be crushed, and the one who crushes it won't even feel it under his foot. I mustn't dwell on it too much. And yet? . . .

256

I wasn't quite asleep, so I wasn't dreaming. It was that moment which I enjoy, when the sense of my responsibilities, which is acute in the waking state, jumps over the wall, and when my imps and my angels circulate freely along my garden paths. In this instance it was I who was walking in front of paintings hung on the walls of a museum in a subprefecture. I like to search by myself for "my" painting. That head attracted me like a magnet, and from then on, nothing else existed for me.

"That is my clown," said my friend.

I tried to tempt him. "Why?" I asked. "Why him? There are also flowers, birds, mountains and lakes in this world. There are—faces!"

"And that is one. Look here, this is what cost me the most work and patience—these two lines, under the eyes."

Under each eye there were two T-squares, two crosses without the vertical prolongation above the arms. Two gallows.

He went on, "I accentuated the lines the farther they get from the eyes. For my clown, it is never finished, you understand? Those paths, under his eyes, lead straight to the outer darkness. Because, don't mistake me: this head is supposed to make you laugh!"

I realized that my friend was a stranger to me. We had often met. His conversation didn't lead to any dreadful unknown depths. I had judged him capable of painting a landscape, a pond with water lilies, a stormless sky strewn with white flakes, a Madonna's face. And here he had just set down the brush which had painted those two lines!

I asked him, "Do you believe in God?"

He answered, "During the night of this past Christmas, I lighted two candles in front of my clown, which I had just finished the day before, and I knelt down and sang hymns. It seemed natural to me, but perhaps it had nothing of faith in it, or at the end of it. I believe in the massacred God of Scripture. That is why I don't dare go into your churches. You have installed God in too comfortable a position. You have made Him look mediocre to me. God isn't at ease, it seems to me, except on the cross. God will never be a resting place for me. And that conviction burns in me so strongly that I would feel I was a heretic (don't hold it against me!) if I held otherwise."

I remember answering, "Jesus Christ isn't ugly. He was and is the handsomest of the children of men."

"Now you force me to do exactly what I didn't want to—praise my clown's beauty. Would you call him ugly? I wanted him to be handsome in his sacrifice, in his acquiescence, handsome beneath his hideous make-up, somewhat as Christ was beautiful beneath the clots of blood. My clown is handsome because he accepts. And in the beauty of his immolation, he is my steppingstone toward the invisible beauty of Christ's immolation. But he is only this one step, the one I can take today. Next year, or in twenty years, will I finally be able to paint Christ? I live in that hope. . . ."

Visitors passed back and forth, stopped, talked among themselves in the stumbling and clumsy manner of self-styled connoisseurs. In these exhibits, the paintings are at home, but the visitors seem out of place. I said to my friend, "Let's get out of here. Come on."

And when we were in the garden, I said, "When did you start to paint your clown?"

"Long before I ever touched a brush. It was when I was studying medicine, so I was still very young. One year, the night before Easter, I decided to go to confession. The church was as dark as one could wish, one of those neighborhood churches all spic and span, where stale perfumes mix and cling. It was sickening. I was going to go out when I saw that one of the confessors was dispatching his penitents at such a rapid rate that I really had no excuse. When I had unburdened myself, this confessor said, 'My son, this morning I

258

read in my breviary, "Let us walk openly, as in full daylight," and again, "The shadows give place to light." Between these two passages lies all of life. Now say your act of contrition.' From that day on I started to paint my clown, looking for the light, trying to move toward it without cheating."

He sat down on a bench, looked straight ahead and added, "The only thing is this: you never reach the end! But you know more about that than I. You are the one who should have painted that clown. He would have had a crown of thorns. No, in all honesty, I can't yet stab them into him."

A shiver ran through my body.

Last night that was about what I saw, but much more sharply.

Part V

The Journey

It is useless now to go on with the dissertation. Useless and impossible. They have come back. Once again I am dominated by the Dean's life, by life itself. That is how life affects us. And what could be the harm in living? I am more and more convinced of the inner stability of this priest. He doesn't reject anything, and he establishes harmony.

He and our neighbor have made plans: The Dean and I are going away. Our kind neighbor is going to take over my parish duties, and we won't be gone long. He is lending us his little car, which the Dean brought back here. He has some kind of two-wheeled affair to get about on, so there is no cause for worry.

When the Dean came in, he first looked into my eyes, and in his I could read his concern for my health. I said, "Don't worry. Everything is all right."

His eyes still bored into mine, but their expression changed to one of youth, laughter, anticipation of my surprise. "We're going away . . ."

He was incapable of leading up to the news, so he blurted it out, carried away by the delight of telling me. Our neighbor, curé pro tem of my parish, was already sitting at my desk. "And here I stay," he said.

They explained their arrangements, and then he said, "Go wherever you like," adding mischievously, "but, come to think of it, where will you go?"

Joy brought tears to my eyes. That rarely happens to me any more, only once in a great while. I never weep for sorrow, I think gritting one's teeth is enough, but I still weep for joy.

"Now I know how you will look when you enter Paradise—handkerchief in hand," said the Dean jokingly.

It was about three in the afternoon. Our neighbor left us, and I turned the chore of packing over to my old woman. I went out, and everything looked new to me.

My youngsters coming out of school greeted me as they passed. A flight of swifts traced their arabesques overhead and piped their sharp cries. I went into the houses, talked, noted my impressions, storing up images. With an air of apology, I announced our departure. No one seemed upset, quite the contrary. "It will do you good, Monsieur le Curé, and Monsieur le Doyen, too."

They are not jealous. I appreciate their simplicity. They are good folk; my complexes are foreign to them. With them everything is "yes" or "no." The Kingdom of God. Even death is simple. I once knew a peasant girl who got herself "in trouble." She stood it as long as she could. Then she went to confession and drowned herself in the well. Lack of courage? Lack of faith? Madness? She simply decided that she had no more right to live. That was all.

I walked as far as the garden, where my dog was already waiting by the gate. We took the path up the hill. My heart was light. The weight of my parish responsibilities, a burden I have carried, day and night, for so many years, already seemed not so heavy. But I wanted to look over my roofs, count them, recall the faces beneath them. It occurred to me that tomorrow we would have to pass through the canton. There is no other road. . . .

I sat down in the shade of a pine and read my breviary. I was taught that the breviary is my special prayer for my parishioners. I stayed there a long time with my prayers and my thoughts. As I went back down the hill, the air was already getting cooler. I felt . . . what? Sadness? Melancholy? (I can't express it) descend on me like fatigue. What am I? Who am I? The grasses bend and straighten up again, rooted in the earth, source of their life. And I? The wind snatches me up, tosses me about, wears me out, like a leaf torn from the branch. The priest, a man between God and men, between Heaven and earth! . . . Did the ones who said that ever watch these movements of the grass? I only know of one who was able to stay between Heaven and earth. . . . He was nailed there! "Save me, O God, for the waters threaten my life."

Be like Him! . . . But where is that going to lead us in the end?

When I came back to the house, my old woman said, "The Dean has been in church for a long while."

I took my big key and entered silently. He was more than kneeling; he was crumpled over, his hands clutching the lowest rungs of a chair. I did not dare go near; he did not stir. Later on he returned, joyful, relaxed, more sure of himself than ever. But on his face I noticed an imperceptible mark, left there by the hand of God. That can be seen, too. . . .

I HOPE—I plan—to devote at least an hour to this Journal every evening.

We loved the trip even as we set out past the hedges, the meadows, the streams. We aren't the least bit interested in speed. And then—it is the only emotion I have kept secret —and then, I am going to see my home! I am almost afraid of the shock, both the joy and the pain.

We have agreed to stop early, to take separate rooms, to recite only part of our breviary together, and not to continue until we have celebrated our Masses, even if it is late in the morning. We expect to be back in time to prepare the Easter solemnities together.

The Dean asked me, "Did you bring your pen?" And not waiting for my reply, added, "Then note this: I am setting out with these two verses from the Psalms in my head: 'Hide not your face from me,' and '. . . in your light we see the light.' And also this phrase of Newman's: 'The Church reserves the right to adapt her messages to the situation, rank and age of her children; to adjust to their ignorance and even their obstinacy; to be silent when it would be inopportune or uncharitable to reveal all of the truth, or when men do not deserve it; to allow their speculations to go far afield, then to recall them to the straight path.' And then this from a modern thinker: 'When we are all guilty, that will be democracy.' And after that, no more philosophy or spiritual reflections. That will keep me until we return."

We passed through the canton, driving slowly. The postman, always jovial, came to attention and greeted us smartly with his hands full. Lifted curtains disclosed invisible presences. At the school the children were at recess in the yard, which is separated from the street only by a low fence. The Dean almost stopped the car. The children rushed forward. They didn't say "Good morning," but, throwing their caps in the air, they shouted, "Long live Monsieur le Curé!"

When we came to the church, he stopped the car. He went inside and I followed him without enthusiasm. He went toward the altar; everything was in disorder. Chairs out of line, altars dirty, dust everywhere. I heard him groan, "How dirty it is!" And, turning to me, "But the altar light is out. Isn't God in this church any more? What is the meaning of this? Let's go, let's go!" He waved his arms. "But no," he said. "Here, lend me a hand." He gave me some vases of withered flowers. "Throw all that out! At least let's not have it stink in here!"

Anger had gripped him. Some women had opened the door. He called to them loudly, "What is going on here? Look at the state your church is in! A stable! Who is in charge? The altar light is out! Have you all become Protestants? What are the nuns doing? Are they dead? Come on, say something, speak up! You always used to have plenty to say."

One of them answered, first by raising her hand in a gesture which meant, "What can we do?" then she said, "They can't get together on it." The others stayed behind, exchanging questioning glances. From time to time the door opened and the group grew more compact. I was leaning against the holy-water stoup on the right, oppressed, anxious about something I couldn't name, wishing to see this painful incident come to a quick end. I turned my eyes toward the stained-glass window, a John the Baptist in the St.-Sulpice style, typically sentimentalized, neither fat nor thin, his crook bedecked with daisies.

"So," he went on, "is this a church or an indoor market? Aren't you ashamed? Is this where you pray? Then you must have invented a new religion. . . . And the others? The others? What are they about?" They understood who he meant. I turned around at that instant and saw them elbow each other. Two or three of them, the eternal penitent Mary Magdalenes, entreated the Dean with looks. These would not speak. It was enough for them to see him again and implore him with their eyes.

The first one who had dared express the general opinion, and who had remained apart from the group, in the lead, answered, "Monsieur le Doyen, you don't know how glad we are to see you getting mad the way you used to! I tell you, they can't get together on anything. We need a chief here. No, it's no kind of a religion any more. And if you could see your presbytery, it's even worse! They hold meetings there, and not to sweep—to talk, to say nothing, to divide the parish a little more. When they come out, they form their enemy camps again in the street."

The Dean answered, "So they haven't changed?"

She answered him, sincerely uncomprehending, "Changed? How do you mean, changed?" And then, thinking it over, "Changed! Oh, yes, it is all changing. We are becoming heathen!"

"And you?"

"Us? Oh, in your time, we——"

"In my time! In my time! If you had been a little bit braver..."

The group was getting excited, and a voice spoke out, "Are you going to leave us like this? Are you going to leave your church in this state? Are you going to leave our children and the old folks who are dying? There was a civil marriage last week——"

Voices murmured, "Tell the whole thing."

The speaker continued in the same vein, "You never saw the like! Everything is going! The church will fall apart. The gutters on the rectory are in a fine state! In a year, I swear, there will be infants without baptism. We are more Christian than you think. You call that a life? But they will get used to it; they are already starting to. Then, what a life! We don't need discussions or all those meetings where they go carrying papers. We need—and they need—a priest who can stir us up, one who isn't afraid. Oh, what a disaster, what a disaster!"

268

Another voice grew bolder, "There aren't fifty . . ." But she didn't finish.

The Dean did not reply, but his eyes were hard. He ought not to have looked at them like that, for they met his eyes fearlessly. I was edging toward the door when a group of boys blocked my path. They quieted down as they entered, but I heard those outside shouting, "The curé is back, the curé is back." They had not changed: their smocks were on crooked; their hair was unkempt; they were twisting their berets in their fingers. One little cripple, his knee bent on a wooden peg, pushed his way painfully and energetically through the crowd. Suddenly everything was back to normal. Their curé, who was such a good storyteller, who made them so mad and was so fond of them, was there. They couldn't get enough of looking at him. Their faces brightened up. They smiled, turning their heads to look at each other, sniffling noisily the way youngsters do. All their smiles were saying, "Now everything will be all right," and "It's a good thing."

One woman (one of the Mary Magdalenes) whispered to her neighbor, "He has aged, but he hasn't changed."

The Dean went over to the disorderly and joyful group of children. His hands were trembling. He stretched them out toward the crippled boy, bent over and kissed him. He took his rosary out of his pocket, slipped it into the little cripple's hand, and said softly, "Here, keep it. It's all I have for you today. At night before you go to sleep, say a decade, or even just two or three Hail Mary's—and think—of me." Then he straightened up his body, his head, and pushed the women back in my direction, without a thought for how I was going to get out, saying, "Come, let's go."

The youngsters, who hadn't understood what was going on, ran after the car as long as they could. I shrank down on my seat, refusing to count the windows that were thrown open.

I HAVE been thinking about this since yesterday: I am less dependent on men than on things. Men help or hinder me. They interest me or bore me. They travel along with me, or leave me by the wayside. I have no enemies, and my friends don't tie me down; they love me and that is a light burden.

But I am much more deeply bound to things. I wouldn't dare admit it out loud, but it is a fact. I am the vine, the meadow, and the wheat. I am the dew and the storm. I enter into communion with things. I live intimately with them. It must be a blood tie that goes back very far, that has inextricable ramifications. My soul and my flesh are involved. My very self. It is a mixing of blood with blood. I realize and admit that this is incomprehensible, impossible to explain.

Still, as we went along this road which is leading us toward our goal, I talked about it a little with the Dean. He suddenly became serious, and said, "There is no point in hiding the fact that for years, and especially since I left my post as Dean, those same ideas have been my secret preoccupation; they have left their mark on me. I am like you. Things move me more than people. Against things, we are helpless: we have to submit to the pain of it. The sign of total honesty, of flawless submission to God, of our acceptance of the light, is surely less our obedience to men than our submission to God's eternal order, which is revealed in the world by what we might call the absolute sincerity of things. The sea doesn't lie, neither does the sun, or the wind, or trees, or beasts. What a terrible lesson! When I was a child, the story of the pelican who pierces his own side so that his greedy and undisciplined offspring won't die of hunger, used to haunt my memory. It is the basis of my pastoral philosophy ..."

He added, "We mature too fast; as our shell hardens, it paralyzes our heart's memory."

He turned to me gaily and said, "Dear and faithful friend, help me to recapture youth. . . ."

It was about four o'clock. The sun was already setting behind the great trees whose branches formed an arch over our heads. It was the first time that this stubborn and violent man had made an appeal to me. The road sloped upward, and broadened unaccountably. Then, at the edge of a circle strewn with sand, I saw a fountain, unlike any other I had ever seen. It was barely three feet high, round like a tree trunk, surmounted by a basin from which the water flowed in thin streams. Who could have built that jewel of a fountain for tourists, under those century-old trees, in that solitary spot? There must be many others who remember it, for the basin's edges were polished by travelers' hands, like the base of a statue in a shrine.

The Dean stopped the car, and went to drink from the basin. He turned to me, his face suddenly shining, and said, "Things! we were just talking about them! . . . Wouldn't it be wonderful to be like this water! make a retreat here at this spring ... to seek God and find Him in abandonment, in song, in obedience, in beauty! And be refreshed—like this!" He plunged his hands into the basin and brought them out full. He dipped his face in the cool water.

"Try it," he said. "To break down our defenses, God doesn't need artillery. A spring, or a cripple's wooden leg. That youngster didn't say anything to me yesterday, and this water isn't speaking a word. He limped. It flows. If this keeps up, this trip will teach us more than our books. There is a secret quality in things. . . ."

To note briefly the event of the day, I should say a word about our dinner in the company of a priest.

All the tables were empty when we entered the inn's dining room, except for his, a table for four. He saw us come in, stood up and bowed to us, then sat down again, leaving us free to choose where we wanted to sit. The innkeeper, frugally, had lighted only the lamp over that table. In any case, we would have sat down there.

The priest was a lecturer, delegated by his bishop to evangelize workers in the halls of country inns and to preach retreats for young people.

The Dean made a face. "An odd ministry," he said.

"Yes, and an odd life to lead! And to think that I wanted to be a country priest, one of the kind who stay in one place, wear themselves out and die there . . ."

"My dear colleague," said the Dean, "don't be under any illusions."

"We all have so many illusions," our new acquaintance replied. "Our life—in its precarious position, between the world and God—lends itself to them. The main thing is to try not to cultivate them, and to be content with our lot. But, tell me, what sort of illusions can a man like me—a roving priest—succumb to?"

"He can believe that he is transforming the world; that he has only to appear for good to be done; that when he leaves a place, he is sure to have left his mark, and chiefly that all parish priests, sedentary by calling, are more or less inept."

The stranger stopped eating. He looked at the Dean over his glasses, like a pathetic, nearsighted pupil, and I had the feeling that he was unhappy.

"Thank you," he said, "Thank you! To tell the truth, I am guilty of all those failings, except entertaining the feelings you mentioned about my sedentary brothers. At least I don't think I do. I admire parish priests. You are one, I suppose.

Well, to stay for ten years, twenty years, a lifetime, in daily contact with mediocrity, and feel it oppressing you—to stick it out and reject as cowardice any desire to escape—you have to be a saint!"

"A saint!"

Are we ever going to get on with this dinner?

"But I also admire the recalcitrant parishioners, in spite of the trials they inflict on one. Can it be another illusion? None of them is really so bad. Souls irrevocably closed are rare, very rare indeed. No matter how stubborn, uncomprehending, and stupid they seem, each one has his secrets, which will come to light the day he is touched by God's grace. The priest's role is to wait. I am not the one to set the example: I merely pass by; it is the one who stands at the door, day and night, a whole lifetime. It must be very hard."

Finally he looked at his watch, didn't take dessert, paid his bill, and left us.

We recited Lauds on a bench under a row of trees leading into the woods already damp with the evening dew. Without looking at the map, I know that we are nearing our destination. We could be there tomorrow, if I wished. Do I really want it?

The Dean was holding his old breviary bound in old, soft leather between his thumb and forefinger, as though weighing it. "Am I right in thinking that that is your first breviary?" I said.

He looked at me affectionately, and answered, "You are right. It was given to me for my subdiaconate. It is a witness——"

"A witness!"

"No use explaining. That is a time when we don't doubt our own truth."

Unidentifiable noises came from the woods. From the

wind's lament, I knew we must be on the top of a hill; it was like a symphony in a minor key, poignant and sorrowful. We listened to it together; it is a sound that grips the heart more deeply than human sobs, setting it adrift on an invisible ocean of cries, of shipwreck, of struggle with death, of solitude and infinity. It is the world's end. The truth starts here, in this melody seeking its key, in this torment and this anguish of things powerless to free themselves from bondage, this birth of despair or of joy.

"This sorcery is painful," said the Dean. "Let's go back." He added jokingly, "I am not acquainted with your province, but it promises to be interesting. If the trees are, as you say, even more spellbinding there, we are likely to meet fairy folk."

I would have liked to speak.

Fairies in my country? It is true they are everywhere. They trail their pink, violet or fawn-colored dresses over the poplars, oaks, and firs; over the meadows, along the sunken paths. Their hands touch the honeysuckle and it bows; they caress the heather and broom on the moors, and speak to them in their own tongue. They visit the water lilies in the evening when the frogs peep out of the ponds. Between the reeds, my fairies hold their counsels. In the alfalfa they urge the reaper on; he pursues them, but they escape laughing and wait for him at the end of the field in the shade of a willow. They drink from the dew, mingling their jewels with it. They travel by leaps and bounds from mountain peak to mountain peak, touching them with a finger, transforming them into blue islands hemmed with fire, lost in the ocean of the sky.

The most beautiful sight is in summer, in June, when they come down over the wheat; when they perfume the vineyards and change the potato fields into Oriental carpets. In that season they sleep only at noon, near fountains, beside streams, behind the hawthorn bushes where nervous birds flutter about their nests. In the evening they light up the stars. The youngest

274

ones, who don't yet fly so high, awaken glow worms, and they take the south wind by the hand and lead it in a dance over the wisps of fog.

But I must stop, otherwise I will feel so homesick that I won't be able to sleep.

THIS MORNING I was awakened by farm noises. I got up and sat by the open window. I hadn't noticed the wide-open gate last night, the sloping farmyard, the low barn, the stable, and off to one side, the farmhouse. The psalms of my Hours passed my lips with a sound of day breaking. I heard the bucket, the milking stool, the clatter of wooden shoes. The four-tongued pitchforks grated on the wet cement of the stable. The light wind carried scents of green grass, of last year's hay in the barn, of the stack of straw against the wall, still piled up almost to the roof. It brought me the strong smell of animals' coats, of the brooding hen, the little drain of dirty water running into the meadow. . . .

I am not home yet, but I will be soon. A few miles more . . . this evening. A charm I have always clung to overpowers all my apprehensions.

But it must be written somewhere that my happiness is to be short-lived. The Dean, who had heard me moving about, knocked on my door and came in without waiting for an answer. His thoughts were certainly not the same as mine!

"I have had all I can take," he said. "I haven't slept. Enough of this! I have finally caught on to your game. You want me to go back, don't you? Then you will have won. Then everything will be perfect, order will be restored. With deep emotion, you will give thanks to the Lord. 'Thank you, O my

God. He has understood at last!' Understood what? The bishop will congratulate me, not too much, just enough, giving it the right slant, referring subtly to my recognition of his sovereign authority. The Colonel's wife and all her followers will rub their hands together—not in front of me, naturally. My church will smell of fresh wax again. My parish will heave a discreet sigh, and my few weeks of wandering will receive a general and generous absolution. But," he roared, "nothing will be changed, *nothing,* NOTHING! I will wear myself out, as our 'lecturer' of last night so nicely put it; I will die there, for the fun of it."

How far away my pretty farm was then! What splendid verse of my Office had I left unfinished? I was on a desert island, devoid of hope, facing my companion, both of us shipwrecked, without provisions, on a rock battered by the waves, strangers to each other. As soon as this man speaks, everything has to be re-examined.

"Don't talk so loud," I said. He had neglected to close the door to my room.

"Don't talk so loud!" He leaned his elbows on the back of the only armchair, his back turned to the door. He lowered his voice, but the words coming from his tense lips seemed only the more violent. "All right. Let's speak softly. As though we were at a deathbed, or in the cell of a man condemned to die. As though we were in the confessional. In this sleeping Church, let no sound be heard except the creaking of the slide. Let us build the Church with inaudible sighs, like nervous conspirators preparing their alibis, with their look-out standing watch in the shadows outside. But the problem goes beyond your desires: it is not a question of whether or not I will return to my parish, but of whether the Church is waking up, whether it will consent to take a stand, not just in words or pious imagery; and of whether we have devoted our lives to bringing a new world to birth, or to accepting in faith

276

—I said in faith, even in faith—the tragic complacency of a Church which has lost its spirit of daring. I thought you understood me. You said as much. But you have forgotten. You were determined to forget—out of cowardly surrender to your complexes (you are not free men!), out of reverential respect for an established order of stagnation, of least resistance, of keeping peace. Not by the strength of faith. Let's disentangle faith from your desires. Faith is something else again!"

He took a few steps toward the window. He looked at the fields, at my farm, then turned back, scowling, fists clenched. He leaned toward me and said, " 'We have been made a spectacle to the world, and to angels, and to men.' Do you understand the Apostle? The Colonel's wife and all her clique—nonentities. My conversation with our 'lecturer' yesterday was the drop that overflowed the bucket. It wasn't his fault, the dear fellow. I answered him in good faith, but I can't abide lecturers. There is no apparent link between cause and effect, there is no telling what brings on these sudden flashes. Take any man who can't manage to succeed as an ordinary parish priest, whose every project has turned out a failure, and when every door is closed to him, when all that he has mistakenly tried to do, based on excellent ready-made ideas and principles extracted from books or from listening to a few irresponsible and influential Jesuits, has gone up in smoke, the time has come to make him into a lecturer. At last he will be a success! And this talkative curé, dismissed for congenital malformation of the intellect, will spend his life instructing his colleagues, and giving them advice on how to run a parish! I repeat, there is no logical connection. It is even apparently senseless. But it is a fact. . . ."

From the moment he quoted St. Paul, I had stopped listening. I wanted to force him to hear the whole passage, but first I wanted to set things straight. I felt guilty.

"Monsieur le Doyen, first of all, I owe you an apology.

It is perfectly true that for some time I have been thinking about your return to the canton. I haven't tried to precipitate anything that would lead you to make this heroic decision, but I have been glad when certain things you have said, or chance happenings (like our passage through your parish yesterday) seemed likely to influence you without my having any part in it. Several times I have been happy to note that what I believed to be the truth had some meaning for you. The two verses from the Psalms which you chose at the out- set of our trip led me to confuse my desires with reality. Al- though I don't owe you an account of my thoughts, and I know you are too discreet to ask for one, I apologize for not having given you one. Because of my lack of frankness and confidence, a shadow has fallen between us. Accept this ad- mission from a man still full of complexes. The Church also suffers from this in her priests. And this imponderable, unadmitted lie, this trifle, is what kills friendship."

His features lost their harshness. "I accept your apologies," he said without anger. "And henceforth, don't break your heart over me. Talk. We'll talk things over together."

"All right then, I have only begun. I have more to say."

"I'm listening."

"The Church needs violent men. If it is true of the King- dom of Heaven that the violent bear it away, you are one of those who will possess it. I admire you, and I have from the beginning. Still, I have sometimes been mistaken in my judg- ment of your attitudes. For example, I thought, last Christmas morning, that your hour had struck, the hour of authenticity. It was only a quarter to, as it turned out. The proof is that your soul has not found peace. I don't have to teach you the catechism, or tell you that we can read whatever we like into Holy Writ. I would like to put your quotation back into Corinthians I where it came from. You see already what I mean! What picture of an apostle does St. Paul paint for his

278

arrogant audience—the Colonel's wife, if you like, the professor, the old doctor, who are simply tiresome individuals, representing no one? St. Paul berates them, whips them, flays them with biting irony, but he is careful not to imitate them. He doesn't take up their arms. He stays on the Cross with Christ Humiliated. I have known this passage by heart since my seminary days.... Do you want it in French or in Latin?"

His hands were trembling, but his face was calm. He leaned against the window, breathed in the air of the fields, bowed his head a little, and said, "In French, so my Colonel's wife can understand."

I felt the immense weight of this Word on my shoulders even before I began. "First Epistle to the Corinthians, Chapter IV. 'For I think God has set forth us the apostles last of all, as men doomed to death, seeing that we have been made a spectacle to the world, and to angels, and to men. We are fools for Christ, but you are wise in Christ! We are weak, but you are strong! You are honored, but we are without honor! To this very hour we hunger and thirst, and we are naked and buffeted, and have no fixed abode. And we toil, working with our own hands. We are reviled and we bless, we are persecuted and we bear with it, we are maligned and we entreat, we have become as the refuse of this world, the off-scouring of all, even until now! ... Now some are puffed up, as if I were not coming to you. But I shall come to you shortly, if the Lord is willing, and I shall learn the power of those who are puffed up, not the promises ...' "

He took up, like an echo, the words, "the power, not the promises ..." Then he said, "Your quotation is correct." He drew away from the window and added, "Thank you." Then he laughed a little and said, "I think you would quote all of St. Paul to me if I let you.... Now it's time to go and present our respects to the local pastor and celebrate our Masses." And after a moment, "If you open the Bible, you are lost."

I answered, "We have to be willing to lose everything so that everything can be saved. Those aren't my words; I don't know where I read them."

He took hold of my arm. "Would you have quoted them to me yesterday?"

"No."

"Then we are making progress in frankness."

The sounds of my farm are audible again. The astounding sincerity of that man's attitudes, words, and manner touches me deeply. Yes, I have to make progress in frankness so that others can do the same. I know that the ambiguous behavior favored by priests of every stamp retards the impetus of truth, and doesn't even correspond to the virtue of prudence. It is a vice of the system. I will talk with him. And never again in riddles. I feel light. I have hope in the Church. Perhaps all she needs is this clarity of soul between men created to love one another—at least I would like to think so.

In the sky, little flakes of clouds are changing from pink to white. It will be another fine day.

The church is small and lovely. A very old church that I can't take time to describe if I expect to get to bed tonight. The altarpiece is composed of two stones inscribed with these words: on the Epistle side: *Stat Crux dum volvitur Orbis* (The Cross is the world's axis), and on the Gospel side: *Haec est victoria quae vincit mundum, fides nostra* (This is the victory which has triumphed over the world, our faith). One feels in communion with an army of monks who have passed on, and with generations of the faithful.

After a breakfast of fresh goat's milk, I said to the Dean, "Today I'll drive."

"It's not a good day to pick. Can you be sure of your reflexes when we get closer to your home place?"

280

"You drive, then. Perhaps today will be a day of strong emotions."

" 'Perhaps' is an understatement. . . ."

From that time on, nothing existed for me except my bluish horizon with the sun suffusing its mists; the scent of the air which went to my head; the half-glimpsed farms with their thick roofs, which seemed to have slipped from the hands of some hasty god and to have been roughly set on the walls; the enclosure divided into two areas: the courtyard for people and the barnyard, behind, for the hay; the field flowers along the ditches and in amongst the rye; the ruins here and there where a door is still outlined, grown over with brambles and nettles, and the traces of soot still on the crumbled chimney; the edge of the well where someone long dead had leaned the plow, now rusted, and the tool which has lost its handle.

Toward noon, we passed through a large town. The weekly market crowded the square. The Dean slowed down, then said, "I want to hear them . . ."

I was amused, for I know that the rest of France considers the people of my part of the country strange. He stopped the car, got out and mixed with the noisy crowd. I couldn't get my fill of just looking at them. Dark-haired women passed to and fro, carrying empty baskets over their arms and tightly clutching their purses. Old grannies made their way with slow steps toward a red bus on which I could read the names of familiar villages. Bent old men, mustached, freshly shaven, dressed in smocks with tucks at the shoulders, were passing the time of day in front of an inn. They were leaning on their smooth, straight sticks, which were too long, the same ones they had been using for twenty years to drive their cattle to pasture. The young men were crowding around a tractor. Stands were all about, like all stands everywhere, but from them came snatches of lively, colorful conversation, in that pungent dialect which I ate up like a ripe apple. Two women

281

stopped near the car. I wanted them to talk to me, just to hear them say something, anything, out of an overwhelming desire to take part in this life that was mine.

"So," I said, "how did the selling go this morning?"

"Selling? Selling? You may as well say we gave things away, but you can't just let them rot."

(Where I come from, that means that we aren't displeased.)

"And your crops?"

"Our crops? They won't be in yet for a while. And with this weather——"

Shyly, I ventured, "It's not such terrible weather."

Their eyes became suspicious. "It's easy to see that you aren't from around here."

They left me, mumbling in dialect, "Another curé wandering about."

As for the Dean, his impression was unequivocal. "Odd birds! I suppose they must have their good points, but they don't make much effort to show them. Gloomy fellows, your compatriots! And you'll have to translate for me, because even when they pretend to speak French . . . what an accent!"

"But, Monsieur le Doyen," I answered sincerely, "we have no accent."

He shrugged his shoulders and burst out laughing.

I added, "And besides, we aren't quite in my part of the country yet."

"Then let's hope it will be a little better. . . . Meanwhile, I'm hungry. And I don't feel like eating in one of these bars." He put his hand on my shoulder. "Far be it from me to hurt your feelings. You might be happy there, and I would be miserable. Take me somewhere where I will be less miserable without making you less happy."

"All right, then. Drive on."

I had him stop in front of a farm.

"Here?" he said. "Do you know these people?"

"Here," I replied. "Without knowing them."

282

He grumbled, "I don't understand what's going on; I must be in the land of miracles."

I went in first. The farm folks were all at the table. I motioned to them not to get up, but the farmer came forward to greet us.

"We are two priests from the south," I said to him. "We are tired and hungry. We will pay you whatever is necessary if . . ."

All eyes were fixed on us. The man said, in the local dialect, "Be careful, woman." And then he went back to his meal.

"What do you want?" the woman asked me.

I was going to give the game away; I couldn't resist: "A good omelette with bacon, a piece of ham, the kind you have hanging up there, some local cheese, and wine from the plain."

Without looking up from his meal, the man said, "I'm telling you, look out. For one thing, that one isn't from the south. . . ."

I went over to him and said in his own dialect, "You are right, I am not from the south. My companion is, though." I felt my chest expand. I kept my eyes fixed on him joyfully. "I come from these parts; I am one of you. I have just these mountains, your mountains, to cross, and I will be home, in the plain, where this wine comes from. Do you recognize me?"

The man stood up and gave a signal. Two chairs were pushed forward. Along the wall, the children crowded together on the long bench and pulled their plates over. The man said to the eldest, "Go and draw wine—from the middle cask—and be quick!" Turning to his wife, he said, "Look at her, standing there like a post. What are you waiting for?" Then to us, "Sit here, one on each side of me." He wiped his mustache, scolded his eldest daughter for not setting our places fast enough, and pointing to the Dean, asked me, "Does that one understand?"

"I think not."

"Then we'll have to try to speak French. . . ."

I could write a whole book about it, but it is getting late. . . .

The branches of broom flaming in the fireplace. That way of beating eggs with the fork and spoon held together, making as much noise as possible. The bacon browning, the omelette served in the frying pan. The ham, very lean, cut in slices as thick and broad as a man's hand. The cheese, already cut into, its creaminess oozing from beneath the rind. And that light, cool wine, which leaves a taste of grapes on the tongue. Everything—even the unmatched knives; the bread, baked a week ago and still not stale. The woman who left her own meal to serve us; the children with whom I tried to make friends; the man, at ease now, saying to me, "Eat, come on, eat! What's the matter, don't you like it? . . . Drink! Come on, drink! That wine comes straight from your neighborhood."

From time to time, when he couldn't restrain himself, he leaned toward me, just as I knew he would, and spoke confidentially, in our patois, poking fun at the Dean: "Where does that one come from? From the sardine country? He knows how to drink just the same."

And the children in turn looked at the Dean, who wasn't feeling very much at ease.

As we left a good hour later, the Dean took it into his head to say, "What do we owe you?"

The man answered dryly, "Good journey." He looked at his watch, and went out toward the stable, adding, "Stop in on your way back."

The weather was very mild. I took a nap under an oak tree.

I knew it would happen just as it did, very simply, at a bend in the road, but I couldn't tell exactly where. The spot isn't different from a dozen others, a little pine grove at the side of a road with grassy embankments which shade it and give it the look of a dried-up river bed; a sudden turn and then, all

284

at once, down below, far below, under our feet, spread out before our eyes, the immense carpet of plain. A bit to the left, the sloping vineyards. Far off in the west, my mountains. From a distance, from where we stood, they were blue, like all mountains, but I know that at a different time of day, they will, alternately, be ashen-colored and flame up, like a pile of glowing embers.

The Dean stopped the car of his own accord. He stretched out his arm and said, "There it is. It can only be there. The Promised Land. I am more fortunate than Moses because I will enter it this evening." He took me jovially by the arm. "Tell me a little about it."

It wasn't as easy as I had hoped. At the end of the afternoon on hot days like this, a whitish mist floats over the villages and towns. It covered the spurs of my mountains. Their peaks rose above it and their outlines appeared clearly enough against the horizon for me to show them to him, and try to tell him their names; so that I could unmistakably point out the one which presides proudly in the midst of its peers, but I was sorry that the sky was not at its best. For me, it didn't matter. I could see enough and the rest I could guess. My eyes were fixed on that superb volcano, that beacon, that friend, to whom I had so often spoken. Between him and me, down there, stretched all that I love. . . .

The Dean stepped back a bit. I was without too strong an emotion, silent, planted there like a stump, a bit disappointed because of the mist. Disappointed for his sake, for I knew that landscape by heart. Everything was in its place. How little things change. A plain of wheat is as immutable as the sea. We plough the earth and the sea, and the furrow closes over.

I know of a certain old cabin in the vineyards which capsized just like a boat, one day during a storm. A wave of brambles, honeysuckle, and wild strawberries engulfed its planks. It was forgotten. No one missed it. The important thing was for this ocean of greenery and flowers to roll on in the ebb and flow of the seasons, for nature not to perish. Entire cities have disappeared, and over their ruins the river flows and trees take root. The cabin, the city, fulfilling men's needs, are of small matter as long as the earth endures, the birds sing, the spring hollows out its bed between the roots, the shade invites us, or the flower calls. Man needs poetry more than bread. And there, before my eyes, beneath those white veils, my land was moving, always the same.

I was the first to break the spell. We had to go down onto that land. In an hour or two it would be night, and we had to reach the straight roads before dark.

Then I wanted to drive. . . .

I knew all the villages and towns by heart now. Night fell quickly. Lights went on. A few late flocks were returning from pasture. Sometimes we had to stop. The shepherdesses in these parts don't put themselves out very much! The animals go along according to their whim. The car had to make its way among them, zigzagging, as well as it could. When the horn or the nose of a heifer would graze the pane, the girl with them would burst out laughing, pretend to intervene, or else not even pay any attention. As for the dog, he was better off not getting mixed up in it. . . . The old-timers were sitting in front of their doorsteps. Soon life began to be concentrated in the houses with their wide-open windows. My countrymen have nothing to hide. I could see the familiar lamps, the long tables, the soup tureens. Then a bit later, the little tots ready for bed, practically naked in their mothers' arms, lively, wriggling with pleasure, like worms. No, nothing had changed anywhere, not even in those low houses, which are without any original touch, without the pots of geraniums or petunias you find in other regions. These people have no time to spare. In my part of the country, flowers are a useless luxury, a rich

286

man's hobby. There are flowers in the fields, tolerated if they aren't in the way, rarely admired, very seldom picked. We can recognize a "foreigner" by many signs; for example, by the fact that he thinks the poppies in the wheat are a pretty sight. "Filthy weeds" my mother used to say. "They ruin the grain." I wonder where my love of flowers came from?

In the early hours of a scented, vibrant night, we entered that ancient city which was named, somewhat out of convention, the "Beautiful." For an hour, two hours perhaps, the Dean hadn't spoken. At times, I forgot him. I didn't miss his voice. He did right to keep silent, but I was not sure that it was out of sympathy. I could tell that the heat haze had disappeared from the way the lights shone at the foot of my mountains, on that spot where the plain had once slipped vertically and fell straight down as though into a trap. A long scar was left there; it is wooded with chestnut trees, and peopled with villages, and enough springs flow out of it to provide a whole province with water to drink. I know of one—I know of twenty, which flow all year round, streams as thick as a man's thigh, even in time of drought. They flow down, skipping over the rocks, and watering the gardens and meadows farther down the mountain.

At last, on my left, crouched in its granite cradle, my town, under my volcano, which protects it from the west winds; my town whose lights, from where I saw them, looked like a torchlight parade. To the south, to the north, these lights gain ground, spread out, invade the hillside, encroach on the vineyards and join the lights of surrounding villages. My heart greeted this forest of stars. They even stirred my Dean out of his meditations.

"Now what are all those lights?"

"They light the city from which the Crusaders set out for the conquest of the Holy Sepulcher."

A trifle ironical, he replied, "And would you find so many people today mad with love for Christ, who would leave everything behind for the chance—if they were lucky—of kissing a few old stones?"

I said, "Why not?" Not because I was so sure, but because where I come from (and here I was on my own soil!) we don't like to be challenged.

"Meanwhile," he went on, "we still have to sleep. Let's stop here in this spot which looks mortally dark and sad to me, and whose paving stones must date from the days of Vercingetorix."

In the morning, on this fourth day, I heard the hours strike on the monumental clock which has been sounding them for centuries, and I suddenly felt at peace. Is this what is called being reborn? Everything was suddenly audible, intelligible, again. Men and women passed beneath my window, walking with that swinging motion of the hips and body which prevents them from rushing. Once more I saw round heads, and those little eyes with thick lashes which always hide some trace of malice, and which look at you as though to weigh you. These people are chary of speech, and never use the word "love" because it is too cumbersome and too fragile; they respect each other. They never surrender themselves. They wait; they wait for each other. They wait all their lives for time, God, or perhaps even the Devil to sort out the true from the false, the worthwhile from the mediocre, the enduring from the chaff which the wind carries away. They are seldom moved, and then only within. They laugh in short gasps, ashamed as they are of laughing, and they never weep. They can stay for hours around a table, three or four of them, listening to each other's souls without moving their lips; and when they get up, each knows what the others were thinking. Their women do not obey. They don't obey their priests any more than their husbands. A woman will spend ten years, twenty if need be, to get her way: to run the parish (no problem there!), but also to rule in her own home, to manage the finances, transform her apparent brute of a man into a tractable sheep, watch from the corner of her eye all his comings and goings, ignoring his temper tantrums, leading him by numberless byways to want what she wants, without even taking the trouble to cultivate the illusion that he is the one who wants it. They say "my" house, "my" children, "my" land as though they were alone in the world; but they devote themselves to their husbands, their children, and those fields with a patience, a perseverance, and a tenacity which might well be called love.

And so I am myself again, sure of being able to distinguish between a "yes" which means "no" and a negative shake of the head which means consent. A man should never be uprooted. The truth is universal, to be sure, but everywhere it wears the local costume. Here, it is the smock down to the knees, the fluted bonnet which makes the women look like false nuns, and the hobnailed sabots. The young people are giving it up, but their shoulders, their heads and their feet have difficulty getting used to the new uniform. Here at the granite level truth smells of heather, of ferns, and wild thyme. Lower down, of apples, grapes, and wheat. And higher up, on the lava slopes, of birch, gentian, whortleberry, and pine. Here the sea means no more to us than China. Here, everything has to be earned; everything is subject to a contract involving work and effort: you earn your living, like everyone else, but you also "earn" Heaven, you "earn" your Easter, you "earn" your diploma, you "have earned" a happy old age, and if you make a little money, you have to explain that "it wasn't stolen." Here the first things to be repaired are the stables for the animals, then the hay barn, and the shed for the machines. At this rate, many people live until they die in a dilapidated

room, and the housewife does the dishes her whole life long
in an old tub of lukewarm water set on the same table where
she has just served supper. Here we are chary of using money.
When we have it, we hoard it, look at it, and count it at fixed
dates; we are afraid of bankers, so we put our money under
the mattress. Even religion has its reminiscences of the druids,
of sorcerers, and sacrificial stone altars; its St. John's Eve celebrations and its witches' Sabbaths. They have one foot in the
Gospel, to be sure, but it is the lifted foot; the other is solidly
sunk in mythology. All of this is seldom attractive to outsiders,
who class us rather cavalierly in the category of congenitally
backward peoples, irredeemable, and barbarian (and if they
knew the whole story . . . !) but my country is so beautiful,
so rich, the souls there are so ardent, the loyalties so true, the
silences so weighted with friendship, our balance so sure, our
ways so honest, our speech so pure and our springs so clear,
that it casts a spell; strangers forget our differences and love
us! We are not surprised, since we are conscious of having
"earned" that love. . . .

It was broad daylight. I had remained at the window. It was
a fine day everywhere, especially in my heart. In these rare
moments of plenitude (I can count three or four in my lifetime) if I still feel a trace of fear, it is of being too happy. It
cannot last!

I would like to see again the little stone bridge we used to
cross, my animals and I, to get to our meadow. It was scarcely
two yards wide, "one-horned," we used to call it, because one
side had been nicked by a cart wheel. It spanned a little ditch,
full of watercress and reeds, mosquitoes and silence. All
through my childhood I called it "my dragonfly ditch" because that was the only place I ever saw them. I used to be
afraid of them, because I thought they might sting like wasps.
I'm still not sure they don't. But they were lovely! During

290

rainy springs, the ditch was full of water for months at a time. Under the bridge, I caught tiny fish in my handkerchief. Just to see that little bridge again would be happiness.

Give every man a little bridge, and dragonflies, two or three poplars tapered like steeples and clicking in the wind like a thousand castanets, a green field to rest his eyes on, a little friendship to fill the measure and a great deal of trust.... They won't become heroes, but they will be happy. And what, after all, is heroism, if not that wild flower which blooms at the end of the path of our joys? A love which has taken root between two mounds of earth?

I was getting ready to go out after writing in this Journal, when I noticed an envelope which had been slipped under my door. I opened it. It was a letter from the Dean:

My dear friend,
Read. Take your time and read. I have had time all this last night to think and write. I cannot decently trouble you any more with my conversations. So I have adopted this easy means of communication. If we never meet again—and even supposing we do meet again somewhere—destroy this letter. I don't trust letters that are saved. I would be ashamed—if it fell into the hands of our superiors—to appear weak to them. I know only too well to what use they would put my words.

I have reached the limit of effort, the moment, that is, when one doesn't look any more for arguments, but for signs. Doubtless you know it. I swear to you that I have not for one moment been play-acting. And I admit that at times everything seems simple to me. I see the Church "resplendent, without spot or wrinkle or any blemish, holy and immaculate." She seems to take my hand and lead me back to my parish. I return; I am there. Everything is normal, orderly, prudent, inoffensive, classical once more. I light my lamp. I compose my Sunday sermon. A boy knocks on my door, or a young couple who would just as soon dispense with the priest and the city hall if they could, or an old granny, who has told me her life story twenty times, and I always answer "Yes" without listening. My blood warms up; my step is firm. I had reached this point when we left. . . .

This state of blessedness does not last.

Suppose our superiors were to read this letter. Don't think I have any grudge against them. What would they accuse me of? Stubbornness, lack of faith, needlessly complicating clear and simple situations, making a fuss over nothing, indulging my own notions, above all of poisoning their existence. They would claim that basically I have only a negative intelligence, good at tearing things down and incapable of proposing the least solution. They would not fail to tell me that true reformers are made of sterner stuff. And they would be right. . . .

Suppose *they* were to read it. (This time I mean my self-righteous parishioners.) What I have to say doesn't interest them—priests' stories, my story of a priest struggling with trumped-up and ridiculous difficulties. They wouldn't understand the first word. (As a matter of fact, what do they "understand"?) They would recognize themselves in a few images and wind up asking, "What have we done to the Lord to deserve such an eccentric curé?" You have to set your watch by their clock if you want to know the right time—the priest had better do the same. Outside of that, what in the world could possibly be of interest to them?

All this makes me think I am really hopelessly dull-witted, and if I refuse to go back to my parish out of weakness and diffidence of faith, I at least ought to return just to avoid becoming totally ridiculous.

And one can fall into that trap, believe me. In the end I would feel the desire to be forgiven, to go back slinking along the walls, to come to them with hanging head and say, "Please forget my foolishness."

This desire to be a coward also fades soon enough. Then what is left? Nothing. There are situations and attitudes which by their very nature cannot be defined. This mania for definitions! I set my inability to continue against their proofs.

They will be right and I will be wrong to the very end. It is an unfair fight. The one who bares his breast never wins.

The hours are slipping by while my life is wavering toward another world. Near our hotel, a bell with the most human sound I ever heard is keeping me company on this night of agony. You are sleeping. Your stars are shining. Today you walked on your own soil. You showed me your volcanoes. Yes, your country is beautiful, and I wish I could have shared your childlike joy. Forgive me. I would be a sorry traveling companion, so you must go on alone to look for happiness in your heather and your grassy meadows. My mind is made up. When you have found your roots here and renewed your strength for another year, two years, go back without me to my home beside the sea. Tell the bishop that I lost my way (use that phrase). One day you will perhaps be Dean in my place. You will succeed where I have failed. You have been very good. But I have reached the end of the road. The sign I sought didn't appear.

You may be sure—and be sure to tell them—that I will not defrock; I will never disgrace the Church which nurtured me and to which I owe everything; I will not cause any scandal. I am disappearing from view, carrying my priesthood in my heart, magnificent and useless. I renounce the exercise of its powers. Every day I will recite my breviary, bowing my head over those Words of fire. My rosary is in my pocket. It was a present on the occasion of my subdiaconate. Our old woman gave it to me then. I have carried it ever since. I charge you to watch over that old woman; she is of the breed of saints. Protect her from the wicked and you will be fulfilling the Scriptures. (See St. James I: 27.) Tell my parishioners that I forgive them, and someday, without making an issue of it, ask them to forgive me, too. I troubled everyone, our superiors and my flock . . .

I do not reject anything. Christ is God. The Catholic Church is the continuation of Christ. My heart has remained, by the special grace of God, free from worldly attachments. I am not even in rebellion any more. But I can't see; I can't go on. I have enough faith for myself, but not enough for others. Before my eyes, within reach of my hands, a wall has sprung up. Christianity is an army on the march. I can't move ahead any more. Who, then, could my parishioners follow? I can't force them to mark time on one spot. Or should I put on an act? . . . God has always preserved me from untruth.

I want to finish before daybreak. The dawn will be too beautiful this morning and I would let it melt my resolution. *Erat autem nox.* . . . No, I am not Judas. In spite of my destitution, if the bread dipped in the dish had been tendered me, I swear to you that I would not have gone forth in the night to the Chief Priests. I am not betraying Him. I love Him enough to die for Him.

But you are stronger than I, and you bolster my courage so well—I can write without risk of shocking you. The day of my subdiaconate, I believed in a Church in which Christ was clearly seen; in a hierarchy which was paternal in heart, not only in words; in a priesthood where one's hands were free; in a faithful people whose hearts were longing for God. Perhaps I could not understand. . . . We have often agreed that only the saints see clearly. And so my failure is no doubt all my own fault. It was part of the logical pattern of a life which was waiting for illumination. "Let your light shine in darkness." I should have been the lamp.

The stars are growing pale. From my window, the ring of your volcanoes stands out in joyous expectation of a light-filled day. In the east, the sky is putting on the colors of the apocalypse. Reds, whites, and blacks clash in a confused and desperate struggle. Soon, above the fray of these moving and desolate half-tones the sun will restore harmony, and joy will possess the world.

Let me depart, O God, while for the space of another hour the world still waits for the light . . . aided and abetted by this half-light; facing, not those volcanoes which are already alight, but this tormented sky fighting against daylight. . . .

I didn't go to his room, since I was sure I wouldn't find him there. I did not reread his letter. I tore it up, but it engraved itself on some obscure region of my memory. I opened my breviary. I probably never recited it with so much feeling.

He obeyed his absolutes. He took all his responsibilities upon his own shoulders. "Poor priest! Poor unfortunate priest!" I have heard that kind of phrase before. That is not my thought this morning. If, perhaps, it was appropriate for others, it is just the opposite of what I think of him at this moment. I say that he has taken the path of supreme fidelity, for, since God is true, it is impossible that He no longer recognizes the Dean as his servant and friend. He went on until the last drop of oil was spent, to the end of his truth. He fell in the struggle. Only cowards will accuse him of cowardice. But has he fallen? Nothing is finished. Everything is beginning. God, whom he loves "enough to die for Him" has the key to this mystery of new beginnings. You have to give up believing, or believe all the way. . . .

He confided in me. I understood him all the better because at one time, like him, I faced that temptation of heroic divestment. Passing fancies! I was satisfied with gazing at the desert from afar. I was afraid of dying of thirst there. I refused to lose myself in it.

If I had to explain my present state of mind (and I do have to), I would say that what I am thinking is not written in the books designed for priests and pious persons. Men are so fashioned that these books, written for them, express a median truth which cannot be called into question without endangering them. But this man has led me so far beyond the commonplace that I have to accept and admit that his way is light and that God is waiting at the end of it, even if he arrives there naked.

Yes, go, my friend, my brother. Go, since I was not strong enough to hold you back; all I had to offer you was the tasteless fare of habit and repetition. If you are wrong to go, this time I am the guilty one. While you were with me, I ought to have made you sense God's presence.

His stay in my presbytery was only an intermission, then. I always realize things too late! The invincible force which thrust him out of his parish couldn't be stopped. He moved forward. He moved forward, and I remained inert. People praised my charity. The Good Samaritan who cared for his wounded brother! ... Which one of us was sicker? If only it had been my courage that they praised; if only, under my roof, he had heard the wind of heroism blow! In my way, I was as poor as all the rest, as empty and calm. (That hideous calm of good Christians, as though they were God's pensioners!) He didn't need that kind of calm; he needed a door to be opened, a veil to be rent, a hand stronger than his to lead him into the desert—in short, to find God in me, the God of Scripture, and if the classic path of Tradition is the only orthodox one, to be unable to stray from it without being diminished in stature.

Now that he has definitely chosen the path of solitude, can I even think of how to spend my time? He left me enough money for several days. What would he advise me to do—for he is the one to whom I turn for advice—to become once again the priest of an authentic priesthood, to find my lost truth in the sands, to face the Gospel squarely and accept its demands, which slowly reinvest words with the terrible weight of things? He would not impose anything on me, and he would say without anger, "It is high time! Your hair is white. The day of reckoning is not so far off. Give up that dreary habit of always depending on someone else. The Church is the Spouse of Christ only on condition that it be composed of free men. Christ freed us from rebellion and from servility. Either the Gospel is nothing but an assortment of contradictions, or it is the liberating Word, our chance to choose between cowardice and courage, the heart's commitment to truth which breaks all chains. In this sense, it is orthodoxy. The idea—what am I saying?—the historical fact of the world's Redemption, as a result of the cogitations of intellectuals fond of their comfort, has been detached from the Cross, put to one side, confused with the vague aspirations of stiff-necked men who, calling themselves Christians, mill about on the very edge of every betrayal. The Crucified remains alone on His cross, while those to whom He said very clearly, 'I have set you an example,' save the world in their comfortable way, claiming they come from Him. And so: the alternative is to flee, or to betray in our turn."

Beneath my window, life has begun for the day. The town has rubbed its eyes, stretched its legs, swept its doorsteps, drawn up the iron curtains of its shops, without too much conviction. They don't expect company today. . . . they won't be in their Sunday best. Children with their school-bags, women with their eternal shopping baskets, men in work clothes. Humanity "milling about on the very edge of every betrayal."

And yet? . . .

I can just hear him say, "Yes, . . . and yet? Don't follow me now; don't ever follow me, since this 'and yet' has insinuated itself between us. Is it the last temptation to be overcome? The diabolical invitation to the easy way out? The mirage? Or the echo, borne down twenty centuries of love, of his *Misereor super turbam*?

"I beg you to abandon me. Neither one of us can answer these questions. I see them as well as you do, those crowds He fed with five barley loaves. If I separate myself from them, am I drawing away from the Cross and leaving them with their burning thirst for the Redeemer's blood? This doubt, the last one about the truth, my truth, pursues me and torments me. That crossroads we have talked about so much is not the intersection of our freedom and our obedience to a bishop; nor is it in the exhausting and commonplace confrontation, less tragic than we pretend, of the integrity of our priesthood with the ridiculous pretensions of our self-righteous villagers; that crossing of the ways is situated precisely on those frontiers of betrayal where a faithful priesthood must have enough audacity to plant the Cross of Christ and enough love to break the bread. But for me this half-glimpsed truth is still at the stage of formulas, words and phrases. Have pity on me; my head hits against that wall I spoke of last night. One thing I am sure of is that no one but I myself can knock it down, the day that those formulas become my blood. When the crucified Christ has accomplished His task in me, He will use me as His instrument to mingle with the crowds and proclaim to them their right to the joy of the Beatitudes. How many threads will have been untangled before that day! How painful is our journey toward the dawn. It is cold there!"

Happy is the man for whom the truth is simple! Happy or unhappy, for the truth is never simple! I have spent my whole life trying to simplify my life, in the hope, always disappointed, of clasping happiness in my hand like a sparrow fallen from the nest. I didn't ask very much. . . . But here I am alone, once more seeking the link between words and my resolutions. I write for the tenth time, perhaps, "When will it ever end?" Once more the ground has buckled and cracked beneath my feet. Again I am poor, ragged, stumbling, a pilgrim in search of certitudes. Alone. And to be truthful without making speeches, I feel an exhilarating impression of lightness. Facile joys oppress me . . .

The details don't matter. His life wavers in another universe whose laws are unknown to me. He has freed himself from the laws of gravity. He will live on a glass of water if he has only that to live on, but he will not stop again until he has become the one who hungers after truth and who is invited to its banquet. He speaks to me of a sign, and doesn't believe in a sign. Still the sign exists, and no one sees it. His eyes will be opened at the precise moment of the final plunge, when there is nothing left around him but the obvious presence of God in things, and when he is no longer anything more than a man who is available.

Just in case . . . I wrote him this note and left it at the hotel desk:

My friend,
Without knowing exactly why, I feel that your day is dawning. To the north, the south, on the mountain or the plain? You cannot lose your way any more, for it is God who leads you on.

There will be no other sign than that of truth. You will recognize it when you can encompass it. And you will one day, since you drew apart from the dishonesty of formulas to commune with silence.

Even if your attitudes since you left the deanery might seem strange to those who are fond of phrases, do not doubt your orthodoxy. We will meet again, I don't know when, but surely, in the Roman and Catholic Church. You have never left it.

Perhaps I will come back here.
                    Yours fraternally.

The idea came to me then to celebrate my Mass, already late, in the cathedral where I was ordained. I drove along a wide road bordered with wheat fields and vineyards, and upon arriving, I entered by the south door, dedicated to Our Lady of Grace, just as I had many years ago, on the morning of the twenty-ninth of June, the Feast of Saints Peter and Paul. I think it is absolutely impossible for a priest to doubt his calling if he goes back to the place where he answered the call. My cathedral was empty, and I was glad. Before I stopped to admire its beauty, I went up to the choir grill. I looked beneath my feet for a diamond-shaped flagstone, just like all those around it, but which I could tell apart from all the rest. A smooth, black stone, imperfectly joined with a cement which had faded to white, laid there centuries ago; my own stone, where I stood up straight the day the bishop, in Christ's name, called me by my name, and from which I took one step forward to answer "yes." I stood up straight on that stone, I took that step again, and I said "yes" out loud. But I realized that I could no longer speak for myself alone. I felt my friend's presence. I took another step forward and repeated that "yes." I felt a hundred leagues from any kind of romanticism, as young and true as on that faraway day of my enthusiasms. I have always thought that in moments like that it would be easy to die. Lose one's faith, they say! . . . One is always held back by some bit of stone. . . .

Then it was that I realized that my cathedral was looking at me. . . . And I know where to stand to receive its blessing: at the back, under the organ loft, up against its great doors which are almost always closed. The hour when it is most alive is the one when the light pierces the stained-glass windows of the nave, and the pillars—almost the only ones in France without capitals—rise toward Heaven, sustained by this sparkling stream of jewels. How many times, on great feast days, did I wait for the moment when, dressed in my surplice, a bit too proud of having been chosen to be part of the procession of young clerics which the crowd's eyes followed tenderly, I would reach this spot under the organ! More than all the speeches, my cathedral convinced me that I was right to believe. More than my teachers, it strengthened me in faith. I asked permission to celebrate my Mass on the altar of the Blessed Sacrament, which was also a witness of my fervor in days gone by. I wanted to relive one last memory: I sat down to make my thanksgiving in one of the choir stalls, and closing my eyes I could hear the chant of the *In manus tuas* as it used to rise up and fade away among the interlacing ribs of the arches at the closing of our evening ceremonies.

RESOLUTION: not to lose contact with things.

In my cathedral, the past, the present, and the future always run together. With my hands I touched the grills of the cloister, the base of a statue, a pillar. Everything was in place. If this stability had been in any way shaken, modified, I would be the most miserable of men. I endure because things endure. An hour ago, I was holding out alone, but one cannot endure for long all alone. My inner unity has to be constantly re-formed. Just now I have a bad pain in my chest. The reason is that I was weak enough to let that old feeling of insecurity come over me, one that has never consented to be drowned in faith. Even if I had a stronger faith, I think it would be the same. This trip is a failure. Everything is dead now. I am on another shore. He has left me, to pursue his dream. But what about me; what is my dream? Yet I defy anyone to prove that I am demanding. I just ask for a little peace, and the chance to love without having my heart broken. A calm parish . . . calm friends. . . . I wanted to see my home again. Is that such a crime? I am marking time again, I am slipping under. If I were to see the Dean again, I would say, "For pity's sake, let's get it over with!" He doesn't want to get it over with. He never wanted to. If I were in his place, I would end it soon enough. There is no solution. So much the worse for man! Let him forget himself and get lost in the system. It isn't man's place to put himself in the wrong against the system. God will be the judge. Whom will He condemn? Who can know beforehand? Everyone thinks he is saved. In that case, who damns himself? Why should anyone want to blaze a trail, when the path to follow has been marked out for us? And if it is cowardly to reason that way, on the other hand, is courage so very profitable? The Message doesn't contain any more surprises. For centuries now it has been annotated, presented, oriented, authenticated in a certain way. It perhaps doesn't manufacture saints by the dozen, but it allows average men not to go too far astray. Well, I am an average man, an average priest. Millions and millions of men are like me. The laws are not written for heroes, but the heroes have to obey them, or else the circle would be broken, and where would that lead us?

My head is empty. I feel quite dizzy. All I need is to have another attack....

It wasn't going to be as clear a day as I had hoped. To escape the haze and the heat in town, I decided to go up the mountains until I was above it. My springs, my stream, my crooked road cut out of the granite, my villages, my peasants, my familiar trees, my hedges, and soon that plateau which gives the traveler the false illusion that his climb is ended. My volcano, seen from close up, in its massive, tranquil majesty.

I went through the mountain pass. I saw my country from "over there" as we used to say; "over there" meant the indeterminate, the unknown, landscapes different from our own, and men whose dialect was less melodious. I ate in a field, beside a clear mountain rivulet, and recited my breviary before the Virgin of the mountains. One comes upon her marvelous church suddenly, and one enters her house, sanctified by centuries of supplications and folded hands, by opening

302

the door before which the pilgrims of times past used to stand to look for the Star! There they stopped, raising their eyes to Heaven, even at high noon, and if they saw it shine, they knew that their prayers were answered.

I prayed to the Blessed Virgin for my friend. She knows where he is, and I seek him before her image. Not knowing where he is adds to my anxiety and fortifies my prayer. Always this mania for the concrete. Has he left the town? Is he wandering about like a gypsy, and in what direction? Has he eaten; can he even be hungry?

Now it is the sweet, scented hour of day which ushers in the evening. Where will he sleep tonight? "Holy Mother of God, You won't abandon him! Watch over him and take his hand to lead him toward that truth which he loves. But what is truth, if not that Child You press to Your heart? The Dean has not denied Him. And although he has not taken the most-traveled road to find Him, who can say that he has lost his way? The much-traveled road, You well know, Holy Virgin of wanderers, so often leads nowhere. . . ."

Night will fall quickly; the mist from the plain didn't lift at noon, and now it is turning to clouds. The stained-glass windows are darkening; the candles burning in front of the statue light up the face of the Madonna and Her Child. No, it isn't possible that a Holy Virgin who once broke the chains of captives will not liberate my friend from his doubts. . . . He will live again! But how? . . . And why always this question?

I only wish I knew where he is. . . .

I took the road along the valley, which glides between the grassy hillocks like a winding river. There are no more towns or hamlets, nothing but those rounded hills, so pleasing to the eye; nothing but those flocks which will stay outdoors all night, forming a circle to sleep; nothing but this road which will end whenever I choose to stop, and here and there on the slopes those low dark huts which we call *burons* and which serve as shelters for herdsmen and their flocks.

Why go any farther to look for a night's resting place?
Not to lose contact with things. . . .

Part VI

The Rendezvous

ONE MORE NIGHT . . .

When I start counting the nights and days (which is not often), my life seems to drag. . . .

I made a hole in the hay. I heard the cattle lowing . . . It may sound simple-minded, but I felt reassured by it. I was absolutely alone with them. Liberated. Free. Not having to think that a tomorrow would dawn from these shadows, taking advantage of the few hours when no one was watching me.

I spread my old sweater out under my head so the hay wouldn't tickle my ears. Old habits are easily revived. In summer, at home, after the midday meal, the men used to take a siesta in the barn on the stack of alfalfa. I always felt comfortable there, just as I did this night. In those days I would unfold an old worn-out blanket, impregnated with the sweat of animals, and before I went to sleep, looking at the daylight that filtered in under the tiles of the roof, I would dream of happiness. Those were the times I slept the best.

At early dawn, the animals, surprised, came to prowl around my car. They drank out of a tree trunk hollowed like a dugout canoe. Then, from very far off, came the call of the herdsman. They heard it and went to be milked. At the

307

moment my only possessions are my rosary, my breviary, this singing rivulet, some bread and cheese and this weightless air, the vehicle of light. I have found my roots and I caress them with my hands. My own things are in my possession. Beyond these simple facts, everything seems to be in darkness.

What day is it? How long ago did I leave my parish? It was yesterday morning that the Dean left me, that is certain. If he had never existed for me, I would let myself be absorbed, like a drop of water disappearing between the leaves, by the happiness of living right in the midst of what is! But—he does exist. He is living somewhere. I discover maternal instincts in myself. Let him think about what he will, but . . . "My little one, aren't they already making fun of you? Aren't you tired, ready to drop with fatigue—the way it was when I was a prisoner, and the Germans kicked my ribs black and blue? 'Up!' they howled, 'or I kill you!' and I saw their little machine-gun muzzles, black and round."

There are so many ways to kill a man!

If only he had come with me! . . . The two of us, in this *buron*—it would have been Paradise.

It looks like rain before nightfall. I have nothing to cover myself with. A minor matter. . . . I'll stop the car and stay inside.

I won't celebrate Mass this morning. I smell of hay. Leaning against the water trough, sometimes trailing my hand in its cool water, I recited my Hours.

I wrote these last pages in front of the *buron,* my notebook on my lap.

I decided not to climb up any higher, but I felt a certain dizziness at having to go back down. The herdsman came toward me; I saw him against the sun. He took his time, a sturdy man, cunning, like all of them; unshaven. His thick, dirty fingers, rubbing his chest and armpits, pressing the blackened skin at the base of his neck, meant that he was wondering about me, but didn't want to show it. He tossed me a short, rough "Good morning" and made as though to pass on. That was exactly the man I would have liked to be, if God hadn't chosen me: the man between sky and earth. Our earth is the same, but our Heavens are not much alike. He wore oversized wooden shoes, simply carved, typical of this region. He wouldn't start the conversation. He turned his back on me. I said, "Will the rain hold off until evening?"

He answered, "The swallows are grazing the earth, the flies are devouring the cattle, the wind is bending the grass. . . . So much the better! It will do the fields good, as long as it doesn't hail. . . ."

"About what time?"

He turned toward the snowcapped mountains, which shone like steel, then darkened, and finally disappeared in copper-colored banks of cloud.

"Between three and four. Not before. Not much later," and he went his way.

I have to go back down, return, seek out other men, draw nearer to my friend, wherever he may be, since he didn't climb up. His adventure is within. A man in his state of mind, who doesn't know the enchantments and secrets of our mountains, stays on the plain.

I have to go back down, in obedience to this devil or angel of mine. The Dean is suffering. I have to enter into that suffering—his, the world's. Happiness is too rare a commodity to hoard for one's self. I mustn't cut myself off. I must live in his air, be in communion with him, even if my presence is useless to him (as it surely will be). On this plateau, with all my happiness, I am worse off, sicker than he is. "Leave off that sad habit of always being dependent on someone else," he said. I never can. The solitude of a man who needs other men is a terrible solitude. It is my torment. I am going back down for

309

him—and for myself. I will be less wretched sharing his pain than here in the silence of pleasant things. And yet the storm would be a fine sight from the foot of these peaks. In our part of the country, in our mountains, the thunder doesn't roar, it cracks, and I love those crashes, like heralds of the Last Judgment. I would take shelter beneath this stone roof, while the rain whipped the earth, and the flocks, the frightened birds, the flies, would come to keep me company. The cows would stretch out their moist noses to me, and I would have time to pet their heads, in the hollow between their horns. Then the moon would come up and everything would turn blue.

But the storm is down below.

I had almost nothing left to eat, and I was hungry. This made me feel lighter, more detached, more transparent, more fraternal—and, one does not die of a little hunger.

I waved good-by to the joy I was renouncing, and I abandoned it beside a spring.

A magnet was drawing me: my lake! Well sheltered, hidden, perched like a nest on the side of the rounded hill, a carved cup full of green water, still and deep. To get there, you climb up a little path. It keeps you waiting, but when you reach its northern side, it assails your eyes, as music does your ears, and completely fills them. Today there were no visitors; I was alone again.

I sat down on a rock which overhangs the water. Only now does it strike me that I was a romantic spectacle there. Not that the label makes any difference when you hear God in the wind, when you see Him as I saw Him, in a bead of water with its thousand luminous facets, when you wait for Him and feel His coming, when you pray to Him and know that storms in the soul also need lifeboats. . . .

It wasn't the first time I had sat in that spot, but I had no heart to revive those happy memories. One day I brought some young people from the Catholic Action group there, and while they practiced rowing, I sat on this rock. It seems to me to belong to another age, when I shared the Church's hope for the spiritual education of the peasants of our region. I don't think I would dare undertake it again. I am old. The world has changed. I don't speak their language any more. I am classed among the fossils. Thus pass men's youth and hopes. But suffering spans the centuries, unchanging. Willing or unwilling, young and old are summoned to its feast. They go all together, holding each other by the hand.

The storm broke on the heights. The lake took fright. Run! I have never been afraid of storms, but I ran for the pleasure of feeling it pursue me.

I barely managed to escape. There was still a blue streak in the east. On the great plain, the light would slowly fade and turn yellow, and soon at my feet the city would look like a great hospital ward with only the nightlight on. My car, pushed forward by the wind, took part in my game. Lower down was where I wanted to be when the storm broke over me.

That is how it used to be long ago. From May through September, atmospheric catastrophes were a constant nightmare to us! I remember one day when we watched the sky all morning. It was so hot and humid that morning that we knew the day could not possibly pass without a disaster. The wheat was just ready to be harvested, the red wheat we grew then, with bearded ears so heavy that they bent the stalks.

In these parts, the hailstorm clouds form toward one thirty in the afternoon, or two o'clock, rarely earlier. At first they are small, minute. My mother said to me, "Look at that one...." A fringe of mist floating innocently along the mountain, a wisp of light smoke, an inoffensive miniature cloud for the angels' entertainment. The sky was extraordinarily clear. In that immense pale blue expanse, the cloud grew, one couldn't say why. It floated, held up by invisible wires. "It is taking shape," my mother said. Like the shepherd I met on the mountain, she knew exactly when those terrible storm-clouds would explode. A light wind came up. "If that goes on, it won't come here, but if it stops. . . . Look at that yellow cloud: that's hail, no doubt of it!"

And soon—that is how it happened that day—the cloud comes majestically forward, like the throne of an accursed god. The whole sky churns; the wind blows stronger, more violently, flattening the harvest as though a roller were passing over it, tearing it, shaking it up in a wild dance. The leaves are torn from the vines, the branches are loosened, the vine props broken. The birds are suddenly still. The cattle turn their horns against the wind as though to defy it.

My mother said, "Let's go in quickly, quickly, my boy. It's coming here all right, and it's a real Hell!" Between two thunderclaps, there was a rumbling like a galloping horse. "See that—it's coming our way. Look! But come, hurry up!"

When we went into the house, my grandmother, on her knees before the hearth, was burning a branch of sacramental boxwood, calling on St. Barbara. Now that chant escapes me, a sort of plaintive canticle which ends, I think, something like this: "When the thunder falls, let it fall neither on us, nor on our family, nor on our friends, nor on our enemies, but in a place where there is no one. . . ."

My father had arrived before us; his tools were thrown down carelessly, contrary to his habit. My grandmother, trembling, rushed toward us, and said in a whisper, "Don't speak to him; he's like a madman. He would beat us!" But he was past seeing any of us. He ran back and forth, waving his arms. His eyes shone like lightning. He crashed into doors, shouting, swearing, filling the house with his enormous anger, blaming God, the Mass, prayer, the saints, priests, everyone, in fact, whose power proved vain against the sovereign, unleashed force of nature. He took a drink and banged his glass violently on the table. Then suddenly he was silent, listening for the inexorable approach of the justification of his rebellion. Then, sure that everything was going to be smashed and disappear, and that his world was crumbling, he swore a stronger oath than before, and started gesticulating again.

I didn't know where to go, so I hid between two old chests in the attic.

At that moment the storm broke.

It began like a game. A little imp tripped across the tiles, dryly tapping out a few notes. A wait, a silence. The imp returned, a bit more resolute. He left; he came back. He left, then returned with ten, a hundred, twenty thousand imps! This infernal drumming lasted, they told us afterward, a quarter of an hour. To me it seemed an eternity. The storm was chopping everything, grinding everything, splitting the grape clusters like a knife blade, beating and cutting the ears of wheat, killing, massacring; insensible, furious, pitiless, blind and deaf. . . . It went just as it had come. Soon there were no more than a hundred, then ten, then only one little imp who played about for a few minutes more, and left on a final arpeggio. . . . The sun came back out, an innocent sun, a sun which had seen nothing, which didn't want to know anything, and which carried on with its job.

I came out of my hiding place.

My grandmother was crying and twisting her hands.

My mother said to us, "Come and eat the soup . . ." but no one touched it.

Today's race against the storm brought back my childhood. Long moments passed without my thinking of the Dean. The road was almost empty, but a few peasants were hurrying along the paths. I could tell from their faces that it wouldn't hail. And so. . . . "It will do the fields good!" I allowed myself

313

a short halt, the one I used to make when the plain unfurled before my eyes. A turn, a wall, and before me, infinitely stretching out, my wheat fields. Then I saw my village. . . .

My mind was made up.

It was a resolution without seed or germination: I would bend beneath the storm, hear the wind, the thunder and the rain; I would see the wheat bow down and the torn leaves chase each other, the water seek the ruts and the toads hop from puddle to puddle, near my village, sheltered somewhere (not in the car) in a stack of straw perhaps or behind a hedge, but there! Afterward I would witness there—still there—there for the last time, the resurrection of the world, when the snails put out their horns, when the birds shake their feathers in the sun to dry them, when my mountains—from which I was running away—intact and renewed, washed, combed, as fresh as a child after his bath, raise up their heads in a sky completely unflawed, and serenade the disappearing storm with their joyous thanksgiving.

And then I would return forever to my parish.

My car was in on the secret. If I hurried, the heaviest part of the storm would not reach me until I was home.

Home! That house in which I could go about with my eyes closed. The old door, the bench, the winding stairway, made of black stone, its iron railing with the fat yellow ball. The cherrywood table that came from Great-grandfather, and its drawer which was the larder, the temptation of my afterschool hours. I remembered how hungry I was, and how it used to contain all the things I will always long for: dark bread; a piece of cold bacon; home-made sausage, for the love of which I would have endured all punishments, even the worst; and sometimes a plate of those *grattons* which I loved, and which I pilfered in secret, making sure to cover my traces by evening out the pile.

Home! The barn always fresh and fragrant, the stable we

314

had built, and, just to the right, the place where my first white bulls were tethered. They were beautiful, and gentle, and built like gods!

Home! It hurt me to think about it in that car which was taking me there! On its pedestal, the statue, never washed, of the Sacred Heart, where we knelt every evening. The room I was born in, where I sometimes pretended to be sick; the one where my mother suffered; and Grandma's room. She died there one hot afternoon, next to her old chest, where she laid her shawl, her black apron, her fluted bonnets and her Alsatian-style ribbons, moiré, and as wide as your hand.

It was in this room that she said to us one day, in that way she had, of the pure in heart, "I hope that you will always love each other. . . ." Alas! If only I could go home, as I did then, free from anxiety, aching with fatigue and overwhelmed with joy! See my grandmother again in front of our steaming bowls of soup! See her bending over the hearth, soup ladle in hand, or sitting in her armchair, her only half-a-square-yard of property, where she huddled herself away to make room for our boisterousness. "Come! Come and eat!" she would say. "The soup is ready and getting cold!" As long as she was there, everything was always ready, in her heart and on the table.

I decided not to go home. Grandma's chair would be empty, and I would have to sit down and make conversation, almost anywhere except in my own place, on the end of the bench, against the wall.

I wouldn't even pass in front of the house. If I did, the car would stop there of its own accord and I would immediately go up to the attic with my pots to catch the rain water from the gutters.

The storm was exerting all its strength, but I paid no attention to it. I took the path along the stream, right through the

315

puddles. I planned to go straight to the end, to the spot where it disappears in the grass and, near the broken bridge, perhaps I would recognize the hut where I used to go to be alone. The rain came down so hard that it drowned the windshield and cut off my view. But I didn't have to see; I could follow the line of the trees. I pushed on through the streaming water in the joy, almost animal and wild, of a past which God revived for me as I had never dared hope: in all its fury and its exaltation of love.

Shall I be able to write what happened then?

It was not a dream: my animals were in my field, huddled together under a willow, horns to the wind. I crossed the ditch over my "dragonfly bridge," I went into my "house-in-the-meadow" and there at the back sat my mother, her shepherd's stick beside her and her dog under her cape, sheltered from the storm.

She didn't get up. She made herself smaller; she squeezed over a little to one side, making room for me on the smooth roots and said, "I was waiting for you ... Hurry and get in out of the rain."

Then: "Here, eat. You must be hungry. I still have some walnuts."

Then: "You are all wet. Hold the dog close to you, he will warm you up."

She looked at me for a second. "You are worried. You have circles under your eyes."

Then: "This rain will do a lot of good. For the peasants, it is raining money. I don't need anything myself. As long as I can come here, to your hut, I will have all I want, and more. My cattle behave well, even along the roads. You'd think they understood. You see, the branches you tied together made a strong roof, and your roots are big enough for me to sit on, like a real bench. What more could I want? I come here every evening. The neighbors don't come any more. I am all alone

316

with your dragonflies, my cows, and my dog. That's quite
enough for me. Too much. I am almost happy here, and that
is why I say, 'too much.' Do you still love storms as much as
you used to? . . . I say my rosary. I do some mending. I leave
when the shadow of the big poplar reaches my feet. I often
think of you. Often? I mean—always. It's quite natural . . ."

A few drops of water trickled through the thick foliage, fell
on our heads, and slid down our necks. The storm kept up its
wild rhythm, but the clouds looked whiter, a sign that it was
ending. Some broken branches passed in front of us, turning
like wheels. I heard the reeds in the ditch rubbing together
like knives being sharpened, and the sound of water flowing
under the bridge. Far off, at the other end of the meadow, we
could make out the hawthorn hedge.

I put my hand over hers on the dog's back. She said, "You
are thinner. I can tell from your fingers."

Was she avoiding the essential thing on purpose? Her
voice was gentle, without passion or mystery. I only felt her
tremble a little when the light came back to the meadow for
good, and the dog, nervous about his flock, went out of the hut.

"The storm is over," she murmured. "You will be going
too. . . . Be careful, the road will be slippery. You haven't said
anything. Is it because you are happy—well, almost happy,
like me?"

I pressed her hand harder. "Tell my brothers that I forgive
them."

She looked straight ahead, far, very far, shivered, then took
hold of herself, and said, like a prayer, "All that is over now.
At my age, it has no more meaning."

She smiled. "My arms and legs are getting stiff. My teeth
have all fallen out. When I sit down, I can't get up again. I
have hardly enough time left for loving; for it is now that I
love—that I love you all. . . ."

She was still smiling. "The only thing that we will bring to

317

God is what we have given away. We have suffered too much. We have caused each other too much suffering. Nothing is ever solved, but it all dies down. When the wheat is ripe, it forgets the storm. It yields to the reaper. Our wheat is ripe...."

The cows came closer. "They want to go home," she said to me resolutely. Then, "Yes, it is all over. It has to be that way so that our purposes can be accomplished.... When you were born ... a few days afterward, as soon as I could get up, I carried you to the church. In front of the altar of that Blessed Virgin you used to love to pray to, I said, 'I give him to you. Do whatever you want with him.' The Blessed Virgin isn't deaf. She took you. She took me. Maybe you have nothing left but your cassock, and I have nothing but your 'house-in-the-meadow' as you used to say. I am happy here, because I find your warmth...."

I helped her to stand.

The sun came out all of a sudden triumphantly. In the ditch, the reeds were already standing straight. The water was flowing under the bridge where I used to fish for sticklebacks. We walked a short way across the grass. The wagtails, coming out of hiding, fluttered about the cows. I saw my sky, not the sky of the coast, but the other, my own, whose blue has reflected the forest, the wheat, the meadows and the vines for centuries beyond recall. The cattle headed off beneath the poplars.

"You know," I said to her, quite low, "I never ... made much of a success of anything."

Then she laughed; it was her old laugh, bursting out, ironical—her laugh of challenge and of triumph! I will always see her that way, this woman who was always so sincere in circumstances which she considered important. Her hand tightened on her stick; she let go of my arm and took her stance in front of me, as straight as a woman of twenty.

"Oh, so, you aren't a success! My son isn't a success! ... Well, then, it's my fault! And I congratulate myself! I made you a farmer. You couldn't adapt to their machinery. You managed your parish like your plough. That is your sin. Oh, I understood very well. . . . They took you for a bungler. My son, a bungler! And they thanked you, like a bungling clerk. What more could you expect? Can you still plough? Do you know how? And sow the seeds after warming them up in your hand? Yes. Well, then, that's all right . . . let them talk, and you just go your way."

The animals now walked single file, the finest in the lead; the dog followed behind. A majestic sun, shining like a monstrance, shed its rays over my mountains. My mother walked with difficulty, slipped, felt for a firm foothold.

"Get into my car," I told her, "We'll drive slowly." Her shoulders drooped. She leaned nervously on her stick.

"Let me kiss you, and then go. Go where you have to go. In an hour it will be dark. You never used to like driving at night. . . . No, don't come to the house. You'll come back when I die. The dead speak better than the living. They have no trouble finding words. Stop at the cemetery on your way, and say a prayer over the family tomb. You'll see it just by the big pine. I will still say my rosary for you every day, in your hut. . . . I'll go back by myself. I won't tell anyone. Tomorrow your dragonflies will be here. I'll say hello to them, the way you used to. . . ."

I took my rosary out of my pocket, as the Dean had done the other day.

"It's all I have to give you," I said.

"We'll exchange, then. Take mine. And . . . may She keep you . . ."

I had forgotten . . .

I had forgotten so thoroughly that it vexed me to remember. The Dean's absolutes once more seemed to be childish obstinacy, games. I enjoy a struggle, against anything, so long as that anything seems to be something. Struggle to live, to start over, to endure. In the old days, I struggled against the frost, against hail, against the cold or the heat. I used to wrestle with the horned sheep in my flock. I would take hold of their horns; there is a trick to it. You twist their necks and hold their heads very low, nose to the ground. It would last a long time. We would roll on the ground together, out of breath. There was no winner or loser. Then they would go off to nibble the grass. We didn't harbor any hard feelings. My horned sheep would come back to me to be petted. I loved those horned sheep. . . .

But men wrestle with ideas! Priests themselves are fond of this kind of struggle. Now, for me, ideas are so much smoke. God is not an idea. And the proof is that His Word was made flesh. Ideas . . . let's understand each other: you have to have a few; clear ones, preferably not too new, firm on their feet, straight and hard like the trunk of an oak. Then you carve one, and out comes what you decided would come out: a table, a plough, a door, a bench, a boat. My house-in-the-meadow taught me that ideas of that kind exist. You pick them like grapes and fill up the vats.

But if things were that way, it would be too easy. . . .

And that is why I am moving forward along this road, why I am already detaching myself from this simple world, from the storm, from the sun disappearing behind my mountains and the first stars; from my reeds, from everything. Without knowing just where, I have crossed the border which separates my two worlds: the one where at this hour, with my stick and a bag in my hand, I would be gathering the snails which had ventured out for a stroll; and the other, the Dean's, where his truth lies, where his fists are clenched and his eyes are staring at a clouded horizon. Now, the childishness seems to be on the side of my fondness for simple impressions, my peasant certitudes, my simple pleasures, my joys which grow by themselves and come tied in bouquets.

320

After my stop at the cemetery where "just by the big pine" I prayed over the tomb of my forebears, I took, without turning back, the road which will perhaps bring me closer to him.

Then the torture began: the torture of headlights, those two unbearable beams of light which slide and shine on the wet asphalt, those two stupid eyes which tear out my eyes. To exist, to live, to think, to try to pray in this servitude to technology, in this slavery and this demented state of a civilization which forbade me to look at the sky! That was what I was reduced to: watching my reflexes, controlling my movements, driving a few inches away from the road posts, and inflicting my headlights on a recalcitrant adversary. Force against force! And two Christians confronting each other! If I were on a bicycle or on foot, the Christian opposite me would take little account of my desire to live! ... So we hold on as long as we have to, dominated by the fear of killing or of dying. I felt tempted to let go, so that the night would return, night in the ditch, waiting for the ambulance, stretched out, broken, but eyes turned upward....

It was in this state of mind that I returned, rather late, to the hotel where we had been staying. The hotelkeeper and his wife were out. One of their employees showed me to my room.

While I write this, all is silent in my room, in the corridor, and in the street. I hear the town clock again. I think of what he wrote, "Near our hotel, a bell with the most human sound I ever heard is keeping me company on this night of agony. . . ." Where is he suffering at this moment? I recited my Office. When he recited it, he must have come to these words:

Save me, O God, for the waters threaten my life; ...
I have reached the watery depths; the flood overwhelms me.
I am wearied with calling, my throat is parched; ...

Those outnumber the hairs of my head who hate me without cause.

Too many for my strength are they who wrongfully are my enemies....

Let not those who wait for you be put to shame through me...

Since for your sake I bear insult...

I have become an outcast to my brothers, a stranger to my mother's sons

Because zeal for your house consumes me....

Let not the flood-waters overwhelm me, nor the abyss swallow me up, nor the pit close its mouth over me....

I looked for sympathy, but there was none; for comforters, and I found none....

But I am afflicted and in pain; let Your saving help, O God, protect me....

In what frame of mind will he read this verse from Prime tomorrow morning—that untranslatable poem of joy contained in a few words: *Et sit splendor Domini super nos* ...

In any case, there is nothing more for me to do here. Tomorrow I will start back to my parish. The miracle didn't take place. The sign didn't appear. My thoughts conflict with each other, and I am trying to pin them down. My thoughts? That is not exactly what I mean. What do you call these deep movements of the soul, these spasms of the heart which in fact obstruct thought and leave no room for anything else, except this pain which I feel in my chest, the suffocation of all my certitudes, an oppression like that of an asthmatic who opens his mouth wide, trying to catch his breath? I thought there were some things that couldn't happen ... but this very night I have seen and grasped in my hand the thread, spun out of my expectations, which binds me to a dead hope. I prayed. I suffered. I cried out. I believed. It seemed impossible that I would go back alone.

I went to the foot of my snow-capped mountains, and I came back down in the storm, with the unformulated yet absolute certainty that I would find the Dean here when I returned. God exists and the priesthood is His invention. Man cannot fly in the face of these facts. God owed it to Himself to save him! A priest whose only sin was burning zeal, whose only passion was to protect God by holding Him in his arms, whose only fear was that his courage might falter. Shall this priest be condemned? Condemned by whom? Condemned to what? Why? Through the tangled branches where he was searching for his path, did Christ then refuse to show His face? It would have taken so little! His eyes. The eyes of the Holy Agony in the Garden of the Divine Suffering; His eyes which saw the Angel sent by the Father . . . the Angel who did not heal Him, but who looked at Him! He would be here tonight. And, not because he understood any better, but because at last he would have believed all the way, we would sing the Easter Alleluia together!

This is the way the world will perish, then, one day . . . not from disease or from famine or from war, but from cold. Souls despairing because of God's silence will fall down dead, stiff. They will snap off, like my buds after a night of frost.

And despite all this, I have faith. . . .

I have faith while I hear the quarter hours strike, while I listen to the night slipping through my fingers like dried grains in a heap of wheat. The heap is getting smaller. Soon the stars will grow pale, my hand will close over shadows and the hour of my departure will have struck. I have faith, as I look out over the rooftops of the sleeping city and feel on my forehead the air cooled by the storm. I have faith as I think of my old woman at prayer, waiting, never having known doubt. I have faith as I press my two hands over the wrinkled leather of my prayer book. I put my questions to it, for it holds the Answer, as well as that imperishable Hope of the Chrysostoms, the Jeromes, and all the Augustines. I believe, not because one must, or because faith is the Explanation of the world, but because faith is the air that I breathe, and I would still cry out that I believe in Him and love Him if this very night He sent a devil to strangle me.

So then, why . . . ?

It is midnight. I want to stay up tonight without sleeping. I feel that this is the last time I will write in this Journal. When I get back, I won't reread it or write in it again. Keeping a Journal requires a youth and vigor of soul that this ordeal has smothered in me. I will work in faith, waiting to see. . . .

I wish I could go out. Walk on the earth, and feel my feet adhere to it. . . . The earth would be mute too, and I would come back without an answer. Besides, I am afraid . . . I am afraid of everything—of opening my door; of lighting the stair light; of going down the wooden staircase, which creaks in spite of its red carpet. Isn't it already too much that my window is still lighted? I wish I could disappear, but that is impossible. Hold out then, without attracting attention, without revealing my presence.

Tomorrow I will say a brief good morning. I will go and celebrate my Mass. I will pay my bill and then run away. Run away . . . only to meet the same problem farther on, but the time of flight is still a kind of solitude. The eyes of strangers don't ask questions. There will be that much gained, lived, past. . . .

"Only the saints see . . ." What do they see? What is it that they understand better than we? What do they read in the Book? What do they decipher, on their knees, in front of a plaster image of Christ crucified? What difference is there between the Dean and a saint? And if there is one (and there surely is, impalpable, imponderable, the speck of dust that tips the scales), it is still true that the world, saved in its entirety by Jesus Christ, needs Jesus Christ in its entirety. In the last analysis it is incomprehensible that only the saints should be illuminated by Jesus Christ. What about the others? Him, me, all the others? The numberless throng of others? And suppose we cannot go any further? Suppose all our effort only brings us to the frontier of light? Suppose, in spite of this effort, we cannot enter alive and joyful, our eyes bathed in fire, into the festival hall where the angels bring the saints the plates of gold on which they find the divine Answer? Suppose our bodies are too heavy, our hearts too fearful of the cold, our hands not full enough? Suppose we were born that way, of an accursed race which has no wings? But in the end isn't it unjust that only the saints see the light, those whose sanctity is enough for them, while we are left without a lamp, we who need only that to take the final step? For whom are the beacons lighted?

I am wandering off the track, or rather, I am blaspheming. All the theologians without one exception would affirm that this is blasphemy. . . . I am not blaspheming, Sirs, I am searching. Are you going to forbid me to search? Isn't orthodoxy simply passivity? Do you understand any better? Do you see any clearer? Do you march forward singing canticles amid a fireworks of obvious truths? Haven't you ever stumbled, drunk with doubt and hunger, before the city gates which no one would open for you? Have the logic and the disciplines of faith always been a comfort to you? Have you read anywhere—and I would like to know where—that the relationships between Jesus Christ and his priest are enough in concordance with your formulas to be sealed as authentic by Jesus Christ? I blaspheme! You who have autopsied the Gospel, codified the Message, held the hand of the one who keeps the Keys, planted markers along our path like conscientious surveyors, measured all our souls' workings on your yardstick, weighed them in your scales, filed them in your catalogues and, before the Judgment, inscribed in your records the names of the damned and the elect, you who are the experts—are you so sure that you are saved? And even if, keeping faith with yourselves, you have observed your rule line for line, would you swear that it has brought you near to the light; would you swear that the enlightened ones, the seers alone, are your attentive disciples? I don't say that you are wrong. I only wish that you would be quicker and more willing to recognize that others might be right. Not right in opposition to you, but right along with you, on condition that you doubt with them. I blaspheme? I will confess this sin of blasphemy only when you swear to me that you are sure that you love.

It is really after midnight that night is night. . . .

Everyone is asleep, heads on their pillows, both the learned and the simple. Joys are asleep and suffering is allayed. The lighted windows are those of the sick, or of madmen, or soldiers. The Dean's window is lighted. Where? My theologians are sleeping. It is the hour when all reasonable people are asleep, after all! Perhaps not all the saints are asleep yet, or perhaps they have already slept, but they are somewhat related to madmen, and they see better at night, like my guitarist. Witnesses who affirm, mystics afire, seers who cast a bridge between the world and God, whether they be mad or sane, tonight they alone have a valid message for me. Come out of your ecstasy, wherever you may be, leave the place where you are and go tell him what the saints say when they speak. What is your role, if not that? Or if you must, by God's will, remain on your knees, let your prayers be strong and resilient enough to rise up to His very Throne and fall back in sparks of fire on the spot where the Dean is struggling against the dark.

We exaggerate at night. We distort, we magnify events. My position is tenable then: I am a man who ought to be asleep but who is keeping watch. Wise men who sleep after the stroke of twelve will give little credence to my notions. But what I would wish, in this moment of digression, is that no one approach my friend in his fugitive state with a satchel of sweets. Then it would really be over. That would kill him, finish him. But approach with humility, search with him in the tangled underbrush—not to distract him or humor him (he would realize it immediately and turn his back)—but because you are like him: you, too, are impatient with a drowsing Christianity; search with him even because you are in a way his disciples (your pardon)—since he is as much a Churchman as you are, and here he has the advantage of a head start.

You may object that the Church, even for those who keep watch after midnight, is not a blind alley—and God knows I believe you! Somewhat out of a lack of interest in argument, more out of conviction. Cut off my head and open my veins, but I would never leave the Church! To go where, Lord? Nor would he, you may be sure! The Jews of old said, "Rather fall in battle than abandon the laws of our God." We have the honor of being priests of Jesus Christ!

He is keeping watch, like me. He is keeping watch; watch with him! Let us watch together. The Book hasn't revealed all its secrets to us. I intend to keep watch. . . .

But what time is it now?

I wanted to watch, and I fell asleep. This night, the last one, will not even be the night of faithfulness! I am no stronger than the rest. No more a watcher than anyone else! The sun is high, children are in school. The city is at work. He is walking, suffering; while he was praying somewhere, I was sleeping! What path did he take while I was asleep? If I had not slept, I would have been in contact with him and following his steps. Now he has disappeared doubly, and I bear the shame of having left him alone. Sleeping fully dressed, my head on my arm on top of these crumpled papers, is sleeping, exactly as though I had gone to bed. Now the shadow is thicker, my shadow. Now I shall never have the courage to stand up and face him. I am thinking straight, I am not magnifying events: it is broad daylight! I have never been able to resist sleep. I slept the night my father died. He watched me sleep. Perhaps he pitied me; he let me sleep. And when I woke up, he could no longer speak. And a few hours ago, I was critical of sleepers! I woke up empty of myself and unworthy of him. I slept on the watch! One night during the war, making my rounds, I had to wake up one of my sentinels. The man was exhausted, but that is never an excuse. I can still see him, lying in front of his machine gun. I was ashamed for him.

I am ashamed of myself! My Journal is finished. I will not search for the Dean any more. I am only good for twilight— I have never had after-midnight courage. I ought at least to have waited for dawn. But I woke up like a townsman: the cattle are tethered, the stable is empty, the swallow is already sated with sun, the dew has fallen, the field is half ploughed. He has celebrated his Mass, recited his Office, bent his heavy head, suffered, suffered again, sought again! And here I am shaving in the bright daylight. Why don't I go? Why don't I run away, too? Let me go quickly back to my parishioners and preach to them about courage! In a few days, preaching the Passion, I will cry out to them that a Christian ought not to sleep while Christ is in agony. . . . Let me grow old, let me finish my days in the mediocrity of a mediocre priest, a quitter, a sleeper, and abandon him in his desert.

It has all been empty phrases, stringing words together. . . .

And the proof is this: it is very possible to disappear . . . from shame!

The train of events is not mine to tell. Henceforth I am only a scribe trying to follow the text. A letter from him is on my table, still unopened. I haven't dared to open it. So he spent this past night near me, in the same hotel, under the same roof; a few yards separated us . . . and I didn't sense it. If I hadn't fallen asleep, I would have recognized his footsteps. But I was asleep! Obviously, I was asleep! My mother used to call me "Sleepyhead," meaning that sleep was more than a need for me, it was a vice. The letter was handed to me when I crossed the hall to go to the church. The hotelkeeper, surprised to see me, said without apparent curiosity, "The priest who was with you the other day left the hotel about an hour ago. He gave me this envelope for you."

My throat tightened. My head buzzed. My blood throbbed in my temples. I said to myself, "Hold on, if only I can hold on!" I leaned on a chair. The hotelkeeper came over to me and said, as he held out his hand to support me, "Are you tired? Perhaps a bad night?"

I was grateful to him for not making the connection between the letter and my pitiful state. I could only do something stupid. I painfully fabricated a lie, for which he hadn't asked me, and which didn't take him in.

"We had to separate. I must have forgotten the exact date of his return. . . ." And then, as though it were a question of no importance, "Did he spend the night here?"

He answered me in a clear and slightly ironical voice, "Your friend, Sir, did not leave town as far as I know. He didn't change hotels. He took all his meals here. . . ."

I thanked him, and bowed awkwardly. I heard him say, "Your friend is a very distinguished person. I believe that he would be incapable of telling a lie." (He emphasized the word "lie.") "Many priests stop here. I have never known one more likable. He took the train. I was sorry to see him go. My other guests will be sorry, too. . . ."

But I was no longer listening. I put the letter in my pocket. The hotelkeeper was watching me. My feet stumbled over the

329

paving stones. I don't remember anything, except what I said to Jesus Christ, after I consecrated the Host ...

"You have consented to come to me once more—and who have You obeyed? But then, too, why did You choose me? I am the one who lost him. Another catastrophe! And this time, what a catastrophe! I lost him last night, by not keeping watch. Intelligent men no doubt would smile at my theory, but I know that it was last night that he made his decision. I was no better at keeping watch than Peter on the night of Your dreadful solitude. Only he is not You. He won't have held out alone! He needed my eyes open, my hands joined on my book, my waiting and praying until dawn. While I kept vigil, I rebelled, but all the same the effort of watching contained its grace, and my rebellion was only a mask for my desire to save him. Sleeping, I was the picture of a coward! My sleeve left a mark on my cheek. ... I don't dare think of it any longer. The thread has come untied. The knot has been loosened. Between him and me these few hours of real courage will always be lacking. They should have been the hands freely outstretched. What You expected of me was that I would open the city gates for him. The call. The pressure of the shoulder against the frontier barrier. And I dared to accuse You of indifference! I dared to say that I would henceforth doubt everything, Your Church, Your learned men, and even, in the last analysis, Your saints! And that is the priest You have just obeyed, whose Mass is being very piously served by an amiable Canon, the curé of this place. Here is your servant—excitable, righter of wrongs, spoil sport, reformer of your Church, resounding windbag, your weary one, who fell asleep! You listen to me because You are God, but Your angels, who are less indulgent, make sport of me, and take turns on this altar so You won't be left alone! ... And this Mass has to continue! I hold the bread in my fingers: *Haec commixtio et consecratio Corporis Domini nostri Jesu Christi fiat ac-*

cipientibus nobis in Vitam aeternam! (May this mingling and consecration of the Body and Blood of our Lord Jesus Christ be to us who receive it effectual to life everlasting.) I have reached the fraction of the Host; I am preparing to partake of Your body; ritually the moment has come for my physical union with You. . . . If the faithful knew of my cowardice! One of Your greatest kindnesses is that You have shrouded Your priest in the opacity of this chasuble! The eyes of the faithful cannot penetrate it. There could be two thousand people in this church and not one would suspect that I did not keep watch this past night, and that while I slept a soul slipped away. . . . I dismiss the angels. What I want to say to You has to be said without witnesses. For, wretched as I am, I still have my life. I am breathing, standing up on my two feet. In a few minutes, I will put on a show of good humor for the priest who is serving this Mass. I am nothing, but I am a nothing whose heart is still beating. If You will, let us make a pact. You, to accept me just as I am, You who said to the great St. Jerome, 'There is something of yourself that you have not given me.'

" 'And what is it, Lord?'

" 'Your sins! Offer me your sins!'

"For him, my runaway, my fugitive, lost through my fault, my offering is not much, but it is all I have left: my life. I thought once that I had given it to You. That was before I fell asleep during his agony, at the moment of his choice, and so it was just another vanity, an illusion, a trick, a young cleric's boast, or the mistake of a priest who despite his white hair cultivated his self-will. It takes a long time for that to wither away. In this desert of thirst where You have lovingly led me, on the burning sand where I writhe with weakness and shame, at this moment of the Mass when, cost what it may, I must partake of Your body, and after the communion I will pronounce these words: *Corpus tuum quod sumpsi et Sanguis*

331

quem potavi, adheareat visceribus meis, et praesta, ut in me non remaneat scelerum macula, quem pura et sancta refere-runt sacramenta. (May Thy Body, O Lord, which I have received, and Thy Blood which I have drunk, cleave to my inmost parts, and grant that no stain of sin may remain in me, whom these pure and holy sacraments have refreshed.) Deign to accept me infirm, so that he can live, redeemed."

I have learned in books and in the saints' teaching that we must not set much store by the impressions our souls feel. All the same, I must add that since that communion, I have lived in great peace.

Now I will open this letter—and affix it to my notebook, whatever it may say . . .

My dear friend,

It is all over, and it happened silently, like the ripening of fruit.

The fruit must have been already ripe. . . .

That is the way God speaks to us. We become like children, without surprise, and we climb back into our boats. The heart consumes a joy it did not sow. The sail takes the wind. The sea calls, "Hurry, the fishing won't keep." Who still condemns? There is no more accused.

"Lord, what would You have me do?"

"Carry on in your life the parable which I purposely left unfinished . . ." *and when they had feasted and the guests had departed, the son looked about him and recognized the house; he went out into the courtyard and caressed the dog; he went to the gate and looked at the sea. The horizon seemed broad to him, the air light; the beach, the waves, the rock seemed familiar. He ventured forward and touched the water with his hand. They had set the bait without him, but the fish were waiting. So then he took his old place among his brothers and went to work.*

332

You notice that the word "prodigal" has not been uttered.

It was not a capitulation or a victory or a reward. But first let me speak to Him . . .

"Now I see, O my God, that You have arranged everything, the world itself, even the use of my time which I thought was my own, even the place of your new call; I see that everything was leading up to this unique event: the joyous acceptance of my state in life as curé of the canton. Since I left my parish, Your Spirit has regulated my life's rhythm with the same precision as the courses of the stars. You waited night and day, watching for the moment when my will would be unsteady enough and strong enough. Now I recognize more intimately, both closer and farther off, the subtleties of your divine tutelage, which over the years, and especially in these last weeks, has fashioned my soul for the love of truth, so that I cannot take another step forward, and so that I have the courage to lose everything, at the very moment that I find myself sinning against the light. Did You prepare the Annunciation with greater care than this? I recognize Your hand from the fact that my eyes were opened without force and that a new heart has replaced my tormented one. But your discretion was evident most of all in the choice of the means. . . ."

And it is here, my brother, that my story begins.

All night the town clock kept watch with me. Its company soothed me. I was writing to you. I slipped my letter under your door and made off.

Made off like a thief in the night, the saying goes. That was not true in my case. You would have let me go; I had no doubt of it. Still there was in this silent and furtive departure a zone of shadow, of which I can only say that it is familiar to me: when I have made a decision, I move forward. Later on things become clear. I have often been proven right in taking such a step. The percentage of cases in which I was wrong is negligible. My resolution was clear: all priests are not curés; I still had my hands to work with; I would serve the Church some other way, with my priesthood intact. How, actually? This "how" would take shape.

The fact that I was not anxious to see you again has a different basis: you would have talked to me, looked at me. And I had nothing more to say to you, whether with looks or words. That is why I call this departure a flight . . . you understand what I mean.

Of course, it could be held that no priest has the right to take it upon himself to make this kind of resolution. In theory, I agree. But the danger that others would follow my example was small. My spiritual itinerary was my own; on this score my conscience was clear. I could not bring myself, with my lofty concept of the priesthood, to debase it to the level of mediocrity without serious forfeit. For me it was the refusal of a sterile humiliation, of a practical failure of the Redemption, hopelessly insoluble in the present state of affairs. Pride hides everywhere, but there is pride and pride, and I prefer the kind which puts the least distance between a man and the truth. I was not fighting for or against anyone. I was looking for a logical solution: this final renunciation offered me one.

This was the heart of the problem, and I was well aware of it. We have it on the word of the authentic servants of God, interpreters and living witnesses of the Gospel, the saints, that "myself" spoken out of context, without mandate or authority except "itself" is an adulterated product. This word alone, used as I used it, contains the formal condemnation of a spiritual disorder which the Church will never baptize in any form. In spite of my assurance, that is where the shoe pinched. How could I be sure, objectively sure, that I could not go on without making Christ dance to their tune, as they say, and make up my mind to leave without the permission of the one, no matter who he was, to whom I had said: *Promitto.*

I want to be sincere: I confess that I meant to ask for an audience with our bishop, and also that I never had the courage to do it. As you know, bishops are often wary of clear and positive decisions; I suppose out of prudence. They are men

334

of government and therefore more easily inclined to maintain the status quo or to choose middle-of-the-road solutions. What does that amount to? It is infinitely simple: they abandon the soul to its thirst, in the hope of faith that the ordeal will make it seek the fountains of holiness where they may be found. In the absolute, still, they are right ... A leader, especially a religious leader, cannot always exactly evaluate the state of a soul. The bishop was not consecrated only for the sanctification of his clergy. In his just conception of the priesthood, the priest's sanctity is the Q.E.D. of Maundy Thursday. But a sanctity according to the administrative rules of sanctity. Therefore the ordeal itself—its nature, its violence—is of slight matter; the kind of Cross does not matter as long as there is a man crucified upon it. Once he has taken his place on the Cross, he will see what he has to see, overlook the details and in the end forget himself. That is the most common form of a bishop's love for his priests. (I am not being ironical, great God!)

As soon as a priest is hanging on this cross, the major problems of his parish are solved. All that remains to be done is to authenticate it, because this crucified priest is still a scandal! A man crucified is ugly, even if he attains to the most perfect beauty of his calling by this ugliness. Slowly reassured by authority—which at first approves timidly, then more boldly when they are sure that it is truly a man crucified, and that he does not thrash about too much—finally the day dawns when his parishioners perceive in his swollen face and writhing body something of Heaven. Even then, it is only after the fact that bishops applaud.

To get to the nails, the thorns, the sponge dipped in vinegar, passive obedience is not enough. The obstacle is a serious one, cerebral in nature: Christ obeyed to this degree, but HE KNEW, and it was His Father whom He obeyed. It was not physically any easier, but it was intelligible, and therefore acceptable. To compare the obedience of a priest to his bishop to that of Christ to the Father seemed farcical to me. In fact that is why, of all the key words in the Gospel, these words,

335

Thou art Peter, and upon this rock I will build my Church
... these few poor words strung together, which no scholar
as far as I know has ever challenged, were my temptation to
despair.

Suppose these words were true?

Well, they are true.

On the other hand, and this time for reasons of the most
elementary human dignity, I could not honestly accept the
so-called compromise solution: a surface reconciliation with
my self-righteous parishioners, out of a semblance of priestly
charity. A visit to our Bishop would thus have been a dialogue
of the deaf. Nothing would have come of it, and it might have
complicated matters even further.

Although it was perhaps not necessary, I felt that I owed
you this review of my problem. You have reflected upon it.
You yourself have endured in other places and at the same
time as I did, the same kind of sufferings. The difference between us was only that the *Tu es Petrus* prevented you from
taking the leap into the ultimate void. I was grateful to you
for your prayers, for the words you spoke, even though I sometimes tripped on their charity and candor. I wanted to ask
you to tell that old woman who keeps watch by the sea—
whom I have known for many years and whose tragic and
glowing story I never told you—how much I had prized her
discretion and her silence. Neither she nor you could have
made me turn back, however, if it were not that a grace of
exceptional weight had been won, perhaps by you or by her,
perhaps by a soul whom I will never meet, perhaps by all of
Christendom on its knees, or even by our bishop who, it is
obvious, was suffering. For I counted for nothing in what I
am going to tell you.

It was barely daylight.

I was walking along over the uneven paving stones, or
rather I was wandering at random.

At the point I had reached, I had to line up my questions,
and therefore with a twofold purpose—first, not run into
you; and second, to deny myself any weakening—I turned my

back on your mountains, since, presumably, you had gone in that direction, and also because their lovely, harmonious lines could only soften my determination.

I sat down on a stone bench at the north of the city.

You know the spot: I suppose it is the old ramparts—a few chestnut trees, a sparse lawn which must be a pleasant place for mothers to stroll with their little ones on summer afternoons. In front of me rose the dark and very dirty walls of what I took to be a prison. . . . Your compatriots do not intrude on a man's solitude, I can assure you. In the early light, a man passed, glanced at me, and went on his way. Groups went by without slowing their pace. One of your young colleagues passed, bareheaded, hurrying, no more curious than the others. My town clock was still striking the quarter hours. Soon frail and timid bells sounded, convent bells without doubt, and then others, energetic and grave, announcing Mass; the bells the parish priest rings when he enters his church in the morning. It was cold. I felt cold. But that, too, was part of the plan. . . . Turning around, I could see a stretch of the plain. The first rays which swept across it accentuated its dull, sad look. You know the scene: the faded red tiles of the lower town, farther on the square wheat fields, a few vineyards, a strange assemblage of straw stacks a bit battered by the winter. On the horizon a village of black, flat houses, whose church steeple, square and totally inexpressive, scarcely dominates it.

If I had had to choose my desert, I would have picked that very spot . . .

My thoughts of you were superimposed on the scene. I have thought of you from the beginning to the end of my spiritual wanderings. My soul drowsed; my heart refused to do any serious work. My head went on living on these few images and the decisions I had made. You were with me on my sands. I waited. I recited my Hours to give you the time to leave town, but the Prophet King did not inspire me. Your young colleague passed by in the opposite direction, slightly more preoccupied. That stone was hard and cold.

337

Don't think I was disheartened. I was where I wanted to be and things were going as I wished. Any notion that you may be entertaining, based on books and your own complexes, of a rebellious priest who begins to gather the tasteless fruits of his decision, would be completely false. When, about nine o'clock, I made up my mind to celebrate my Mass, it was from an impulse of love, not out of the need of weakness.

This town possesses two churches. The one with the pointed spire didn't attract me. Its exterior is mute. I went down the street and entered the other church, dedicated to Our Lady, as I learned afterward. I celebrated Mass without spiritual complications, without "colloquies" or effusions. A half-hour spent with our invisible, impalpable God, a God without weight or dimension, Who has granted me the grace of believing in His living presence in the Sacrament and also the equally great favor of never having needed any proof of it. The church was empty and the sacristan was discreet. After that Mass I realized that I did not want food or drink, that I had the whole morning left to decide what to do, and that a lateral chapel politely invited me to prayer, which would last, as I estimated, until noon.

Then it was that I saw Her ...
I saw Her in Her smile....
I saw nothing of Her but that smile.

The chapel was dark. I was sitting rather far back from the sanctuary rail. The statue was therefore about ten yards away from me. Don't worry, it didn't light up or move. It remained just what it was, a block of carved stone. The miracle was that in the half-light in which everything was blurred, all I could make out of Her—Her Child, Her pedestal, the altar She stood over—was Her lips, and Her lips were smiling.

Our colleague once alluded to this smile in front of us, and that came back to my mind. Since then, I have learned that She has a beautiful name. For me she will always be the smiling Virgin.

For, dear friend, I had never seen such a smile, a smile of that quality. No smile on a man's or a woman's face has ever

338

come close to it. The artist who sculpted those lips did not copy them from a model. No one could have been, to such a degree, mother and Holy Virgin.

In that smile of Eve before the fall, the memory of the lost Paradise was held out to me, the reflection of the promised Paradise to come, the echo and the music of the inexpressible Word, hope's answer to all my questions, the serene audacity to transform all my humiliations into humility, Peace, Joy, at last—Joy! At first I said to myself: There is the exact expression of the poem and song of a sacrificed soul; that is how we will smile in God's presence. Then I thought: Just this Woman's smile is the witness to the truth of the dogma about Her birth: it contains the Law and the Prophets, the entire Book, from Moses to the Apocalypse. And then, very softly, that smile entered into me by a door I thought was no longer open, and I understood that a smile from the Virgin cannot be other than extraordinary, capable of uplifting, of overturning, of transforming the visible and the invisible world . . . and I was surprised that I had not known it before. I reached the point of thinking: If the Virgin smiles at me, it is because She has no other way of saying what She wants to tell me: that revelation of a crushing truth, a truth victorious over everything, the humble and triumphant smile of the One who has overcome.

That was how the Virgin smiled at me. . . .

And to be alone as I was, in the presence of that smile; absorbed in that smile; attracted, fascinated, vanquished by that smile, victorious and free because of it . . . well, my friend, all at once you understand all of dogmatic and moral theology; the decisions you made an hour before fly off like swallows in the fall; you hear yourself answering "yes" with astonishing firmness, and once again you see men as you did your first year in the seminary. You aren't dreaming; you are no more a mystic than you were yesterday; your two feet are firmly on the ground; you can see, you can speak—but there it is. . . . You watch the movement of those lips and the whole world is renewed, its faded colors are freshly painted, the turbulent flood of contradictions flows back to its source and water bursts forth from another rock, the one in the luminous Garden of long ago. A man's pain, a priest's doubts, his burdens and his "what's the use?" run away like the wind. . . .

And I realized that my soul was smiling.

It was so new that I wanted to see myself smiling. This is what happened:

I was holding my head in my hands, although I detest that gesture. I felt a physical sensation of well-being. Another man (you, perhaps) would have fallen to his knees. It was more ordinary: I felt like stretching out flat, like a child, on the grass, relaxing my whole body and going to sleep, because at last I would be able to sleep. My soul's wrinkles were smoothed away; I breathed freely; my blood flowed like a stream in the meadows that waters the flowers, a hand had lifted the enormous weight of shadow which was crushing my head.

Then I heard:

Sleep, my little one. Sleep on the dew of which my prophet speaks. Sleep in the accepted harmony of the Message, in your betrothal to Truth. Sleep and smile at me in your sleep. To fall asleep, you see, all you needed was a smile. . . .

Some women approached the railing. The sound of their feet made me lift up my head. They were carrying shopping bags full of household provisions. They knelt and looked at the statue, praying as fast as they could, almost aloud. Then they left. Others came and prayed in the same rhythm, and lit candles. I don't know now whether I envied them. I hardly wanted to see them. The Virgin smiled at them, too. I noticed that I was not praying. Not the way they were, verbally. I looked at Her now, saying to myself, "Is it possible?" I am dreaming. Of course, it is a dream! I have the impression of a physical and supernatural reality, yet I am dreaming. But my eyes had only to meet that smile to find reassurance. I immediately stopped analyzing. Each time I found the total Explanation, unformulated but complete. The whole sea, they say, is in a drop of water. The smile of the Virgin contained the whole Explanation in the same way. And if I was dreaming, it was the kind of dream which reflects life, the clear water of beaches where our sails are mirrored, the tremor of the youth who sees himself as a man. I thought, or rather I believed, that this dream was true and that before it happened, and before I saw that smile, I had been wandering at random on beaten paths. I understood that in order to live, one has to cast one's whole life into a dream at every moment, and that it is by virtue of this same law that the trees spread their shade, that the flower anticipates the fruit and the darkness goes on all night long and each morning keeps its rendezvous with the sun.

And I heard:

> *Dream, my little one.*
> *The hour of dreams has struck....*

Your open hands. Your life stretched out on a stone of sacrifice. Your breast worn out from loving. Your hope to make the world enter into your dream and ... your smile! You understand me: the smile of your subdiaconate. Everything was so simple on that day. Your lips were smiling; men were astonished to find themselves believing in the Redeemer, and you went toward them and invited them to the feast. Now you are smiling at yourself again. You are being born again. You are recreating your life as fast and as well as when God said: Let there be light! Forget all the speeches. Reality, on this morning when I was waiting for you, is to believe, smiling, that your dream goes on. ...

I am writing this letter almost two days after the "event." You are impatient to know the outcome. Let me tell it my way. One cannot come into possession of joy and keep secrets. I am drawing up an exact account of precise states of soul, like an honest bookkeeper.

So the Mother of God did not blame me. She smiled at me. She taught me to smile again. I was overcome with astonishment at this delicacy, uncommon in our relationships with men. She said to me, "Sleep, dream!" She called me "My little one." I did not invent these words. I certainly was not expecting them. My heart received them as the heart receives the inaudible Word, in silence. Were they a door? A way? A beacon? I devoured them . . . wasn't that enough?

That is where I was: all the women had left. It must have been time to prepare the midday meal. The sun had moved. The windows of the vault were lighter, and the Virgin's smile was very subtly changed. Now she was smiling in a new and more human way, and I could see her Child better.

The door opened and closed, and I felt someone approach me after making a long genuflexion: I recognized the curé of the parish from the easy way he moved about: he was at home in his church.

He spoke to me straightforwardly, as though to a tourist. "My dear colleague, you can't see Her well enough. I will die before I succeed in lighting Her intelligently. Let me turn on the lights."

"Is intelligence so indispensable, Monsieur le Curé?"

"Intelligence, no. Light, yes."

I didn't need the light from the window now, but I felt him standing behind me, and decided to leave. His presence oppressed me. The adventure seemed to be over. He stepped forward, preventing my gesture, and held out his hand very courteously. "Beautiful as she is, it is noon," he said. And after a hesitation, "Can I invite you to lunch with me?"

I particularly wanted to avoid that. "I prefer to stay here. But before you go, would you explain why the Child is making a gesture as though drawing back?"

"The artist was a man of the Middle Ages, simple, pious, more naïve than we—which did no harm—and a sensitive theologian. He imagined that the Child was caressing a bird, and that the ungrateful creature pecked his finger. He hasn't yet made the connection between his caresses and the injury. So he is suffering from . . . amazement. It is a human reaction. We ourselves . . . He had only to think of it and imprint it on stone."

342

"And his Mother? . . ."

The curé sat down heavily on a chair beside me, but I don't think it was because he was put out at having to postpone his lunch. He lowered his voice, and I felt less sure that he was speaking to instruct me. Silences punctuated his words.

"The smile of that Mother cannot be put into words," he said. "You look at it . . . you close your eyes quickly . . . and you listen to it. If the Mother of God had written what she felt at the moment of Her Child's surprise, She would have made good literature out of good sentiments, which supposedly is impossible for men like us. Men destroy, and destruction gives them a feeling of inspiration . . . Look at Her! She mends everything with a smile. She reconciles, rejecting the absurd. For this Woman, there is only one adventure, that of faith. If we consent to enter into Her smile . . . look at Her Child . . . retreat is unthinkable for Him now. He will say to Her, 'I was stupid . . .' and kiss Her. It is the opposite of middle-class morality. What I mean is that She doesn't offer Him a packet of bandages. Her pity goes beyond, it has its meaning . . . beyond; it simplifies . . . resolves contradictions . . . Look at her."

I was looking at her, in fact, and I forgot that he was there. I was "listening" to a smile.

He went on: "The Child's pain is nothing . . . a little dust has blown across His sun. It would be false to attach any importance to it. He doesn't understand; suddenly He is divided . . . He is looking for a key; He needs—more than a word or a gesture—music. No doubt that is why our mothers used to sing to us when we had a fever. But beyond music, there is something more . . . silence . . . and a Mother's smile in this universal hush. The serenity and assurance of a smile that rises up from the depths of all things . . . from the soul. When it is the Mother of God, from a soul which is the inviolate center of the invincible Truth, Peace, the fathomless well of Joy, the contrary of refusal, the 'yes.' What can remain of the Child's injury after seeing this smile? He has courage to forget the bird's peck and return to life—in faith, smiling."

He left. I was in tears. He was very discreet, and perhaps took me for a madman. And I heard:

Weep, my little one! ...

That is the way the sky weeps to make the earth fruitful. The way the grapevine weeps, heralding spring. The way the sea weeps along the flanks of laden ships. The way a child weeps when he cannot contain his joy. That is the way I wept beneath the Cross. The way all the poor weep, all the hungry, all God's beggars ...

And I who have always reacted against any show of tenderness, who have trained myself, harshly schooled myself to resist any kind of softheartedness which brings tears to the eyes, I who do not believe in emotion, who for years have safeguarded my inner freedom by surrounding it with a wall of dry, cold stones—in that moment I wept without shame because I felt that those tears were unlike any others. I leave it to you to draw up the list. You can write, after whatever else you want, that there are tears which shine like your stars and which light the way for those who shed them. Perhaps they flow only once in our lives. I had never known them. As a child I wept from sorrow, disappointment, helplessness, fear. Then I never wept again, because I was determined to be a man. I wept freely that day for the first time, because I glimpsed in a smile a truth that at last was pure, and because that smile made me consent to love it. In that smile my tears found their source. And if you tell me again that truth tears one apart, I will answer (one must be honest all the way) that when you love it, weeping for love of it, you clasp it so close that you cannot see any trace of a break on your heart.

And so, you think, I have only to sign my name. Unity is restored. The soldering will hold. In your terms, always the same, discouraging in their flat beatitude, I have been converted, I am a man converted. You wouldn't dare say to what. You would leave the question unanswered if it were put to you. You would let him who questioned understand more or less this: that I had been restored to a form of life, a mode of

344

thought which suddenly transformed me, more cowardly than before, into a passive and benign servant of a beribboned Christianity. A snicker from the Devil might, I imagine, lead a priest who listened sympathetically to him, to this capitulation, this denial, this renunciation plastered over with piety and ratified on Satan's ledger. My dear fellow, not a smile from the Virgin! No, indeed. Not Her smile, who in this church where She arranged for me to come to Her, diverts Her son's attention from His hurt finger, from His childish surprise, and immediately turns His heart in another direction, toward the true way, and to talk like you, re-converts Him to the Ideal of the Redeemer, just by the force of Her radiant motherhood shining in her smile. Would you be willing to say that She is smiling at Him only to make Him accept defeat, and that She is saving Him from one evil only to let Him fall into another that is worse?

Enough of this—let us not fall into blasphemy. We love Her too much for that, both of us. Let us accept the fire of those tears.

So I won't sign my name yet, although my clock has just struck midnight. I won't sleep tonight. I am thinking of those who, out of charity, keep watch for wanderers. Which one have I to thank?

When I got back to the hotel, they were clearing the tables. The dining room was noisy and full of smoke. No one seemed in a hurry. I was happy to pass the time of day with your compatriots.

Sometimes I try to speak by comparisons, which is easier and makes things clearer. One often hears it said that a memory, a thought or a smile—since that is what I am talking about—follows us. In my case this was not true. That smile did not follow me; nor did it go before me. I did not carry it about as though it had remained an exterior reality for me, like a piece of luggage that one can set down and pick up again. It had not become, as they say, part of my flesh, which would give an impression of something heavy and cumbersome. It had united with my immaterial soul, and I know now

345

what communion is. Animals cannot experience communion with anything, nor can trees or stones. Communion means the harmonious fusion of two immaterial realities. And thereafter separation is impossible without a violent effort, which is like an agony. That must be what is called the sin against light. I have always preferred to die rather than commit it.

Up to that moment, however, I had not considered the question of returning to my parish. I was living in the joy of my restored equilibrium, without practical consequences. This question, furthermore, could not come up mechanically, like an artificial ending to a play. Without yet thinking about it, I bore within myself the free responsibility of a response which might or might not conform to the quality of that smile. I was made aware of it specifically when the hotel-keeper asked me whether I was planning to spend the next night under his roof. My hesitation in answering would have reopened the wound if my soul had been as it was "before." I said "yes" without understanding why, except that I could not answer otherwise.

The room had emptied. Everyone had returned to his own occupations. I realized that I had to decide what to do with my time, and that another visit to the church would not bring me any new joy or assurance. At what moment, in the depths of what silence, in what luminous and impenetrable mystery does God's Spirit act in us? It has always seemed to me that I act on my own decisions, and it is only afterward that I realize that Another has already chosen for me. I felt the need both to be alone and to be surrounded by other men. That desire took shape and quivered on the surface of my soul, and I could call it my own much as the sea might consider its own the waves stirred up on its surface by the winds and the moon. So I decided to walk straight ahead, keeping my secret and taking advantage of contacts with other men.

It was the day before yesterday; market day. Crowds filled the street. I went back past my church and walked slowly up the street. The market was closing, and the street looked like a battlefield after an engagement, or a river just about to go dry. What happened then has no chronology. It happened and I experienced it all at once.

Imagine a curé of a canton, a Dean, suddenly freed from calculations, meannesses, malice, even innocent malice, from multiple and varied intrigues, from plans, red tape and the hieroglyphics of all the Scribes and Doctors of the Law, and from his own fear of making blunders . . . that was what I was. I had made an enormous bundle of all this nonsense, and it was all carried away by a wave, and disappeared. And then at last I acknowledged myself a priest, a man chosen and consecrated; able to preach the Gospel, inspired by the Gospel alone; able to find orthodoxy in the Sermon on the Mount, to disentangle the Word from passions, complacency, arguments and controversies, from the ever-changing forms of thought and action, from supposedly opportune adaptations, and able to accept the responsibility, not for the impossible orientations of a hundred sterile egoisms toward God, but for the flowering of Love. I was back at the beginning. The Church was young again in my heart. I walked among men, my hands emptied of formulas, methods and tricks. Something in me had been broken and repaired. Peter and Paul called to me and I followed them. Something in me had been renewed and what up to that moment had been no more than an intuition was transformed into a luminous certainty: that all our pretentious attitudes (including mine) and all our poses (also including mine) are only masks for a frightful poverty of soul! I wanted to ask pardon of the angels, the saints, the whole world, and of Peter and Paul and all their successors who at that moment might have been my judges if the Mother of God, living in me in Her smile, had not provided guarantees for me.

You say that (God knows!) I had always lived outside the system, and that I had abandoned my parish only to free the Gospel from their narrowness. How then could that have lightened my burden? Your logic was good . . . before. Since, the intersecting point of my self-righteous parishioners and myself was no longer at the same crossroads. Yes, it is mad,

347

but do you absolutely insist that I commit the sin against the sun? I wanted to ask them pardon, too, although they have not changed. For, my dear brother in the same priesthood, who can keep his lamp burning if he doesn't receive any oil, and who can warm himself at a fire which has gone out? Who is to blame, except the one who forgot to love? And what is the meaning of ransom if not turning their system around backward and paying with a smile in their place, until the time comes when they pay?

I saw our vanities sink into the sea and they are still present to me. I am not falling again, I am passing beyond. I am not humiliating the Cross, I am nailing a humiliated victim to it. Some have gone astray and I am the one to recall them. I am not saying that they are right ... simply that I love them.

I didn't love them.

That is why I was no stronger than they. The clash of our vanities gave rise to nothing but the absurd, which we once discussed. The house was crumbling, for a house can crumble in the wind of wild ideas. Avenging God's honor is a magnificent formula, just one more, and an abstract one, a bureaucracy, even if everything seems in order as long as God's Knight brandishes the sword. Love them, to save them, or else (I can't see any other way) defrock, so as at least not to lose them! The worst scandal is certainly the priest who pretends to defend God by smothering Him in the wrappings of his own egoisms. And the more noble they are, the more dangerous.

All I needed was a smile, and to hear, *Sleep, my little one, sleep and dream, and weep* ...

Even the *Tu es Petrus* would only be a system among others, a bureaucracy, if it were not warmed by the heart of a priest; and obedience offered passively, coldly, dryly, even intelligently, to men, even to our superiors in the hierarchy, would be only a higher kind of cowardice if our obedience were not based on a logic other than that of the mind, which is as cold as ice. The mind alone is not enough to see us through. The miracle (or say, the sign) consisted in the fact

that I understood, in the smile of the Mother of God, that
loving is not a defeat, and that the most beautiful thoughts
are empty, useless, and cruel if they reject tenderness. Before,
I was vanquished, but clear-headed. And the strange thing is
that I don't think I have become foolish.

By three o'clock the street was empty. But for a long time
men pushed me, crushed me between their bodies, pressed me
against the stalls of the venders. They are likable people, I
swear, and I smiled at them.

At nightfall, when I had walked all over the town, I went
back to Her chapel and spoke to Her:

"Holy Virgin, here am I who once was Your wayfarer of
the spirit. It took me a long time to get here. It took a great
deal of intelligent foolishness; I had to follow many and devi-
ous ways, spend long days and nights among thorns; I had to
try on different masks, deepen my wrinkles, hear the words
of many men and speak many in my turn; I had to cast a lot
of my ballast into the sea, before I could offer You the joy of
transforming me into a wayfarer of the heart. I was all that can
be imagined, the worst and the best, and even a traditionalist
without realizing it . . . but not a redeemer. I was satisfied with
looking at Your Son's hurt finger. I was a good policeman
whose egoisms in noble guise went hand in hand with his
pieties."

I would have liked to continue for an hour. Humiliate myself. Tell Her that . . . *now* . . .

But I heard,

Leave now, my little one.

*Your flowers from yesterday are just withering. Don't
water them.*

*Go without looking back. The children are asking for
bread. . . . It is not too late. It is time.*

I did not leave Her right away, I admit. I said to Her,
". . . and if they still make fun of me? If the professor, the
Colonel's wife, the Canon . . ."

You will look at my smile within you.

". . . and if they hurt your little One?"

I never protected Him. I offered Him to them.

"And if I begin to think that I am stupid . . . again . . . sometimes?"

It will mean that you have forgotten Me.

"I can never forget You."

Then why are you waiting? The Redemption is moving onward through you, my wayfarer of the heart. You have only one presentable habit now, my smile made your own. That is enough for you. You are handsome to see since my smile came over your face.

"One last word, Mother. Who helped me?"

All of them. All. Your colleague, in his shy, warm way. That old woman, you know it yourself. All the baptized Christians of your parish in their unformulated desire for God, and even your self-righteous parishioners. Believe me, your bishop too, whose smile is one of patience . . . Now, will you obey Me?

Finally I parted from Her. Night had fallen. I hoped you would come all day yesterday. In the afternoon, a storm rolled down in anger from your volcanoes and passed over the town. Where were you? Where are you now? I wished you could have been with me when the sun came out. I spent all this last night writing to you. You will come back here. I take the train in a quarter of an hour. I am going back. Soon we will sing with St. Augustine, "It is the Night, the Night of which it is written: it will light us as the day!" The clear, sweet, radiant Night of Easter's Alleluias, the night of Faith.

350

THIS JOURNAL has to be finished by me, the Dean . . .

He didn't add anything more.

He left his province soon after I did, and certainly didn't stop along the way. When he came into my house, which I had reached a few hours before he did, it was well along into the night. I was sweeping out my kitchen, preparing a meal for myself and for him, for, to tell the truth, I was expecting him. He helped me and we ate together. We made some pastoral decisions for celebrating the coming Pascal feasts. He said nothing to me about my letter, but all of our words, even the most distant from our preoccupations of those last days, were full of peace and humility. He kept apologizing, and I had to forbid him to refer to what he called his singular blunders, the weakness of his spiritual understanding, of his faith and charity. Listening to him, convinced and sincere, a sort of sacred emotion caught at my throat and these words from the Gospel came to my mind: "For where two or three are gathered together for my sake, there am I in the midst of you." His conversation was a prayer, the most beautiful kind.

The next day, my mind was completely enlightened: not knowing what more to do, to say or suggest, this man whom I had led, by my attitudes, to the extreme limits of the choice between faith and despair, had offered his life for me, and this offering had been accepted. I read it later in his notes, but, from that moment on, I was convinced of it.

He went back to his house tired. He announced the news of my return to the canton to our old woman, without any commentary. She had lighted a fire, expecting his arrival. Then he went to bed. At dawn, he did not appear in the church to celebrate his Mass. The old woman found him on his bed, bathed in perspiration and panting. The doctor assured me that he would hold out for a week, which proved to be true. His right arm and leg were paralyzed. He had difficulty speaking, and soon could not speak at all. I stayed with him night and day, until the end.

At the outset, I related some of the details of his lucid agony. In the soul and heart of this priest, Heaven and earth were at last reconciled. Now he could love it all, his earth, his sun, his flowers, and God—all at once. When I ventured to ask him, "Why did you do it?" he answered very softly, "The leaf falls, the grapes are crushed, the wheat is milled, the dawn comes out of the night. Christ knew it, and stretched Himself out upon the Tree. One law, one Love, one and the same sacrifice, the same sap, one single poem. . . . I only imitated Him. Without bloodshed, there is no ransom."

He was smiling like the Virgin of my revelation.